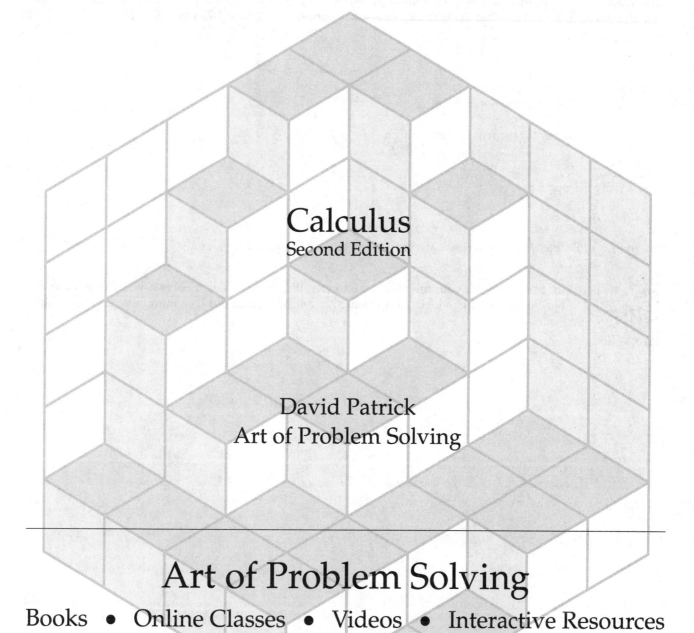

# Calculus
## Second Edition

David Patrick
Art of Problem Solving

# Art of Problem Solving

Books • Online Classes • Videos • Interactive Resources

www.artofproblemsolving.com

Published by:    AoPS Incorporated
15330 Avenue of Science
San Diego, CA 92128
books@artofproblemsolving.com

ISBN-13: 978-1-934124-24-6

Visit the Art of Problem Solving website at http://www.artofproblemsolving.com

Scan this code with your mobile device to visit the Art of Problem Solving website, to view our other books, our free videos and interactive resources, our online community, and our online school.

Cover image designed by Vanessa Rusczyk using KaleidoTile software.

Printed in the United States of America.

Second Edition. Printed in 2023.

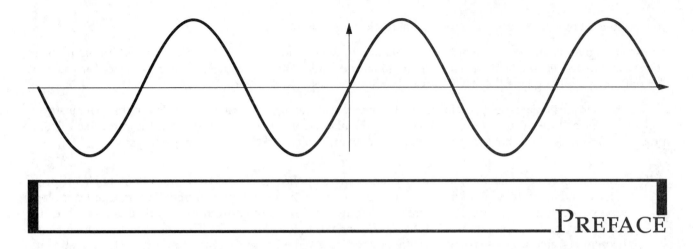

# PREFACE

## INTRODUCTION

Calculus is a branch of mathematics that, broadly speaking, introduces concepts and tools to describe and analyze functions. Although some parts of calculus were known to the ancient Greeks, Egyptians, and Chinese, the modern version of calculus that we use today was largely developed in the 17th century, independently by the great mathematicians Isaac Newton and Gottfried Leibniz. Calculus is not only an important branch of mathematics in its own right, but also provides the rigorous mathematical foundation of physics, engineering, and many other branches of science.

Unfortunately, most students first learn calculus as a bag of tricks: a number of seemingly unrelated algorithms to be memorized and then endlessly applied to problem after problem without motivation. Calculus is sometimes seen as the pinnacle of high-school mathematics, and passing a college placement exam in calculus is the ultimate goal. Students who learn calculus this way—and this describes most high-school and college students who take calculus—will likely never appreciate the beauty or richness of the subject.

Our goal for this book is to present calculus with a substantial theoretical underpinning. Calculus, at its heart, is a few fundamental ideas that come together to create a rich subject, and is not a collection of definitions, formulas, and algorithms. Our hope is that students who complete this book will *understand* calculus, both as a theoretical subject and as a problem-solving tool.

## WHO SHOULD STUDY CALCULUS USING THIS BOOK

The target audience for this book is motivated high school students who have mastered the high school curriculum and have developed the mathematical maturity necessary to handle the level of mathematical rigor in this text. At a minimum, students must have mastered algebra, plane geometry, and trigonometry before considering continuing on to calculus. This is true for any course of calculus study, and especially important for the more rigorous calculus treatment in this book. We strongly recommend a robust precalculus curriculum, such as that in [**Ru**], before proceeding with this text. (Note: bold letters in brackets such as [**Ru**] refer to the References on page 303.)

Students—even highly skilled students—who rush into calculus too soon are likely to be frustrated and will not be able to appreciate the richness and subtleties of the subject. Such a student will only learn calculus as a set of algorithms to be memorized, and even though this may be sufficient to progress on to the next subject, it will rob the student of a key step in his or her mathematical development.

We strongly recommend that students, especially younger students, be exposed to both nontrivial problem solving and to discrete mathematics (such as combinatorics and number theory) *before* "continuing on" to calculus. Art of Problem Solving has other textbooks and online courses in both of these areas.

This book in particular is designed for students who want a deeper understanding of calculus than a mainstream high-school or college calculus text provides, and who also want exposure to a variety of non-routine calculus problems. Specifically, this book differs from a "mainstream" calculus book in two major ways:

1. A more rigorous presentation, including proofs where applicable. For example, this book begins with set theory and the construction of the real numbers, including a discussion of suprema, infima, and completeness. We cover the rigorous $\delta$-$\epsilon$ definition of limit, which is omitted from many calculus texts. We also prove many of the important results of calculus, including the Mean Value Theorem and the Fundamental Theorem of Calculus; these results are often merely asserted without proof in standard calculus treatments.

2. An assortment of nontrivial problems. This book has fewer routine "drill-and-kill" exercises than most calculus texts, and instead has a wider array of problems that require the students to go beyond rote memorization of algorithms and instead to think more deeply about how the different aspects of calculus are interrelated. We have taken many nontrivial problems from two of the premier math contests that include calculus: the high-school level **Harvard-MIT Mathematics Tournament** (HMMT) and the college-level **William Lowell Putnam Mathematical Competition**. The HMMT is an annual math tournament for high school students, held at MIT and at Harvard in alternating years. It is run exclusively by MIT and Harvard students, most of whom themselves participated in math contests in high school. More information is available at www.hmmt.co. The Putnam Competition is a long-running North American undergraduate math competition held every December—2023 will be the 84$^{th}$ annual contest—which consists of *extremely* difficult problems across the entire undergraduate mathematics curriculum. More information is at www.maa.org/math-competitions/putnam-competition.

Students who are preparing for college calculus placement examinations may wish to supplement their study with a test-preparation workbook. The key to success on such placement examinations is repetition of routine calculations, which this textbook largely eschews in favor of a variety of more difficult, non-routine problems.

## STRUCTURE OF THE BOOK

Chapter 1 is a review of important foundational material: sets, real numbers, functions, graphs, trigonometry, exponentials, and logarithms. We urge students not to skip this chapter, even if they think that they already know this material. We present the material at a level of detail and rigor that students may not be used to, and will be introducing terminology and notation that is not typically covered in a precalculus class.

Chapter 2 introduces the first core idea of calculus: the limit. We present the full $\delta$-$\epsilon$ treatment of limits, which is often not covered in a high-school calculus course, but we feel that exposure to the rigorous definition of limit is an important part of students' mathematical development. In particular, stating key definitions rigorously is necessary to prove later results, and our goal will be to prove (and not merely assert) as much as possible.

Chapters 3–5 are the heart of the subject: differentiation (Chapters 3 and 4) and integration (Chapter 5). These are the core concepts of calculus.

Chapters 6 and 7 deal with the concept of "infinity," of which most students have a vague understanding but which we will attempt to make precise. Chapter 7 also includes the very important topic of Taylor series, which is a fundamental topic of analysis.

Chapters 8 and 9 are essentially independent, and each serve as an introduction to the broader world of analysis beyond calculus. Chapter 8 covers plane curves, including curves in polar coordinates, and is a nice introduction to topics that will be covered more thoroughly in multivariable calculus (typically the next calculus course after a student has mastered the topics in this book). Finally, Chapter 9 is an introduction to the theory of differential equations, a very broad subject which we only touch on in this book, but which is the subject of (several) courses of study beyond calculus.

Throughout the book, you will see various shaded boxes and icons.

**Concept:** This will be a general problem-solving technique or strategy. These are the "keys" to becoming a better problem solver!

**Important:** This will be something important that should be learned. It might be a formula, a solution technique, or a caution.

**WARNING!!** Beware if you see this box! This will point out a common mistake or pitfall.

**Sidenote:** This box will contain material which, although interesting, is not part of the main material of the text. It's OK to skip over these boxes, but if students read them, they might learn something interesting!

**Bogus Solution:** Just like the impossible cube shown to the left, there's something wrong with any "solution" that appears in this box.

Most sections end with several **Exercises**. These will test students' understanding of the material that was covered in the section. Students should try to solve *all* of the exercises. Exercises marked with a ★ are more difficult.

All chapters conclude with several **Review Problems**. These are problems that test basic understanding of the material covered in the chapter. Students should be able to solve most or all of the Review Problems for every chapter—if unable to do so, then the student hasn't yet mastered the material, and should probably go back and read the chapter again.

All chapters also contain several **Challenge Problems**. These problems are generally more difficult than the other problems in the book, and will really test students' mastery of the material. Some of them are very, very hard—the hardest ones are marked with a ★. Students should not expect to be able to solve all of the Challenge Problems on their first try—these are difficult problems even for experienced problem solvers.

Many chapters will have one or more advanced sections after the end-of-chapter problems. These sections are denoted with a letter (such as 1.A). These sections are optional and often cover topics at a more theoretical level than in the main text. Eager students who work through these sections should find them rewarding, but it is acceptable to skip them.

# HINTS

Many problems come with one or more hints. Readers can look up the hints in the Hints section in the back of the book. The hints are numbered in random order, so that when looking up a hint to a problem students will not accidentally glance at the hint to the next problem at the same time.

It is very important that students first try to solve each problem without resorting to the hints. Only after one has seriously thought about a problem and is stuck should one seek a hint. Also, for problems which have multiple hints, use the hints one at a time; don't go to the second hint until having thought about the first one.

# SOLUTIONS

The solutions to all of the Exercises, Review Problems, and Challenge Problems are in the separate Solutions Manual. There are some very important things to keep in mind:

1. Students should make a serious attempt to solve each problem before looking at the solution. Don't use the solutions book as a crutch to avoid really thinking about the problem first. Think *hard* about a problem before deciding to look at the solution. On the other hand, after serious effort has been made on a problem, students should not feel bad about looking at the solution if they are really stuck.

2. After solving a problem, it's usually a good idea to read the solution. The solutions book might show a quicker or more concise way to solve the problem, or it might have a completely different solution method.

3. If the reader is unable to solve a particular problem and has to look at the solution in order to solve that problem, he or she should make a note of it. Then, the student should come back to that problem in a week or two to make sure that he or she is able to solve it without resorting to the solution.

# RESOURCES

Here are some other good resources for students to pursue further their study of mathematics:

- The Art of Problem Solving's *Precalculus* textbook by Richard Rusczyk, in particular the chapters covering trigonometry. The other major subjects covered in *Precalculus*—complex numbers and linear algebra—are not necessary for this calculus book, but are very important for students' future math studies.

- *The Art of Problem Solving* books, by Sandor Lehoczky and Richard Rusczyk. Whereas the book that you're reading right now will go into great detail of one specific subject area—calculus—*the Art of Problem Solving* books cover a wide range of precalculus problem solving topics across many different areas of mathematics.

- The www.artofproblemsolving.com website. The publishers of this book also maintain the Art of Problem Solving website, which contains many resources for students:

  - a discussion forum
  - online classes
  - resource lists of books, contests, and other websites
  - a LATEX tutorial

– a math and problem solving Wiki

– and much more!

- Students can hone their problem solving skills (and perhaps win prizes!) by participating in various math contests. For U.S. high school students, some of the best-known contests are the AMC/AIME/USAMO series of contests (which are used to choose the U.S. team for the International Mathematical Olympiad), the American Regions Math League (ARML), the Mandelbrot Competition, the Harvard-MIT Mathematics Tournament, and the USA Mathematical Talent Search. Links to these and many other contests are available on the Art of Problem Solving website.

## TECHNOLOGY

Most students who study calculus will do so with the aid of a graphing calculator, and we encourage students using this book to do so as well. Once students have mastered the basics, a graphing calculator can remove some of the tedium from long calculations, and can also serve as a valuable check of students' work. Additionally, much of calculus is visual in nature, and being able to sketch, quickly and accurately, a graph of a function with a few keystrokes is very beneficial. However, students should be aware of the following cautions:

1. There is a famous saying: "garbage in, garbage out." That is, a graphing calculator is only as good as its user—if you enter bogus data into it, you will get bogus results. You also need to know how to properly use your calculator, and to make sure that it is in the correct mode (for example, while doing calculus, your calculator should be in "radians" mode and not in "degrees" mode).

2. Make sure your calculator is sufficiently sophisticated. A "scientific calculator" may not have enough features to be broadly useful for calculus. Ideally, your calculator should be able to (a) graph functions with an arbitrary viewing window, (b) solve equations numerically, and (c) numerically compute derivatives and definite integrals. (Don't worry if you don't know what all these things mean yet—that's what this book is for!) Top-of-the-line calculators are also able to do (b) and (c) symbolically (that is, in terms of variables) as well as numerically.

3. If you are planning to take a standardized calculus examination, then make sure your calculator doesn't do too much. While most calculus examinations permit (or even require) the use of calculators, a "calculator" that is actually a handheld computer or PDA will likely not be permitted. Check with the organization administering your placement test to see if they have a list of approved calculators.

We also recommend the use of symbolic computation websites. One of the best is Wolfram|Alpha (available at wolframalpha.com), which makes many of the features of the computational software *Mathematica* available on the web. (In fact, the author of this book used Wolfram|Alpha to check many of the calculations.)

## ACKNOWLEDGEMENTS

This book is a collaborative effort of the staff of the Art of Problem Solving. Richard Rusczyk and Jeremy Copeland each read many drafts of this book and made many, many helpful suggestions; Naoki Sato also proofread much of the solutions manual. Much of this book was influenced by the online calculus course that was held on artofproblemsolving.com in 2008-09 and again in 2009-10; we thank the students in those classes for their enthusiasm and for many helpful in-class discussions that have greatly improved this textbook. We also thank the teaching assistants for those courses—Sam Elder, Palmer Mebane, Dimitar Popov, and Max Rosett—not only for their assistance in the course, but also for selecting and/or writing first drafts of many of the problems and solutions in this book. Samson Zhou, Thomas Belulovich and Qiaochu Yuan also assisted with selecting problems for the book, and Vanessa Rusczyk designed the cover.

For the second edition, we would like to thank the following readers who gave us helpful comments or corrections: John Beaulieu, Philip Bonneville, Ravi Boppana, Andy Dienes, Chetak Hossain, Jon Joseph, Dan Kneezel, Marcus Neal, Matt Owen, Nathan Phan, Andres Saez, Jason Shi, Justin Stevens, Michael Wang, Alex Watt, and the many students who have taken our online Calculus course at Art of Problem Solving over the past few years.

This book was written using the LaTeX document processing system. The diagrams were prepared using Asymptote.

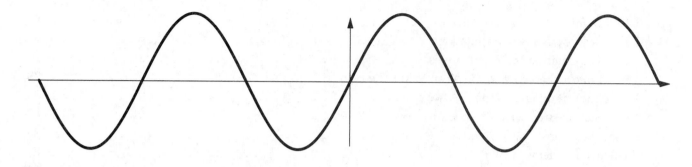

# CONTENTS

# 4    Applications of the Derivative      88

# 5    Integration      125

# 6   Infinity      191

# 7   Series      220

# 8   Plane Curves      259

# 9   Differential Equations      279

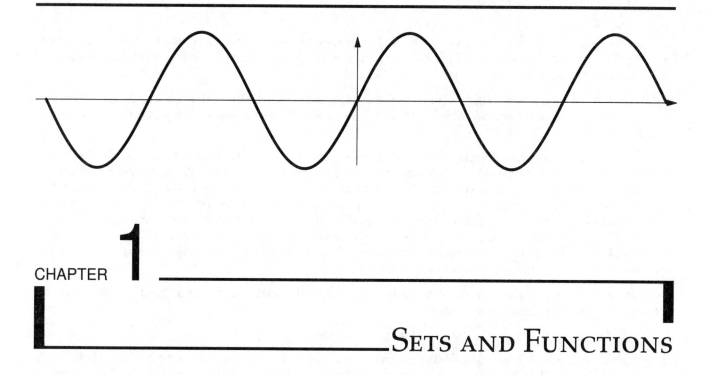

# CHAPTER 1

# SETS AND FUNCTIONS

Before we can dive into calculus, we need to make sure that we have a rigorous understanding of some basic mathematical concepts, such as sets, numbers, and functions. Some of these concepts will seem obvious, and one can certainly learn the mechanics of calculus without worrying about rigorous details, but to *understand* calculus, it's important to pay attention to details.

We will also review some special functions that play a crucial role in calculus: the **trigonometric** functions, and the **exponential** and **logarithm** functions. You should already have some prior experience with these functions. These types of functions are used throughout calculus, so it is important to have a thorough understanding of them. When you first learned about these functions (in a precalculus or intermediate algebra course, for example), some of their properties may have seemed like magic. In this chapter we'll try to add a bit more rigor to these functions.

## 1.1 SETS

Sets are the building blocks of mathematics. Like many other fundamental mathematical concepts (such as "point" or "number"), sets are difficult to define precisely, and we're not going to try to be terribly precise here.

Roughly speaking, a **set** is a collection of objects. The objects can be anything: numbers, functions, other sets, any combination of these, or nothing at all. The order of the objects in the set is unimportant. All that matters is what objects are in the set. There might only be a **finite** number of objects in the set (meaning that we could count them if we liked), in which case the set is called a **finite set**. Otherwise we call it an **infinite set**. The objects in the set are called the **elements** or **members** of the set.

There are two basic ways that we can describe a set. The first is to list its elements. For example:

$$A = \{2, 9, 22\}.$$

This is a set with three elements, namely 2, 9, and 22. This is often the simplest way to define or describe a set: We list the elements inside of curly braces, and separate the different elements by commas. As we said above, the order of the elements doesn't matter, so $A = \{9, 22, 2\}$ is exactly the same set as $A = \{2, 9, 22\}$. Also, each element can only be in the set once, so for example $B = \{3, 6, 3\}$ is not a legal set (alternatively, we can think of the second "3" in $\{3, 6, 3\}$ as being redundant and write $\{3, 6, 3\} = \{3, 6\}$).

Sometimes it's impractical to list a big set, so we use ellipses if the pattern of the elements in the set is clear. For example, we feel pretty safe describing a set as $\{1, 2, 3, \ldots, 99, 100\}$ and knowing that this is the set of the first 100 positive integers.

If a set is infinite, then we obviously have no hope of being able to list all the elements, since such a list would go on forever! But if it is clear which elements are in the set, then we can list the elements using ellipses. For example, the set of all positive integers can be written as $\{1, 2, 3, \ldots\}$, because the pattern is clear. As another example, we can be pretty sure that $\{1, 2, 4, 8, 16, 32, \ldots\}$, without any further description, is the set of all positive integers that are powers of 2. Be careful though: you should only do this if your pattern is absolutely clear. Listing a set as $\{1, 2, 4, \ldots\}$ is pretty ambiguous: is it the set of all nonnegative powers of 2, or the set of all positive integers not divisible by 3, or something else that we didn't think of? It's not at all clear, so we need more sample elements to make the pattern clear, or some words describing the set.

Aside from listing the elements, the other basic way to describe a set is to provide a property that precisely defines the elements of the set. For example:

$$B = \{x \mid x \text{ is an integer}\}.$$

In this example, the set $B$ consists of all the integers. Some people use a colon (:) instead of the vertical bar; in either case, you should read the symbol as "such that." For example, we would read our set $B$ above as "the set of all $x$ such that $x$ is an integer." Another common example is an interval on the real line; for example,

$$\{x \mid x \text{ is a real number and } 2 < x \le 3\}$$

is the interval of all real numbers that are greater than 2 and less than or equal to 3. One of the major strengths of this way of describing a set is that we can use this even if we don't know explicitly what the elements are. For example,

$$\{y \mid y \text{ is a real number and } 2y^4 - y^3 + 6y^2 - 11y + 12 = 0\}$$

is perfectly valid, even if we don't necessarily know at first glance exactly what values of $y$ are in the set, or even if there are any elements in the set.

If an object $x$ is an element of $S$, we write this as $x \in S$. If $x$ is not an element of $S$, we write $x \notin S$. For any object $x$ and any set $S$, either $x \in S$ or $x \notin S$, but (of course) never both. Indeed, this is the whole point of sets: a set is a collection of the objects that belong to it, and everything else does not belong.

There is a very special set called the **empty set**, denoted by $\emptyset$. This is the set with no elements at all. For example,

$$\{x \mid x \text{ is a real number and } x^2 < 0\} = \emptyset,$$

because there is no real number satisfying the property that its square is less than 0. Note that $x \notin \emptyset$ for any $x$. We sometimes also write the empty set as a list: $\emptyset = \{\}$. Of course, it's an empty list, since the empty set has no elements.

If $S$ is a finite set, then we let $\#(S)$ denote the number of elements of $S$. We say that $\#(S)$ is the **cardinality** of $S$. (Note that many sources use the notation $|S|$ in place of $\#(S)$.) For example, if $S = \{2, 4, 9, 11\}$ then $\#(S) = 4$, since $S$ has four elements. Note that $\#(\emptyset) = 0$, since $\emptyset$ has zero elements. If $S$ is an infinite set (such as the set of all integers), then we cannot define $\#(S)$ without resorting to so-called *transfinite cardinal numbers*, which we will not need in this book.

A set $A$ is called a **subset** of a set $B$ if every element of $A$ is also an element of $B$. We think of $A$ as a smaller set that is made up of some of the elements of $B$. More informally, we think of $A$ as sitting "inside" $B$. The notation that we use is $A \subseteq B$. For example,

$$\{3, 8, 11\} \subseteq \{2, 3, 8, 10, 11, 14, 16\}$$

and

$$\{x \mid x \text{ is an even integer}\} \subseteq \{x \mid x \text{ is an integer}\}.$$

If $A$ is a subset of $B$, we also say that $B$ is a **superset** of $A$.

Notice that, by definition, every set is a subset of itself. It is convenient to have a notation for when a set is a **proper subset** of another set, meaning that it is a subset but not equal to the larger set. For example, $\{1, 2, 3\}$ is a proper subset of $\{1, 2, 3, 4\}$, but $\{1, 2, 3, 4\}$ is not a proper subset of $\{1, 2, 3, 4\}$, although it is a subset. We use the notation $A \subset B$ to denote that $A$ is a proper subset of $B$. (This is very similar to the notations $<$ for "less than" and $\leq$ for "less than or equal to": $3 < 4$ and $3 \leq 4$ and $4 \leq 4$, but $4 \not< 4$.) Another way to think of this is that $A \subset B$ means that $A$ is a subset of $B$, but there is some element of $B$ that is not in $A$. For example, $\{1, 2, 3\} \subset \{1, 2, 3, 4\}$ because 4 is not in $\{1, 2, 3\}$.

> **WARNING!!** Unfortunately, this notation is not universally agreed upon. Many authors use $A \subset B$ to mean that $A$ is any subset of $B$, not necessarily proper. Some of these authors then use the notation $A \subsetneq B$ or $A \subsetneqq B$ to mean that $A$ is a proper subset of $B$.
>
> However, in this book, we will always use $A \subseteq B$ to mean that $A$ is a subset of $B$, possibly equal, and use $A \subset B$ to mean that $A$ is a proper subset of $B$.

> **WARNING!!** The concepts and notations can get a bit confusing, and it takes a little bit of practice to use them properly. For example, if $A = \{1, 2, 3\}$, then it is correct to say that 1 is an element of $A$ and that $\{1\}$ is a subset of $A$. In notation, we would write
>
> $$1 \in A \quad \text{and} \quad \{1\} \subseteq A.$$
>
> But it is *not* correct to say that $\{1\}$ is an element of $A$.

Let's practice with some basic exercises involving elements and subsets:

**Problem 1.1:** Consider the following sets:

$$A = \{1, 2, 3, 4, 5\}, \qquad B = \{2, 3, 4\}, \qquad C = \{3, \{4, 5\}\}.$$

(a)  Is $A \subseteq A$? Is $A \subset A$?

(b)  Is $B \subseteq A$? Is $B \subset A$?

(c)  Is $C \subseteq A$? Is $C \subset A$?

(d)  Is $4 \in B$? Is $4 \in C$?

(e)  List all of the subsets of $B$. How many are there?

*Solution for Problem 1.1:*

(a)  The elements of $A$ are 1, 2, 3, 4, and 5. All of these elements are elements of $A$, so $A \subseteq A$. However, $A = A$, so $A$ is not a proper subset of $A$. Therefore, $A \not\subset A$.

(b)  All of the elements of $B$ are also elements of $A$, so $B \subseteq A$. Further, $A$ contains elements (namely, 1 and 5) that are not in $B$, so $B$ is a proper subset of $A$; that is, $B \subset A$.

(c)  One of the elements of $C$ is $\{4, 5\}$. This is not an element of $A$ (it is a subset of $A$, which is not the same thing). Thus $C \not\subseteq A$ and by the same reasoning $C \not\subset A$.

(d)   4 is an element of $B$, so $4 \in B$. However, 4 is not an element of $C$. The set $C$ has two elements, the number 3 and the set $\{4, 5\}$. Thus $4 \notin C$.

(e)   We can list the subsets of $B$:

$$\emptyset, \{2\}, \{3\}, \{4\}, \{2,3\}, \{2,4\}, \{3,4\}, \{2,3,4\}$$

(Don't forget that $\emptyset$ and $B$ itself are subsets of $B$. More about $\emptyset \subseteq B$ in Problem 1.2 below.) Thus, there are 8 subsets of $B$.

□

Note some properties of subsets:

- Every set is a subset of itself; that is, $A \subseteq A$ for any set $A$.

- The empty set is a subset of any set; that is, $\emptyset \subseteq A$ for any set $A$.

- If $A, B$ are two sets such that $A \subseteq B$ and $B \subseteq A$, then $A = B$. In fact, this is often how we prove that two sets $A$ and $B$ are equal: we show that $A \subseteq B$ and $B \subseteq A$. (Note the analogy to real numbers: if $x \leq y$ and $y \leq x$, then $x = y$.)

- If $A$ and $B$ are any two sets, then we cannot have both $A \subset B$ and $B \subset A$. (Also note the analogy to real numbers: we cannot simultaneously have $x < y$ and $y < x$.)

Let's explain one of these properties now, and you'll be asked to explain the others in the exercises.

---

**Problem 1.2:** Show that the empty set is a subset of any set.

---

*Solution for Problem 1.2:*   By the definition of subset, we know that $\emptyset \subseteq A$ if every element of $\emptyset$ is an element of $A$. But $\emptyset$ has no elements. So it is true that every element of $\emptyset$ is in $A$, and thus $\emptyset \subseteq A$. This may seem strange, but you can think of it this way: if you can give me an element of $\emptyset$, then I can show that it is in $A$. I know I'm safe making this claim, because I know that you can't give me an element.

Many people find the above argument confusing; here's another way to think about it. We know that $\emptyset$ is *not* a subset of $A$ if and only if there exists some $x \in \emptyset$ such that $x \notin A$. But such an element $x$ cannot possibly exist, because $\emptyset$ has no elements! Thus, is it *not* true that $\emptyset \nsubseteq A$, and therefore $\emptyset \subseteq A$. (Even though the logic in this paragraph uses a double-negative, many people find this argument easier to follow than the argument in the previous paragraph.) □

---

**Sidenote:**   The empty set is a weird object, and can lead to counterintuitive conclusions. For example, the statement

> If $x \in \emptyset$, then $x$ is a flying yellow pig.

is a true statement: because $\emptyset$ has no elements, there is no such $x$. Thus we don't care what the "then" part of the statement says, because the "if" part of the statement is never satisfied.

---

Just as we can perform operations on numbers, such as addition and multiplication, to get new numbers, we can perform operations on sets to get new sets. We start by defining the two primary operations on sets.

---

**Definition:**   The **union** $A \cup B$ of two sets $A$ and $B$ is the set of all objects that are elements of $A$ or of $B$.

---

We can write this more formally as:

$$A \cup B = \{x \mid x \in A \text{ or } x \in B\}.$$

Note that our use of the word "or" in the definition does *not* mean "one or the other, but not both." Instead, we use the word "or" to mean "one or the other, or possibly both." (This is always the way that mathematicians use the word "or.") Elements that are in both $A$ and $B$ are also in their union.

Here are some examples:

- $\{2, 3, 8\} \cup \{1, 7, 11, 13\} = \{1, 2, 3, 7, 8, 11, 13\}$.

- $\{4, 8, 9\} \cup \{2, 4, 9, 11\} = \{2, 4, 8, 9, 11\}$. (We don't list 4 or 9 twice, even though they appear in both sets, since elements are not duplicated in a set.)

- $\{1, 2, 4\} \cup \{1, 2, 4, 8\} = \{1, 2, 4, 8\}$.

- $\{x \mid x \text{ is an even integer}\} \cup \{x \mid x \text{ is an odd integer}\} = \{x \mid x \text{ is an integer}\}$.

> **Definition:** The **intersection** $A \cap B$ of two sets $A$ and $B$ is the set of all objects that are elements of both $A$ and $B$.

We can write this more formally as:

$$A \cap B = \{x \mid x \in A \text{ and } x \in B\}.$$

Some examples:

- $\{3, 5, 9, 11\} \cap \{2, 5, 8, 11, 13\} = \{5, 11\}$.

- $\{2, 6, 9, 11\} \cap \{2, 9\} = \{2, 9\}$.

- $\{4, 9, 11, 16\} \cap \{2, 8, 10, 14\} = \emptyset$, since these two sets have no elements in common.

- $\{x \mid x \text{ is an even integer}\} \cap \{x \mid x \text{ is an odd integer}\} = \emptyset$.

- $\{x \mid x \text{ is an even positive integer}\} \cap \{x \mid x \text{ is a prime number}\} = \{2\}$.

A special case of union and intersection is shown in the following problem.

> **Problem 1.3:** Suppose $A$ and $B$ are sets such that $A \subseteq B$.
> (a) What is $A \cup B$?
> (b) What is $A \cap B$?

*Solution for Problem 1.3:*

(a) If $A \subseteq B$, then every element of $A$ is also an element of $B$. This means that any element in $A$ or $B$ must be in $B$. Therefore, $A \cup B \subseteq B$. On the other hand, every element of $B$ is also an element of $A \cup B$, so $B \subseteq A \cup B$. Hence, $A \cup B = B$.

(b) Any element in $A$ and $B$ must be in $A$, so $A \cap B \subseteq A$. On the other hand, every element of $A$ is also an element of $B$, and thus also an element of $A \cap B$, so $A \subseteq A \cap B$. Therefore, $A \cap B = A$.

$\square$

> **Important:** Two sets are equal if and only if they contain exactly the same elements. To show that two sets $A$ and $B$ are equal, we show that every element of $A$ is also an element of $B$, and we show that every element of $B$ is also an element of $A$. If we only do one of these but not both, then all we're showing is that one set is a subset of the other. For example, if we show that every element of $A$ is also an element of $B$, then we've shown that $A \subseteq B$. In order to show that they're equal, we have to show that $B \subseteq A$ as well.

It is useful to have a word describing when two sets have no elements in common:

> **Definition:** If $A \cap B = \emptyset$, then we say that $A$ and $B$ are **disjoint**.

Our two operations—union and intersection—are distributive with respect to each other. We'll prove one of the distributive laws and leave the other as an exercise.

> **Problem 1.4:** Prove that if $A$, $B$, and $C$ are sets, then
> $$A \cap (B \cup C) = (A \cap B) \cup (A \cap C).$$

*Solution for Problem 1.4:* To prove that two sets are equal, we must show that they have the same elements. This means that we must show that every element in one set is also in the other set, and vice versa.

We start by letting $x$ be an element of $A \cap (B \cup C)$. This means that $x \in A$ and $x \in (B \cup C)$, which means that

$$x \in A \text{ and } ((x \in B) \text{ or } (x \in C)).$$

This can be rewritten as

$$(x \in A \text{ and } x \in B) \text{ or } (x \in A \text{ and } x \in C).$$

Now, rewriting our statement using union and intersection of sets, we have

$$x \in ((A \cap B) \cup (A \cap C)).$$

Thus, all elements of $A \cap (B \cup C)$ are also elements of $(A \cap B) \cup (A \cap C)$, which means that

$$A \cap (B \cup C) \subseteq (A \cap B) \cup (A \cap C). \tag{$*$}$$

We're not done! We have to show the reverse as well. To do so, let $y$ be an element of $(A \cap B) \cup (A \cap C)$. Then

$$(y \in A \text{ and } y \in B) \text{ or } (y \in A \text{ and } y \in C).$$

This can be written as

$$y \in A \text{ and } (y \in B \text{ or } y \in C),$$

which means that $y \in A \cap (B \cup C)$. Thus,

$$(A \cap B) \cup (A \cap C) \subseteq A \cap (B \cup C). \tag{$**$}$$

Combining ($*$) and ($**$), we see that $A \cap (B \cup C)$ and $(A \cap B) \cup (A \cap C)$ have the same elements, so they are equal. $\square$

We have one more important operation on sets to define; we will leave its properties as an exercise.

> **Definition:** The **set difference** of two sets $A$ and $B$ is
> $$A \setminus B = \{x \in A \mid x \notin B\}.$$

That is, $A \setminus B$ consists of all elements of $A$ that are not in $B$. For example, if $A = \{1, 2\}$ and $B = \{2, 3\}$, then $A \setminus B = \{1\}$, because $1 \in A$ and $1 \notin B$, and 1 is the only element with this property. Similarly, $B \setminus A = \{3\}$.

Set theory is a very rich subject, and we have only scratched the surface of it. We could fill a whole book discussing set theory (and many such books have been written). But the set theory that we've done in this section is really all we'll need for calculus.

---

## EXERCISES

**1.1.1** Show that if $A \subseteq B$ and $A \subseteq C$, then $A \subseteq (B \cap C)$. Show that the same statement is *not* true if we replace every "$\subseteq$" with "$\subset$".

**1.1.2** Prove that for any sets $A$, $B$, and $C$,

$$A \cup (B \cap C) = (A \cup B) \cap (A \cup C).$$

**1.1.3** Prove that $A \subseteq A$ for any set $A$.

**1.1.4**

(a) Is set difference commutative? That is, must we have $A \setminus B = B \setminus A$? (If true, prove it; if false, give a counterexample.)

(b) Is set difference associative? That is, must we have $(A \setminus B) \setminus C = A \setminus (B \setminus C)$? (If true, prove it; if false, give a counterexample.)

(c) Prove that for any sets $A, B, C$, we have

$$A \setminus (B \cup C) = (A \setminus B) \cap (A \setminus C) = (A \setminus B) \setminus C.$$

(d) What is $A \setminus \emptyset$? What is $\emptyset \setminus A$?

**1.1.5★** Show that, for any sets $A, B, C$,

$$A \cup (B \setminus C) = (A \cup B) \setminus (C \setminus A).$$

**Hints:** 53

---

## 1.2 NUMBERS AND INTERVALS

There are some special sets that consist of numbers. You're almost certainly already familiar with these sets, but let's discuss them with an eye towards what makes each of them special.

We can start with the **positive integers**, which are our basic counting numbers:

$$\{1, 2, 3, 4, \ldots\}.$$

An average 3-year-old is pretty comfortable with positive integers (although he or she probably doesn't yet know the word "integer").

---

> **Sidenote:** Some mathematicians call the positive integers the **natural numbers**, denoted by the symbol $\mathbb{N}$:
> $$\mathbb{N} = \{1, 2, 3, 4, \ldots\}.$$
>
> Other mathematicians consider 0 to be a natural number as well, so
> $$\mathbb{N} = \{0, 1, 2, 3, 4, \ldots\}.$$
>
> Unfortunately, there is not general agreement in the mathematical community as to whether 0 should be a natural number or not. There is similar ambiguity about the terms **whole numbers** and **counting numbers**, which (depending on who you ask) each refer to the set $\{1, 2, 3, \ldots\}$ or the set $\{0, 1, 2, 3, \ldots\}$.
>   We will sidestep the issue by referring to the set $\{1, 2, 3, \ldots\}$ as "positive integers" and the set $\{0, 1, 2, 3, \ldots\}$ as "nonnegative integers."

But positive integers, by themselves, have a lot of limitations. First of all, zero is missing. Second of all, we can't always subtract: for instance, $1 - 3$ is undefined as a positive integer. So we include 0 and negative integers to get the entire set of **integers**, denoted by $\mathbb{Z}$:

$$\mathbb{Z} = \{\ldots, -4, -3, -2, -1, 0, 1, 2, 3, 4, \ldots\}.$$

Integers are a great improvement: now we can add and subtract, and we have 0. In fact, addition in $\mathbb{Z}$ satisfies these other nice axioms as well:

- **commutativity**: for any $a, b \in \mathbb{Z}, a + b = b + a$.

- **associativity**: for any $a, b, c \in \mathbb{Z}, (a + b) + c = a + (b + c)$.

- $\mathbb{Z}$ has an additive **identity element**, namely 0: for any $a \in \mathbb{Z}, a + 0 = 0 + a = a$.

- $\mathbb{Z}$ has additive **inverses**: for any $a \in \mathbb{Z}$, there exists $b \in \mathbb{Z}$ such that $a + b = b + a = 0$. (Of course, $b = -a$.)

Of course, we know that $\mathbb{Z}$ has a second operation—multiplication—that is also commutative, associative, and has an identity element, 1. Additionally, the two operations together satisfy the **distributive** property:

$$\text{for any } a, b, c \in \mathbb{Z}, a(b + c) = (ab) + (ac).$$

However, we don't have multiplicative inverses; that is, we can't divide. For example, $2/3$ is undefined in $\mathbb{Z}$. To remedy this, we move up to the **rational numbers**, denoted by $\mathbb{Q}$ (for "quotient").

The elements of $\mathbb{Q}$ are ratios of integers:

$$\mathbb{Q} = \left\{ \frac{m}{n} \mid m, n \in \mathbb{Z} \text{ and } n \neq 0 \right\}.$$

Note in particular that we don't allow 0 in the denominator.

However, this doesn't tell the whole story, since a lot of these fractions are equal. For example, $\frac{1}{2} = \frac{2}{4} = \frac{5}{10}$, and in fact there are infinitely many fractions that represent each rational number. We don't think of $\frac{1}{2}, \frac{2}{4}$, etc. as separate elements of $\mathbb{Q}$; rather they are different ways of representing the same number.

The set $\mathbb{Q}$ together with the operations of addition and multiplication is what is called a **field**: we can add, subtract, multiply, and divide any two elements of $\mathbb{Q}$ (except that we can't divide by 0, of course), and these operations satisfy all the nice properties that we want them to have (commutativity, associativity, and distributivity). So it seems like we have everything we need for our number system.

But there's still something fundamental missing from $\mathbb{Q}$. For instance:

**Problem 1.5:** Show that there is no number $x \in \mathbb{Q}$ such that $x^2 = 2$.

*Solution for Problem 1.5:* The proof that follows is one of the most famous examples in mathematics of **proof by contradiction**. Our strategy will be to assume that there *is* a number $x \in \mathbb{Q}$ such that $x^2 = 2$, and then show that this leads to a logical impossibility. This implies that the original assumption cannot be true.

If $x \in \mathbb{Q}$, then we can write $x = p/q$, where $p$ and $q$ are integers that have no common factors (other than 1 and $-1$). We will show that this assumption leads to a contradiction. Note that $p$ and $q$ having no common factors means in particular that $p$ and $q$ are not both even. We will now prove that $p$ and $q$ in fact *are* both even, which is our logical impossibility.

The fact that $x^2 = 2$ gives us $(p/q)^2 = 2$, so $p^2 = 2q^2$. But this means that $p$ is even, so let $p' = p/2$. Thus, we have $(2p')^2 = 2q^2$, which simplifies to $2(p')^2 = q^2$. But this means that $q$ is even. Therefore, $p$ and $q$ are both even. This is our contradiction! Thus, our assumption was false, and there is no number $x \in \mathbb{Q}$ such that $x^2 = 2$. $\square$

Of course, when we extend our set of numbers to the **real numbers** (denoted $\mathbb{R}$), a solution to $x^2 = 2$ exists, namely $\sqrt{2}$. But what exactly are real numbers? In other words, how can we define numbers such as $\sqrt{2}$ using what we already have, which (for the moment) is just rational numbers?

One idea starts with how we naturally think of $\sqrt{2}$, and that is as the positive number whose square is 2. Slightly more formally, we can "define" $\sqrt{2}$ as the positive solution to the equation $x^2 - 2 = 0$, which is an equation that only contains rational numbers. When we add all such numbers to the set $\mathbb{Q}$—that is, we include all numbers that are solutions to some polynomial equation with rational coefficients—we get the set of **algebraic numbers**, denoted $\overline{\mathbb{Q}}$. But $\overline{\mathbb{Q}}$ still lacks of lots of useful numbers, such as $\pi$, or indeed any other **transcendental** number that is not the solution of a polynomial equation with rational coefficients. So what can we do?

Instead, we are motivated by the idea that we typically think of $\mathbb{R}$ as being equivalent to the "number line": a line in which every point represents a real number, and in which every real number corresponds to a unique point on the line. When thinking of numbers as lying on a number line, we see that $\mathbb{Q}$, by itself, contains lots of "holes" on the line.

For instance, to go back to our earlier example, we can think of the number $\sqrt{2}$ as the number that fills the hole between the sets $\{x \in \mathbb{Q} \mid x < 0 \text{ or } x^2 < 2\}$ and $\{x \in \mathbb{Q} \mid x > 0 \text{ and } x^2 > 2\}$. Note that we can very easily describe the above two sets just using rational numbers, and the sets contain only rational numbers. But the "hole" between them is the number $\sqrt{2}$. When we fill in all the numbers that create such holes in $\mathbb{Q}$, we get the real numbers $\mathbb{R}$.

It is possible, with a lot of work, to make the construction of $\mathbb{R}$ rigorous. But for the purposes of our study of calculus in this book, it's enough to think informally of the real numbers as all the points on the number line without any holes. The essential axiomatic fact about $\mathbb{R}$ that we'll need for calculus is called **completeness**, which essentially means "no holes." Before stating exactly what completeness is, we'll need a few definitions:

---

**Definition:** Let $S$ be a subset of $\mathbb{R}$.

- A number $x \in \mathbb{R}$ is called an **upper bound** for $S$ if for all $y \in S$, we have $y \leq x$. If an upper bound for $S$ exists, we say that $S$ is **bounded above**.

- A number $x \in \mathbb{R}$ is called a **lower bound** for $S$ if for all $y \in S$, we have $y \geq x$. If a lower bound for $S$ exists, we say that $S$ is **bounded below**.

- If $S$ has an upper bound and a lower bound, we say that $S$ is **bounded**.

---

Some bounds are very special:

> **Definition:** Let $S$ be a subset of $\mathbb{R}$.
>
> - A number $x \in \mathbb{R}$ is called a **least upper bound** (or **supremum**) of $S$ if $x$ is an upper bound for $S$ and if for every $z \in \mathbb{R}$ such that $z$ is an upper bound of $S$, we have $x \leq z$.
>
> - A number $x \in \mathbb{R}$ is called a **greatest lower bound** (or **infimum**) of $S$ if $x$ is a lower bound for $S$ and if for every $z \in \mathbb{R}$ such that $z$ is a lower bound of $S$, we have $x \geq z$.

In other words, an upper bound of a subset $S \subseteq \mathbb{R}$ is any number greater than or equal to all of the numbers in $S$. If we can find a smallest possible upper bound for $S$, then this number is the least upper bound of $S$. Similarly, a lower bound of $S$ is a number that is less than or equal to all of the numbers in $S$. If we can find a greatest possible lower bound for $S$, then this number is the greatest lower bound of $S$.

> **Problem 1.6:** Suppose $S$ is a subset of $\mathbb{R}$. Show that if $S$ has a least upper bound, then this least upper bound is unique.

*Solution for Problem 1.6:* Suppose $x$ and $y$ are each least upper bounds of $S$. Then $x \leq y$ (since $x$ is a least upper bound and $y$ is an upper bound), but also $y \leq x$ (since $y$ is a least upper bound and $x$ is an upper bound). Since $x \leq y$ and $y \leq x$, we must have $x = y$. So the least upper bound is unique. $\square$

The least upper bound, or supremum, of a subset $S \subset \mathbb{R}$ is denoted $\sup S$ (if it exists). Similarly, the greatest lower bound, or infimum, of $S$ is denoted $\inf S$ (if it exists)—we will leave it as an exercise to prove that if it exists, it must be unique.

We can now precisely say what it is that makes $\mathbb{R}$ "better" than $\mathbb{Q}$:

> **Important:** $\mathbb{R}$ is **complete**, meaning that every nonempty subset $S \subset \mathbb{R}$ that has an upper bound has a least upper bound.

This may seem obscure, but it is the fundamental property that distinguishes $\mathbb{R}$ from $\mathbb{Q}$. By way of example, let's again look at $\sqrt{2}$ by considering the set

$$A = \{x \in \mathbb{Q} \mid x^2 < 2\}.$$

As a subset of $\mathbb{Q}$, this subset certainly has an upper bound (2 is a trivial example of an upper bound of $A$), but it has no *least* upper bound: there is no single number in $\mathbb{Q}$ that is an upper bound of $A$, but smaller than all other upper bounds of $A$. However, as a subset of $\mathbb{R}$, the set $A$ has a least upper bound: $\sup A = \sqrt{2}$ because $\sqrt{2}$ is an upper bound of $A$ (that is, all numbers in $A$ are less than or equal to $\sqrt{2}$) and any other upper bound of $A$ must be greater than $\sqrt{2}$.

The most important subsets of $\mathbb{R}$ that we will be regularly using are **intervals**:

> **Definition:** A subset $I$ of $\mathbb{R}$ is called an **interval** if, for any $a, b \in I$ and $x \in \mathbb{R}$ such that $a \leq x \leq b$, we have $x \in I$.

Informally, an interval $I$ is a subset of $\mathbb{R}$ without any "holes"—if $a$ and $b$ are in $I$, then all the numbers between $a$ and $b$ are also in $I$. Two types of intervals are most commonly used:

> **Definition:** Let $a \leq b$ be any two real numbers. The **open interval** $(a, b)$ is defined as the set
>
> $$(a, b) = \{x \in \mathbb{R} \mid a < x < b\}.$$
>
> The **closed interval** $[a, b]$ is defined as the set
>
> $$[a, b] = \{x \in \mathbb{R} \mid a \leq x \leq b\}.$$

It is easy to check that open intervals and closed intervals are indeed intervals (we leave this as an exercise). We think of intervals as segments of the real line. Open intervals do not include the endpoints, but closed intervals do. We denote intervals on a number line as follows:

Notice that we use an open circle to indicate that the endpoint of the interval is not included in the interval (as in the case of an open interval), and a filled-in circle to indicate that the endpoint of the interval is included in the interval (as in the case of a closed interval).

If we set $a = b$ in our definition above, we get that $(a, a) = \emptyset$ and $[a, a] = \{a\}$. So the empty set is an open interval, and a single point is a closed interval. For technical reasons, the empty set is also a closed interval, even though it is not of the form $[a, b]$ for some $a \leq b$. (One way around this technical loophole would be to allow $a > b$ in our definition of $[a, b]$.)

We also often use the following notations for intervals that include one endpoint but not the other:

$$[a, b) = \{x \in \mathbb{R} \mid a \leq x < b\},$$
$$(a, b] = \{x \in \mathbb{R} \mid a < x \leq b\}.$$

Such intervals are referred to as **half-open** intervals.

> **Problem 1.7:** Let $a \leq b$ be any two real numbers.
> (a)  What are $\sup[a, b]$ and $\inf[a, b]$?
> (b)  What are $\sup(a, b)$ and $\inf(a, b)$?
> (c)  Comparing your answers to (a) and (b), what is the distinguishing feature that differentiates $[a, b]$ from $(a, b)$?

*Solution for Problem 1.7:*

(a)  If $x \in [a, b]$, then $a \leq x \leq b$. This immediately tells us that $a$ is a lower bound and $b$ is an upper bound. In particular, by definition $\sup[a, b] \leq b$, since any upper bound (in particular $b$) is at least $\sup[a, b]$. On the other hand, $b \leq \sup[a, b]$ since $b$ is in the set $[a, b]$. Thus $b = \sup[a, b]$. Similarly, $a = \inf[a, b]$.

(b)  If $x \in (a, b)$, then $a < x < b$. As in part (a), this immediately tells us that $a$ is a lower bound and $b$ is an upper bound. Any real number less than $b$ (but greater than $a$) is in the interval, so no number less than $b$ can be an upper bound. Therefore, $\sup(a, b) \geq b$. But $\sup(a, b) \leq b$ by definition (since $b$ is an upper bound), so $\sup(a, b) = b$. Similarly, $a = \inf(a, b)$.

(c)  From (a) and (b), we see that $\sup[a, b] = \sup(a, b) = b$ and $\inf[a, b] = \inf(a, b) = a$. The difference is that in part (a), the supremum and infimum are elements of the interval, whereas in part (b), they are not. In other words, $\sup[a, b] \in [a, b]$ and $\inf[a, b] \in [a, b]$, but $\sup(a, b) \notin (a, b)$ and $\inf(a, b) \notin (a, b)$.

□

The last problem motivates a new definition:

---

**Definition:** Let $S$ be a subset of $\mathbb{R}$. If $\sup S \in S$, we say that $\sup S$ is the **maximal element** of $S$ (or simply the **maximum** of $S$). If $\inf S \in S$, we say that $\inf S$ is the **minimal element** of $S$ (or simply the **minimum** of $S$).

---

As we saw in Problem 1.7, although a bounded subset of $\mathbb{R}$ must have a supremum and an infimum, it need not have a maximum or minimum.

We often use unbounded intervals too:

---

**Definition:** Let $a, b \in \mathbb{R}$. We define the following intervals:

$$[a, +\infty) = \{x \in \mathbb{R} \mid a \leq x\} \qquad (a, +\infty) = \{x \in \mathbb{R} \mid a < x\}$$
$$(-\infty, b] = \{x \in \mathbb{R} \mid x \leq b\} \qquad (-\infty, b) = \{x \in \mathbb{R} \mid x < b\}$$

---

---

**WARNING!!**     It is common to use just $\infty$ instead of $+\infty$, especially when the context is clear.

---

---

**Important:**     The symbol $+\infty$ is read "positive infinity." However, it is very important to not think of $+\infty$ as a number—rather, it is a conceptual symbol that vaguely means "arbitrarily large" or "growing without bound," but whose specific meaning depends on its context.

---

Because we never think of $+\infty$ or $-\infty$ as a number, we don't think of the interval as containing $+\infty$ or $-\infty$, and thus the "infinite" end of the interval is always open. In particular, we never would write $[a, +\infty]$. Nonetheless, the intervals $[a, +\infty)$ and $(-\infty, b]$ are closed intervals, because they contain their endpoint, even though they appear to be open at the unbounded end. The intervals $(a, +\infty)$ and $(-\infty, b)$ are open intervals, because they do not contain their endpoint.

---

**Problem 1.8:** Let $a \in \mathbb{R}$. What are $\sup[a, +\infty)$ and $\inf[a, +\infty)$?

---

*Solution for Problem 1.8:* By construction, the interval $[a, +\infty)$ has no upper bound, since it contains arbitrarily large elements. Thus $\sup[a, +\infty)$ is undefined. On the other hand, $\inf[a, +\infty) = a$ by the same argument that shows $\inf[a, b] = a$ for any $b \geq a$. $\square$

Finally, we can write the entire set of real numbers as an interval as $\mathbb{R} = (-\infty, +\infty)$. This interval is both open and closed. Indeed, the only two intervals that are both open and closed are $\emptyset$ and $\mathbb{R}$.

## EXERCISES

**1.2.1** Let $S \subset \mathbb{R}$. Show that if $S$ has a greatest lower bound, then this greatest lower bound is unique.

**1.2.2** Prove that for any $a \leq b$, the open interval $(a, b)$ and the closed interval $[a, b]$ are indeed intervals (using our original definition of interval). **Hints:** 243

**1.2.3**

(a) Show that the intersection of any two intervals is an interval.

(b) Show that the union of any two intervals need not be an interval. **Hints:** 123

**1.2.4★** If $A, B$ are bounded intervals with $A \cap B \neq \emptyset$, then show that $\sup(A \cap B) = \min\{\sup A, \sup B\}$. **Hints:** 113, 220

## 1.3 FUNCTIONS

A **function** is a mathematical device that associates an input with a unique output. For example, we write

$$f(x) = 3x - 5$$

to mean the function which, for any given input $x \in \mathbb{R}$, outputs the real number $3x - 5$. The $x$ in our function definition above is a **dummy variable** that takes the place of the input. This dummy variable can be anything, so

$$f(x) = 3x - 5, \qquad f(t) = 3t - 5, \qquad f(\xi) = 3\xi - 5$$

are all representations of the same function.

More formally:

> **Definition:** A **function** $f$ from a set $A$ to a set $B$, denoted $f : A \to B$, associates to each $a \in A$ an element $f(a) \in B$. The set $A$ is called the **domain** of $f$ and the set $B$ is called the **codomain** of $f$. We let $\mathrm{Dom}(f)$ denote the domain of $f$ and $\mathrm{Cod}(f)$ denote the codomain of $f$.

In calculus, the codomain of our functions will almost always be $\mathbb{R}$, and you can assume that a function has codomain $\mathbb{R}$ unless otherwise specified. Such a function is called **real-valued** for the obvious reason. If we don't explicitly specify a domain, then it is understood that a function has as its domain the largest subset of $\mathbb{R}$ for which the function definition makes sense. For example, the function $f(x) = \sqrt{x}$ has domain $[0, +\infty)$, since we cannot (in $\mathbb{R}$) take the square root of a negative number. However, sometimes (depending on the situation) we may find it convenient to consider a function whose domain is a subset of its "allowed" domain.

There is another point to make about $f(x) = \sqrt{x}$. Even though the codomain of this function is $\mathbb{R}$ (as it will be for virtually all functions we consider in this book), the function only actually outputs values that are nonnegative real numbers; that is, $f(x) \geq 0$ for all $x \in \mathrm{Dom}(f)$. To indicate this, we say that the **range** of $f$ is $[0, +\infty)$.

> **Definition:** The **range** of a real-valued function $f$, denoted $\mathrm{Rng}(f)$, is the set of values that $f$ outputs; that is,
>
> $$\mathrm{Rng}(f) = \{y \in \mathbb{R} \mid y = f(x) \text{ for some } x \in \mathrm{Dom}(f)\} = \{f(x) \mid x \in \mathrm{Dom}(f)\}.$$

As a simple example:

> **Problem 1.9:** Find the domain and range of the function $f(x) = \dfrac{1}{\sqrt{x^2 - 1}}$.

*Solution for Problem 1.9:* There are two conditions on the domain of $f$. First, since we can only take the square root of a nonnegative number, we must have $x^2 - 1 \geq 0$. But we also cannot have a denominator equal to zero, so we must have $x^2 - 1 > 0$. This means that $x^2 > 1$, so $x > 1$ or $x < -1$. Thus, the domain is $(-\infty, -1) \cup (1, +\infty)$.

Since the denominator can be any positive real number, the range is $(0, +\infty)$. $\square$

We can perform various operations on real-valued functions:

- We can add two functions $f$ and $g$:
$$(f + g)(x) = f(x) + g(x).$$

Note that this is only valid at $x$ where both $f$ and $g$ are defined, so $\mathrm{Dom}(f + g) = \mathrm{Dom}(f) \cap \mathrm{Dom}(g)$. Similarly we can subtract, multiply, and divide:

$$(f - g)(x) = f(x) - g(x), \quad (fg)(x) = f(x)g(x), \quad (f/g)(x) = f(x)/g(x).$$

All of these have the same domain as $f + g$, with the exception of $f/g$ that has the added restriction that $g(x) \neq 0$.

- We can multiply a function $f$ by a constant $c \in \mathbb{R}$:

$$(cf)(x) = c \cdot f(x).$$

It is clear that $\mathrm{Dom}(cf) = \mathrm{Dom}(f)$.

- We can **compose** two functions:

$$(f \circ g)(x) = f(g(x)).$$

Note that, for $(f \circ g)(x)$ to be defined, we must have $x \in \mathrm{Dom}(g)$ and $g(x) \in \mathrm{Dom}(f)$. Notice also that the order of the functions is important: $f \circ g$ is in general not the same as $g \circ f$.

As we progress through the text we will see additional operations that we can perform on functions.

Composition also gives us a new notion:

---

**Definition:** Let $f$ be a real-valued function. A real-valued function $g$ is called an **inverse** of $f$ if $f(g(x)) = x$ for all $x \in \mathrm{Dom}(g)$ and $g(f(x)) = x$ for all $x \in \mathrm{Dom}(f)$. We denote this by $g = f^{-1}$.

---

Notice that if $g$ is an inverse of $f$, then $f$ is also an inverse of $g$, by the symmetry of the definition. Further, since $f$ and $g$ essentially "undo" each other, the result of the next problem should make sense:

**Problem 1.10:** Show that if $g$ is an inverse of $f$, then $\mathrm{Dom}(f) = \mathrm{Rng}(g)$ and $\mathrm{Dom}(g) = \mathrm{Rng}(f)$.

*Solution for Problem 1.10:* Since $g(f(x)) = x$ for all $x \in \mathrm{Dom}(f)$, we see that $x \in \mathrm{Dom}(f)$ implies that $x \in \mathrm{Rng}(g)$. So $\mathrm{Dom}(f) \subseteq \mathrm{Rng}(g)$. On the other hand, if $y \in \mathrm{Rng}(g)$, then $y = g(x)$ for some $x \in \mathrm{Dom}(g)$, and thus $f(y) = f(g(x)) = x$. In particular, $y \in \mathrm{Dom}(f)$, so $\mathrm{Rng}(g) \subseteq \mathrm{Dom}(f)$. Combining these two subset inclusions gives us $\mathrm{Dom}(f) = \mathrm{Rng}(g)$.

By the symmetry of the definition of inverse, we also have that $f$ is an inverse of $g$, and thus the previous argument shows that $\mathrm{Dom}(g) = \mathrm{Rng}(f)$. $\square$

The next problem shows that we can refer to "the" inverse of $f$ rather than "an" inverse of $f$:

**Problem 1.11:** Show that if $f^{-1}$ exists, then it is unique; that is, show that if $g$ and $h$ are both inverses of $f$, then $g = h$.

*Solution for Problem 1.11:* By Problem 1.10, we know that $\mathrm{Dom}(g) = \mathrm{Rng}(f) = \mathrm{Dom}(h)$. Let $x$ be an element in the shared domain of $g$ and $h$; we will show that $g(x) = h(x)$. Since $x \in \mathrm{Rng}(f)$, there is some $y \in \mathrm{Dom}(f)$ such that $f(y) = x$. But then

$$g(x) = g(f(y)) = y = h(f(y)) = h(x).$$

So $g(x) = h(x)$ for all $x$ in their (shared) domain, and thus the functions are equal. $\square$

There are a couple more definitions regarding functions that will be useful for us to have later on. In particular, it's useful to have a way to describe what happens to a set when we apply a function at each point in the set, and it's useful to describe all the points that get mapped to a certain set.

---

**Definition:** Let $f$ be a function and $A \subseteq \mathrm{Dom}(f)$. The **image** of $A$ under $f$, denoted $f(A)$, is

$$f(A) = \{y \in \mathrm{Cod}(f) \mid y = f(x) \text{ for some } x \in A\}.$$

Let $B \subseteq \mathrm{Cod}(f)$. The **preimage** of $B$ under $f$, denoted $f^{-1}(B)$, is

$$f^{-1}(B) = \{x \in \mathrm{Dom}(f) \mid f(x) \in B\}.$$

---

Informally, the image of $A$ is the set where $A$ "gets sent to," and the preimage of $B$ is the set "that gets sent to" $B$. Notice that, by definition, $f(\mathrm{Dom}(f)) = \mathrm{Rng}(f)$ and $f^{-1}(\mathrm{Rng}(f)) = \mathrm{Dom}(f)$.

**WARNING!!** Note that $f^{-1}$ has two different but related meanings. If $f$ has an inverse, and $x \in \mathrm{Rng}(f)$, then $f^{-1}(x)$ denotes the image of $x$ under the inverse function of $f$. On the other hand, if $B \subseteq \mathrm{Cod}(f)$, then $f^{-1}(B)$ denotes the preimage of $B$ under $f$; we do not require that $f$ have an inverse in order to define $f^{-1}(B)$. In the former, $x$ is a number, whereas in the latter, $B$ is a subset.

Here is an example of this notation:

**Problem 1.12:** Let $f(x) = x^2 - 3$.
(a)  Find $f((0,3))$ and $f([0,3])$.
(b)  Find $f^{-1}((1,2))$.
(c)  Find $f^{-1}((-5,-4))$.

*Solution for Problem 1.12:*

(a)  Note that $f(0) = -3$ and $f(3) = 6$. Furthermore, we see that $f$ is "continuously" increasing from $-3$ to $6$ as we increase $x$ from $0$ to $3$. Thus we should have that $f((0,3)) = (-3,6)$ and $f([0,3]) = [-3,6]$. We have somewhat cheated a little here: the word "continuously" is not well-defined, and is certainly not rigorous. But if you glance ahead a little bit, you'll see that this is the topic of the next chapter.

(b)  If $x^2 - 3 = 1$, then $x^2 = 4$, so $x = \pm 2$. Also, if $x^2 - 3 = 2$, then $x^2 = 5$, so $x = \pm \sqrt{5}$. Thus,

$$f^{-1}((1,2)) = (-\sqrt{5}, -2) \cup (2, \sqrt{5}).$$

This shows that the preimage of an interval, even using a "nice" function like $x^2 - 3$, does not necessarily have to be an interval.

(c)  There is no value of $x$ such that $-5 < f(x) < -4$, since $f(x) \geq -3$ for all $x \in \mathbb{R}$. Hence $f^{-1}((-5,-4)) = \emptyset$. More generally, if $B$ contains no values in $\mathrm{Rng}(f)$, then $f^{-1}(B) = \emptyset$.

$\square$

Images and preimages are not necessarily inverse operations, despite their suggestive notation. The next problem is trickier than it looks:

**Problem 1.13:**
(a)  Let $f$ be a function and $A \subset \mathrm{Dom}(f)$. What is the relationship between $A$ and $f^{-1}(f(A))$?
(b)  Let $f$ be a function and $B \subset \mathrm{Cod}(f)$. What is the relationship between $B$ and $f(f^{-1}(B))$?
(c)  Let $f$ be a function and $B \subset \mathrm{Rng}(f)$. What is the relationship between $B$ and $f(f^{-1}(B))$?

*Solution for Problem 1.13:*

---

(a) If $x \in A$, then by definition $f(x) \in f(A)$. And since $x$ is an element that gets mapped into $f(A)$, we have $x \in f^{-1}(f(A))$. This means that $A \subseteq f^{-1}(f(A))$, since every element of $A$ is also an element of $f^{-1}(f(A))$. However, if we try to reverse this argument, it doesn't work. Indeed, consider the example $f(x) = x^2$ and $A = [0, 2]$. Then $f(A) = f([0, 2]) = [0, 4]$, and $f^{-1}(f(A)) = f^{-1}([0, 4]) = [-2, 2]$, which is strictly larger than the original set $A$. Thus, all we can say is that $A \subseteq f^{-1}(f(A))$.

(b) If $y \in f(f^{-1}(B))$, then by definition there is some $x \in f^{-1}(B)$ such that $f(x) = y$. But, again by definition, $x \in f^{-1}(B)$ means that $f(x) \in B$, and since $y = f(x)$ this means $y \in B$. Hence, every element in $f(f^{-1}(B))$ is also in $B$, and thus $f(f^{-1}(B)) \subseteq B$. As in part (a), the converse is not true: for example, take $f(x) = x^2$ and $B = [-4, 4]$. Then $f^{-1}(B) = [-2, 2]$ and $f(f^{-1}(B)) = f([-2, 2]) = [0, 4] \subset B$. Thus all we can say is $f(f^{-1}(B)) \subseteq B$.

(c) The reason that the converse fails in part (b) is that $B$ might contain elements that are not in the range of $f$. But if $B \subseteq \mathrm{Rng}(f)$, then every element $y \in B$ satisfies $y = f(x)$ for some $x \in \mathrm{Dom}(f)$. Then we have $x \in f^{-1}(B)$, and thus $y = f(x) \in f(f^{-1}(B))$. This proves that $B \subseteq f(f^{-1}(B))$, and this combined with part (b) gives us $B = f(f^{-1}(B))$.

□

> **WARNING!!** ☢ Images and preimages often behave in "unintuitive" ways. Be careful when working with them!

## EXERCISES

**1.3.1** Find the domain of $f(x) = \dfrac{x - 2}{\sqrt{x^2 - 7x + 12}}$.

**1.3.2** Find the domain and range of $f(x) = |2x - 3| + 5$.

**1.3.3** Can a function have domain $\emptyset$? Can a function have range $\emptyset$? Explain your answers. **Hints:** 229

**1.3.4** Show that if $A \subseteq B$ and $f$ is a function whose domain includes $B$, then $f(A) \subseteq f(B)$. If $A$ is a proper subset, that is if $A \subset B$, must we have $f(A) \subset f(B)$?

**1.3.5★** If $f$ is a function with inverse $f^{-1}$, and $y \in \mathrm{Rng}(f)$, what is the relationship between $f^{-1}(y)$ and $f^{-1}(\{y\})$? **Hints:** 103

## 1.4 GRAPHS OF FUNCTIONS

You should already be familiar with graphing functions. For example, the picture to the right shows the graph of $y = x^2 - 2x - 3$. The investigation of geometric properties of graphs of functions is one of the cornerstones of calculus, and we will be dealing with graphs of functions throughout the book. In this section, we'll give a slightly more formal definition of a graph than you may be used to, and we'll review the important basics about graphs of linear functions. It's important to have these basics mastered because you'll need them to be almost automatic as we continue through the book.

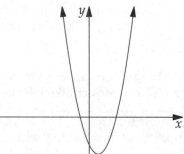

Graphs are constructed on the **Cartesian plane**, as in our picture to the right. The Cartesian plane is the set of all ordered pairs of real numbers; in other words, it is:

$$\{(x, y) \mid x, y \in \mathbb{R}\}.$$

This is often denoted $\mathbb{R} \times \mathbb{R}$ or $\mathbb{R}^2$.

You should know from your past mathematical experience that a point $(x, y)$ is in the graph of a function $f(x)$ if and only if $y = f(x)$. In other words, the graph of $f$ is the set of all points $(x, f(x))$ where $x \in \mathrm{Dom}(f)$. We'll use this as our formal definition of a graph:

---

**Definition:** The **graph** of the real-valued function $f$ is the set

$$\{(x, f(x)) \mid x \in \mathrm{Dom}(f)\}.$$

---

This may seem like a strange definition: we've defined a graph to be a *set* rather than a geometric object. But sets and functions are the things that we can handle most rigorously. Of course, when we draw the picture of a graph in the Cartesian plane, we are identifying the graph with a geometric object. We'll use the word "graph" interchangeably to mean both the set of ordered pairs $(x, f(x))$ and the geometric object that results when we plot all of these ordered pairs on the Cartesian plane.

We'll start with the fundamental geometric property of graphs of functions:

**Problem 1.14:** Let $f$ be a function. Explain why every vertical line in the plane intersects the graph of $f$ in at most one point.

*Solution for Problem 1.14:* For any $a \in \mathbb{R}$, the vertical line $x = a$ in the plane is the subset $\{(a, y) \mid y \in \mathbb{R}\}$. However, there is at most one point in the graph of $f$ with first coordinate $a$, and that is the point $(a, f(a))$. (This is just a restatement of the fact that a function produces a unique output for each input.) Therefore, the vertical line $x = a$ will intersect the graph of $f$ in the point $(a, f(a))$ if $a \in \mathrm{Dom}(f)$. Of course, if $a \notin \mathrm{Dom}(f)$, then there is no point in the graph of $f$ with first coordinate $a$, and hence the line $x = a$ does not intersect the graph of $f$ at all. □

This is called the **Vertical Line Test**:

---

**Important:**  The **Vertical Line Test**: for any function $f$, any vertical line (that is, any line given by $x = a$ for some constant $a \in \mathbb{R}$) must intersect the graph of $f$ in at most 1 point. Conversely, if there is a subset $S$ of the Cartesian plane for which there is some vertical line $x = a$ that intersects $S$ in more than 1 point, then $S$ cannot be the graph of a function.

---

The intuition of the converse portion of the Vertical Line Test should be clear: if some line $x = a$ intersects $S$ in two distinct points $(a, b)$ and $(a, c)$, then there's no way $S$ could be the graph of a function $f$, since we'd need $f(a) = b$ and $f(a) = c$, but $f(a)$ can only equal one number.

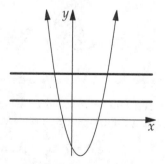

There's no such restriction about horizontal lines. For example, looking back at our parabola $y = x^2 - 2x - 3$, shown at right, there are lots of horizontal lines that intersect the graph in more than one point. However, graphs in which every horizontal line intersects the graph in at most one point have a very special property:

**Problem 1.15:** Let $f$ be a function, and suppose that every horizontal line $y = b$ intersects the graph of $f$ in at most one point. Show that $f$ has an inverse $f^{-1}$.

*Solution for Problem 1.15:* Suppose the line $y = b$ intersects the graph of $f$ at $(a, b)$. We know that $b = f(a)$ by definition, since it lies on the graph of $f$, so our inverse for $f$ will have to map $b$ back to $a$. This tells us how to define the inverse.

Define a function $g$ as follows: if the line $y = b$ intersects the graph of $f$ at the point $(a, b)$, then $g(b) = a$. Note that $\text{Dom}(g) = \text{Rng}(f)$. Since any such horizontal line will intersect the graph in at most one point, the function $g$ is well-defined. By construction, we have $g(f(a)) = a$ for any $a \in \text{Dom}(f)$. Furthermore, if $b \in \text{Dom}(g)$, then the line $y = b$ intersects the graph of $f$ at some point $(a, b)$, so $f(g(b)) = f(a) = b$.

Thus $g = f^{-1}$. $\square$

This leads to:

---

**Important:**  The **Horizontal Line Test**: given a function $f$, if every horizontal line (that is, any line given by $y = b$ for some constant $b \in \mathbb{R}$) intersects the graph of $f$ in at most 1 point, then $f$ has an inverse $f^{-1}$. Conversely, if there is some horizontal line $y = b$ that intersects the graph of $f$ in more than one point, then $f$ does not have an inverse.

---

We have not proved the converse part of the Horizontal Line Test—we will leave this as an exercise.

The most basic and important graphs in calculus are lines. You should already know how to work with lines in the Cartesian plane. Specifically, the graph of $f(x) = mx + b$ is the line with slope $m$ that passes through the point $(0, b)$. If $m = 0$, this is just the horizontal line $y = b$. Note that a vertical line $x = a$ is not the graph of a function, since it does not pass the Vertical Line Test.

Conversely, given a non-vertical line $\ell$ in the plane, we can select any two distinct points on the line, $(x_1, y_1)$ and $(x_2, y_2)$. Then the slope of the line is

$$m = \frac{y_2 - y_1}{x_2 - x_1},$$

and thus $\ell$ is the graph of $y = mx + b$, where $(0, b)$ is the $y$-intercept of the graph.

The last important graph skill that we'll cover in this section is the ability to identify and draw "related" graphs of a function. The following exercise is typical:

---

**Problem 1.16:** Shown at right is the graph of a function $f$. Sketch the graphs of the following related functions (don't worry about exact accuracy or scale, just try to show the general behavior):

(a) $g(x) = f(x + 1)$

(b) $g(x) = f(x) + 1$

(c) $g(x) = f(-x)$

(d) $g(x) = f(2x)$

(e) $g(x) = 2f(x)$

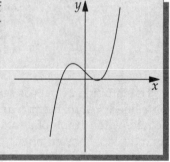

---

*Solution for Problem 1.16:* In all of the pictures in this solution, the original graph of $f$ is shown as a dotted curve, and the graph of $g$ is shown as a darker, solid curve.

(a) Note that if $(x, y)$ is on the graph of $f$, then $(x - 1, y)$ is on the graph of $g$, since

$$g(x - 1) = f((x - 1) + 1) = f(x) = y.$$

In other words, each point on the graph of $g$ is 1 unit to the left of the corresponding point on the graph of $f$. Thus, the graph of $g$ is just the graph of $f$ shifted 1 unit to the left, as in picture (a) below.

(b) If $(x, y)$ is on the graph of the $f$, then $(x, y + 1)$ is on the graph of $g$, since $g(x) = f(x) + 1 = y + 1$. That is, each point on the graph of $g$ is 1 unit above the corresponding point on the graph of $f$. Thus, the graph of $g$ is just the graph of $f$ shifted 1 unit upwards, as in picture (b) below.

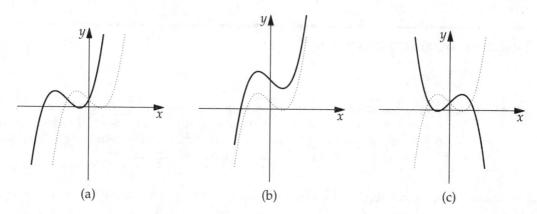

(a)　　　　　　　　(b)　　　　　　　　(c)

(c)　If $(x, y)$ is on the graph of $f$, then $(-x, y)$ is on the graph of $g$, since $g(-x) = f(x) = y$. Thus, every point $(x, y)$ on the graph of $f$ is reflected over the $y$-axis to the point $(-x, y)$ on the graph of $g$. Thus, the graph of $g$ is the graph of $f$ reflected over the $y$-axis, as in picture (c) above.

(d)　If $(x, y)$ is on the graph of $f$, then $(x/2, y)$ is on the graph of $g$, since $g(x/2) = f(x) = y$. So each point $(x, y)$ on the graph of $f$ gets contracted horizontally by a factor of 2 towards the $y$-axis to the point $(x/2, y)$ on the graph of $g$. Thus, the graph of $g$ is the graph of $f$ contracted horizontally by a factor of 2, as in picture (d) below.

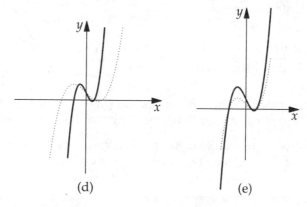

(d)　　　　　　　　(e)

(e)　If $(x, y)$ is on the graph of $f$, then $(x, 2y)$ is on the graph of $g$, since $g(x) = 2f(x) = 2y$. Thus, each point $(x, y)$ on the graph of $f$ gets expanded vertically by a factor of 2 away from the $x$-axis to the point $(x, 2y)$ on the graph of $g$. Therefore, the graph of $g$ is the graph of $f$ expanded vertically by a factor of 2, as in picture (e) above.

□

## Exercises

**1.4.1**　Prove that if $f$ is a function and there is a horizontal line $y = b$ that intersects the graph of $f$ in more than one point, then $f$ cannot have an inverse. (This is the "converse" part of the Horizontal Line Test.)

**1.4.2**　Suppose that $f(x) = x^2 - 2x$ and $g(x) = \sqrt{1 - x}$.

(a)　Find the domain and range of $f$ and $g$.

(b)　Find $(f \circ g)(x)$, $(g \circ f)(x)$, and their domains and ranges.

(c)　Graph $f(x)$ and $f(x - 2) + 3$.

(d)　Graph $g(x)$, $4g(2x)$, and $-g(-3x + 1)$.

**1.4.3**　Show that the converse of the Vertical Line Test is true: that is, if $A \subset \mathbb{R} \times \mathbb{R}$ satisfies the Vertical Line Test, then $A$ must be the graph of some real-valued function $f$.

## 1.5 TRIGONOMETRIC FUNCTIONS

> **WARNING!!** The discussion of trigonometric functions in this section is intended to be
> review. You should already have significant experience with trigonometry
> before attempting to learn calculus. Art of Problem Solving's *Precalculus*
> textbook contains a thorough treatment of trigonometry.

You are already familiar with the trigonometric functions of a right triangle. If $A$ is an acute angle of a right
triangle, then:

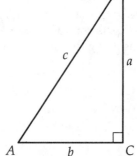

$$\sin A = \frac{\text{length of side opposite } A}{\text{length of hypotenuse}} = \frac{a}{c},$$

$$\cos A = \frac{\text{length of side adjacent to } A}{\text{length of hypotenuse}} = \frac{b}{c},$$

$$\tan A = \frac{\text{length of side opposite } A}{\text{length of side adjacent to } A} = \frac{a}{b} = \frac{\sin A}{\cos A}.$$

Because any two right triangles with the same angles are similar, the ratios of corresponding sides are equal.
Therefore, the trigonometric functions depend only on an angle and not on a particular choice of triangle.

In calculus (as with most of higher mathematics), we always measure our angles in **radians**. Radians are
a much more natural system of measurement than degrees (which depend on the fairly arbitrary choice of 360
degrees in a circle).

> **Definition:** Let $C$ be a circle of radius 1, and let $A$ be a central angle of $C$ (that is, an angle
> with its vertex at the center of $C$). The measure of $A$ in **radians** is equal to the length of the
> arc that is subtended by $A$.

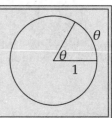

In particular, we can compute the radian measure of some common angles:

- A right angle measures $\frac{\pi}{2}$, since it subtends one-quarter of the circle. The circumference of the circle is $2\pi$,
  so the length of the subtended arc is $\frac{2\pi}{4} = \frac{\pi}{2}$.

- In an isosceles right triangle, the two acute angles each measure $\frac{\pi}{4}$.

The key fact to remember when computing radian measures is that

$$2\pi \text{ radians} = 360 \text{ degrees.}$$

So, we can always easily convert between degrees and radians by setting up a ratio.

**Problem 1.17:**

(a)  Suppose angle $A$ measures $d$ degrees. What is its measure in radians?

(b)  Suppose angle $B$ measures $r$ radians. What is its measure in degrees?

*Solution for Problem 1.17:*

(a)  Let the radian measure of $A$ be $r$. Then we must have the ratio

$$\frac{r}{d} = \frac{2\pi}{360}.$$

Solving for $r$, we see that $r = d\left(\frac{\pi}{180}\right)$.

(b)  Let the degree measure of $B$ be $d$. Then we must have the ratio

$$\frac{d}{r} = \frac{360}{2\pi}.$$

Solving for $d$, we see that $d = r\left(\frac{180}{\pi}\right)$.

□

| **WARNING!!** | If you are using a calculator in your study of calculus, make sure that you put it in "radians" mode and not in "degrees" mode. |
|---|---|

There are two basic right triangles that you should know. They are shown at right with their angles labeled in radians.   You should already know these triangles from your previous study of geometry. In degrees, the one on the left is a 30-60-90 triangle and the one on the right is a 45-45-90 triangle. But from now on, we always want to be thinking about them in terms of radians. We can make the following chart of the trig functions for the acute angles in these triangles:

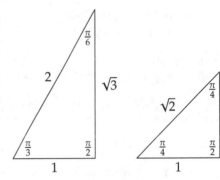

|  | sin | cos | tan |
|---|---|---|---|
| $\dfrac{\pi}{6}$ | $\dfrac{1}{2}$ | $\dfrac{\sqrt{3}}{2}$ | $\dfrac{\sqrt{3}}{3}$ |
| $\dfrac{\pi}{4}$ | $\dfrac{\sqrt{2}}{2}$ | $\dfrac{\sqrt{2}}{2}$ | $1$ |
| $\dfrac{\pi}{3}$ | $\dfrac{\sqrt{3}}{2}$ | $\dfrac{1}{2}$ | $\sqrt{3}$ |

| **Concept:** | You should learn the above table. It should be internalized to the extent that it is as basic as addition. You shouldn't have to think very hard about what $\sin\left(\frac{\pi}{6}\right)$ is; it should be *automatic* that this is $\frac{1}{2}$. |
|---|---|

Using right triangles, we can define our trigonometric functions for any angle $\theta$ such that $0 < \theta < \frac{\pi}{2}$, since any acute angle measures between 0 and $\frac{\pi}{2}$ (in radians, of course!).

However, we want sin and cos to be functions with domains of all of $\mathbb{R}$. To extend their definitions beyond acute angles, we use the **unit circle**. The unit circle is the circle with radius 1, centered on the coordinate plane at the origin $(0,0)$. We construct a right triangle with one leg along the $x$-axis and hypotenuse equal to a radius of the circle, and with acute angle $\theta$ in the first quadrant, as in the picture to the right. We can then determine the lengths of the sides of the triangle, and we see from the picture that the point on the circle corresponding to the angle $\theta$ is $(\cos\theta, \sin\theta)$.

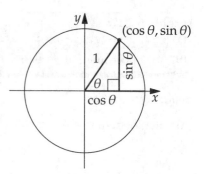

| WARNING!! | A common mistake is to incorrectly write points on the unit circle with their coordinates backwards. Remember, cos is the $x$-coordinate and sin is the $y$-coordinate. (An easy way to remember this is that cos comes before sin alphabetically, just as $x$ comes before $y$.) |
|---|---|

The advantage of using the unit circle to define sine and cosine is that we can easily extend this to any angle, as in the picture to the right. The angle $\theta$ is between $\frac{\pi}{2}$ and $\pi$ in radians. Just as we did with acute angles, we can define $(\cos\theta, \sin\theta)$ to be the point on the circle corresponding to a central angle $\theta$. Note now, though, that $\cos\theta$ is *negative*, since the $x$-coordinate of the point on the circle corresponding to the angle $\theta$ lies in the second quadrant.

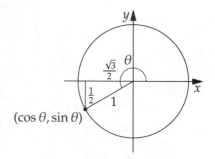

You should become proficient in computing the sine and cosine of any angle that is an integer multiple of $\frac{\pi}{6}$ or $\frac{\pi}{4}$. Here is an exercise to practice:

**Problem 1.18:**
 (a) Compute $\cos\left(\frac{7\pi}{6}\right)$ and $\sin\left(\frac{7\pi}{6}\right)$.
 (b) Compute $\cos\left(\frac{7\pi}{4}\right)$ and $\sin\left(\frac{7\pi}{4}\right)$.
 (c) Compute $\cos\left(-\frac{4\pi}{3}\right)$ and $\sin\left(-\frac{4\pi}{3}\right)$.

*Solution for Problem 1.18:*

(a) We draw an angle of $\theta = \frac{7\pi}{6}$ at right. We see that this puts us in the third quadrant, so both the cosine and the sine will be negative. We can now essentially read from the picture that $\cos\left(\frac{7\pi}{6}\right) = -\frac{\sqrt{3}}{2}$ and $\sin\left(\frac{7\pi}{6}\right) = -\frac{1}{2}$.

(b) We draw an angle of $\theta = \frac{7\pi}{4}$ at right. We see that this puts us in the fourth quadrant, so the cosine will be positive and the sine will be negative. We have that $\cos\left(\frac{7\pi}{4}\right) = \frac{\sqrt{2}}{2}$ and $\sin\left(\frac{7\pi}{4}\right) = -\frac{\sqrt{2}}{2}$.

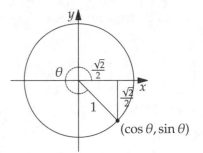

(c) We draw an angle of $\theta = -\frac{4\pi}{3}$ at right—note that this angle goes in the clockwise direction starting from the positive $x$-axis, because the angle is negative. We have that $\cos\left(-\frac{4\pi}{3}\right) = -\frac{1}{2}$ and $\sin\left(-\frac{4\pi}{3}\right) = \frac{\sqrt{3}}{2}$.

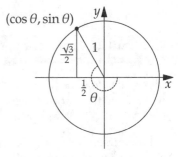

□

We define tangent for (almost) any angle in terms of sine and cosine. Specifically, for any angle $\theta$ such that $\cos\theta \neq 0$, we define

$$\tan\theta = \frac{\sin\theta}{\cos\theta}.$$

If $\cos\theta = 0$, then $\tan\theta$ is undefined.

**Problem 1.19:**
(a) Compute $\sin 0$, $\cos 0$, and $\tan 0$.
(b) Compute $\sin\frac{\pi}{2}$, $\cos\frac{\pi}{2}$, and $\tan\frac{\pi}{2}$.

*Solution for Problem 1.19:*

(a) An angle of 0 means that we don't move off the positive $x$-axis at all. Hence the point on the unit circle corresponding to an angle of 0 is $(1,0)$, the point where the circle intersects the positive $x$-axis. Thus, $\cos 0 = 1$ and $\sin 0 = 0$. Also, we have $\tan 0 = \frac{\sin 0}{\cos 0} = \frac{0}{1} = 0$.

(b) An angle of $\frac{\pi}{2}$ means that we move one-quarter of the way around the circle (counterclockwise starting at the positive $x$-axis). Hence the point corresponding to an angle of $\frac{\pi}{2}$ radians is the point $(0,1)$. Thus $\cos\frac{\pi}{2} = 0$ and $\sin\frac{\pi}{2} = 1$. Then, we have $\tan\frac{\pi}{2} = \frac{\sin\frac{\pi}{2}}{\cos\frac{\pi}{2}} = \frac{1}{0}$, which is undefined. So $\tan\frac{\pi}{2}$ is undefined.

□

**Problem 1.20:** What are the domains and ranges of sine, cosine, and tangent?

*Solution for Problem 1.20:* Using our unit circle formulation, we see that we can define sine and cosine for any real angle, so $\text{Dom}(\sin) = \text{Dom}(\cos) = \mathbb{R}$. Since all points on the unit circle have coordinates that are between $-1$ and 1 (inclusive), we have $\text{Rng}(\sin) = \text{Rng}(\cos) = [-1, 1]$.

Tangent is defined only for angles at which cosine (the denominator of tangent) is nonzero. By looking at the unit circle, we see that cosine is 0 at the angles where the circle crosses the $y$-axis, so $\cos(\theta) = 0$ if and only if $\theta$ is an odd integer multiple of $\frac{\pi}{2}$, that is, if and only if

$$\theta \in \left\{ \ldots, -\frac{5\pi}{2}, -\frac{3\pi}{2}, -\frac{\pi}{2}, \frac{\pi}{2}, \frac{3\pi}{2}, \frac{5\pi}{2}, \ldots \right\}.$$

Thus we get that

$$\text{Dom(tan)} = \mathbb{R} \setminus \left\{ \frac{\pi}{2} + \pi k \;\middle|\; k \in \mathbb{Z} \right\}.$$

It is also easy to see that Rng(tan) = $\mathbb{R}$. □

**Problem 1.21:** Let $\theta$ be any angle. How is $\sin(\theta + 2\pi)$ related to $\sin \theta$?

*Solution for Problem 1.21:* Adding $2\pi$ to an angle $\theta$ corresponds to making a complete revolution around the unit circle, since the entire circle has angle $2\pi$. So $\theta$ and $\theta + 2\pi$ give us the same point on the unit circle, and thus $\sin(\theta + 2\pi) = \sin \theta$ for any angle $\theta$. □

Of course, the same argument shows that $\cos(\theta + 2\pi) = \cos \theta$ and $\tan(\theta + 2\pi) = \tan \theta$. This sort of situation comes up frequently in mathematics, so we have some terminology for it:

**Definition:** Let $f$ be a function. We say that $f$ is **periodic** if there exists a positive real number $k$ such that $f(x) = f(x + k)$ for all $x \in \text{Dom}(f)$. The smallest such $k$ (if it exists) is called the **period** of $f$.

In light of Problem 1.21, we can show that the sine and cosine functions are periodic with period $2\pi$. (In fact, tangent is periodic with a smaller period—we will leave this fact as an exercise.) Graphically, this means that the graphs $y = \sin x$ and $y = \cos x$ repeat every $2\pi$ units along the $x$-axis. We can sketch the graphs by plotting the points that we know: the points where $x$ is a multiple of $\pi/6$ or $\pi/4$. Plotting these and then "connecting the dots" gives us our graphs of sine and cosine:

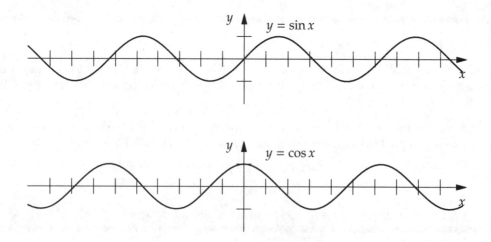

You probably notice that the graph of cosine appears to be the graph of sine shifted $\frac{\pi}{2}$ units to the left. In fact, $\cos x = \sin\left(x + \frac{\pi}{2}\right)$ for all $x$. You'll be asked to explain this and other trig relationships as an exercise.

There are three other trigonometric functions that are commonly used. They are simply the reciprocals of the functions that we already have.

$$\textbf{secant:} \quad \sec\theta = \frac{1}{\cos\theta},$$

$$\textbf{cosecant:} \quad \csc\theta = \frac{1}{\sin\theta},$$

$$\textbf{cotangent:} \quad \cot\theta = \frac{\cos\theta}{\sin\theta}.$$

Notice that $\cot\theta = \dfrac{1}{\tan\theta}$ where both sides are defined. However, we have $\cot\frac{\pi}{2} = 0$ whereas $\tan\frac{\pi}{2}$ is undefined.

> **WARNING!!** ☢ Note that *co*secant is the reciprocal of sine and secant is the reciprocal of *co*sine.

We also need to discuss the inverses of the trig functions. Of course, they do not have inverses as we defined "inverse function" in Section 1.3, as their graphs pretty badly fail the horizontal line test. For example,

$$\sin 0 = \sin 2\pi = \sin 4\pi = \cdots = 0,$$

so we can't explicitly determine $\sin^{-1}(0)$—there are infinitely many $\theta$ such that $\sin\theta = 0$. But we'll cheat and "define" $\sin^{-1}$ by restricting the domain of the sine function to an appropriate interval.

> **Definition:** The **inverse sine function**, denoted $\sin^{-1} x$ or $\arcsin x$, is the function with domain $[-1, 1]$ that satisfies $\sin^{-1}(\sin x) = x$ for all $x \in \left[-\frac{\pi}{2}, \frac{\pi}{2}\right]$.

Thus, $\sin^{-1}$ is the function that takes a value between $-1$ and $1$ (inclusive) and outputs the angle in $\left[-\frac{\pi}{2}, \frac{\pi}{2}\right]$ whose sine is that value. Note that this is not technically an inverse of sine; however, it is the inverse of the function we get by restricting the domain of the sine function to $\left[-\frac{\pi}{2}, \frac{\pi}{2}\right]$.

We can define the inverse cosine function too, but we need to make a slight modification.

> **Problem 1.22:** Define $\cos^{-1}$ in a similar fashion as we defined $\sin^{-1}$. How do the domain and range differ?

*Solution for Problem 1.22:* We want $\cos^{-1}$ to have the same domain $[-1, 1]$ as $\sin^{-1}$, because the range of cosine is $[-1, 1]$. However, the range of $\cos^{-1}$ can't be $\left[-\frac{\pi}{2}, \frac{\pi}{2}\right]$, since cosine only takes nonnegative values for angles in this interval. We need the range of $\cos^{-1}$ to be an interval on which cosine takes all values in $[-1, 1]$. The most obvious choice is the interval $[0, \pi]$, so we have our definition:

> **Definition:** The **inverse cosine function**, denoted $\cos^{-1} x$ or $\arccos x$, is the function with domain $[-1, 1]$ that satisfies $\cos^{-1}(\cos x) = x$ for all $x \in [0, \pi]$.

□

> **WARNING!!** ☢ Most calculus books use the two inverse trig notations interchangeably. In this book, we will frequently switch between $\sin^{-1}$ and $\arcsin$ to get you used to seeing both notations.

Naturally, we also have an inverse tangent function, with the appropriate modifications to the domain and range:

> **Definition:** The **inverse tangent function**, denoted $\tan^{-1} x$ or $\arctan x$, is the function with domain $\mathbb{R}$ that satisfies $\tan^{-1}(\tan x) = x$ for all $x \in \left(-\frac{\pi}{2}, \frac{\pi}{2}\right)$.

## Exercises

**1.5.1** Determine the domains and ranges of sec, csc, and cot.

**1.5.2**

(a) Write $\sin(-\theta)$ in terms of $\sin \theta$.

(b) Write $\cos(-\theta)$ in terms of $\cos \theta$.

**1.5.3** Show that $\tan(\theta + \pi) = \tan \theta$ for any $\theta \in \mathbb{R}$ such that $\theta \neq \left(k + \frac{1}{2}\right)\pi$ for any integer $k$.

**1.5.4** Find $\sin\left(\frac{\pi}{2} + \theta\right)$ and $\cos\left(\frac{\pi}{2} + \theta\right)$ in terms of $\sin \theta$ and $\cos \theta$.

**1.5.5** Find the following quantities in terms of $\sin \theta$ or $\cos \theta$:

(a) $\cos\left(\frac{\pi}{2} - \theta\right)$    (b) $\sin(\pi - \theta)$    (c) $\cos(\pi + \theta)$

**1.5.6** Prove that sin and cos each has no period smaller than $2\pi$. Is the same true for tan?

**1.5.7** Compute the following:

(a) $\cos^{-1} 0$    (b) $\sin^{-1} \frac{1}{2}$    (c) $\cos^{-1}\left(-\frac{\sqrt{3}}{2}\right)$    (d) $\tan^{-1}(-1)$

**1.5.8** Find an angle $\theta$ such that $\cos^{-1}(\cos \theta) = \theta$ but $\sin^{-1}(\sin \theta) \neq \theta$. **Hints: 254**

## 1.6 Basic trigonometric identities

In this section we'll prove some basic identities for the trig functions. The first identity is the most fundamental and also the most useful.

> **Problem 1.23:** Prove that, for any $\theta \in \mathbb{R}$,
> $$(\sin \theta)^2 + (\cos \theta)^2 = 1.$$

*Solution for Problem 1.23:* We recall that, for any $\theta \in \mathbb{R}$, the point $(\cos \theta, \sin \theta)$ is, by definition, on the circle centered at $(0,0)$ with radius 1. But of course any point $(x, y)$ on that circle satisfies the equation $x^2 + y^2 = 1$, and that proves our identity! $\square$

By convention, we usually write powers of trig functions with a notational shorthand: $\sin^2 \theta$ denotes $(\sin \theta)^2$ and similarly $\cos^2 \theta$ denotes $(\cos \theta)^2$. Thus, our fundamental identity becomes simply:

> **Important:** For any $\theta \in \mathbb{R}$,
> $$\sin^2 \theta + \cos^2 \theta = 1.$$

It's hard to overstate how fundamental this identity is to calculus, and we'll see it reappear time and time again throughout the rest of the book.

Next, we have the angle addition and subtraction formulas. These are a bit difficult to prove (see Section 1.A for some further discussion), so we will just present them without proof:

> **Important:**  For any $\alpha, \beta \in \mathbb{R}$,
>
> $$\sin(\alpha + \beta) = \sin \alpha \cos \beta + \cos \alpha \sin \beta$$
> $$\sin(\alpha - \beta) = \sin \alpha \cos \beta - \cos \alpha \sin \beta$$
> $$\cos(\alpha + \beta) = \cos \alpha \cos \beta - \sin \alpha \sin \beta$$
> $$\cos(\alpha - \beta) = \cos \alpha \cos \beta + \sin \alpha \sin \beta$$

While these formulas in their general form are not especially useful for calculus, some specific applications of them are very important. In particular:

**Problem 1.24:** Find simple formulas for $\sin 2\theta$ and $\cos 2\theta$ in terms of $\sin \theta$ and/or $\cos \theta$.

*Solution for Problem 1.24:*  We can just use our angle-addition formulas from above. Specifically,

$$\sin 2\theta = \sin(\theta + \theta) = \sin \theta \cos \theta + \cos \theta \sin \theta = 2 \sin \theta \cos \theta.$$

Similarly,

$$\cos 2\theta = \cos(\theta + \theta) = \cos^2 \theta - \sin^2 \theta.$$

The latter formula is sometimes simplified using $\sin^2 \theta + \cos^2 \theta = 1$ to write it only in terms of sin or of cos:

$$\cos 2\theta = \cos^2 \theta - \sin^2 \theta = 2 \cos^2 \theta - 1 = 1 - 2 \sin^2 \theta.$$

$\square$

The formulas from Problem 1.24 are called the **double-angle formulas**:

> **Important:**  Double-angle formulas:  for any $\theta \in \mathbb{R}$,
>
> $$\sin 2\theta = 2 \sin \theta \cos \theta,$$
> $$\cos 2\theta = \cos^2 \theta - \sin^2 \theta$$
> $$= 2 \cos^2 \theta - 1$$
> $$= 1 - 2 \sin^2 \theta.$$

As an exercise, you'll be asked to find formulas for $\sin \frac{\theta}{2}$ and $\cos \frac{\theta}{2}$. Not surprisingly, these are called the **half-angle formulas**.

The formula in the next problem is also commonly used in calculus:

**Problem 1.25:**  Prove that $\tan^2 \theta + 1 = \sec^2 \theta$ for all $\theta \in \mathbb{R}$ where both sides are defined.

*Solution for Problem 1.25:*  Our first step is a common trig-problem strategy:

> **Concept:**  When dealing with a trigonometric expression, it is often helpful to write everything in terms of sines and cosines.

We write the left side of our desired identity as

$$\tan^2 \theta + 1 = \frac{\sin^2 \theta}{\cos^2 \theta} + 1.$$

Putting this over a common denominator gives us

$$\frac{\sin^2 \theta + \cos^2 \theta}{\cos^2 \theta}.$$

But the numerator is just 1—remember, this is our most basic trig identity (from Problem 1.23). Thus, our expression is just $\frac{1}{\cos^2 \theta}$, which by definition is $\sec^2 \theta$. □

Finally, let's see how some of these identities work in a nontrivial trig problem.

**Problem 1.26:** Given that $t \in \mathbb{R}$ satisfies $(1 + \sin t)(1 + \cos t) = \frac{5}{4}$, compute $(1 - \sin t)(1 - \cos t)$. *(Source: AIME)*

*Solution for Problem 1.26:* It's not immediately clear how to start, so we can begin by assigning a variable to what we want to compute.

**Concept:** In general, when trying to evaluate a complicated expression, set some variable equal to the complicated expression. Then try to combine this new equation with the given data to solve for the variable.

We let $x = (1 - \sin t)(1 - \cos t)$ be the expression that we want. This gives us a system of equations:

$$(1 + \sin t)(1 + \cos t) = \frac{5}{4},$$
$$(1 - \sin t)(1 - \cos t) = x.$$

There doesn't seem to be any good choice other than to multiply out the two left sides.

$$1 + \sin t \cos t + \cos t + \sin t = \frac{5}{4},$$
$$1 + \sin t \cos t - \cos t - \sin t = x.$$

We notice that all of the left side terms are the same (but some with different signs), so adding and subtracting the equations will make some terms cancel. In particular, adding them gives

$$2 + 2\sin t \cos t = \frac{5}{4} + x, \tag{1}$$

and subtracting them gives

$$2\cos t + 2\sin t = \frac{5}{4} - x. \tag{2}$$

You might recognize the double-angle formula for sine in equation (1), and try to replace $2\sin t \cos t = \sin 2t$. But that doesn't really get us closer to our goal of solving for $x$. We want to make all the $t$ terms cancel. Instead, a better idea is to square equation (2), because that will create $\sin^2 t$ and $\cos^2 t$ terms that we should be able to eliminate completely. Squaring (2) gives us

$$4\cos^2 t + 8\sin t \cos t + 4\sin^2 t = \frac{25}{16} - \frac{5}{2}x + x^2. \tag{3}$$

This is good, because $4\cos^2 t + 4\sin^2 t = 4$. So (3) becomes

$$4 + 8\sin t \cos t = \frac{25}{16} - \frac{5}{2}x + x^2. \tag{4}$$

Aha! Multiplying (1) by 4 and subtracting from (4) will cancel all the $t$ terms! We get

$$4 - 8 = \left(\frac{25}{16} - \frac{5}{2}x + x^2\right) - 4\left(\frac{5}{4} + x\right).$$

This is just a quadratic in $x$, which after simplification is

$$x^2 - \frac{13}{2}x + \frac{9}{16} = 0,$$

so by the quadratic formula the solutions to the quadratic are $x = \frac{13}{4} \pm \sqrt{10}$. But which solution do we want?

> **Concept:** Sine and cosine have ranges $[-1, 1]$, and these ranges often put bounds on possible values of expressions defined in terms of sine and cosine.

We recall that we defined $x = (1 - \sin t)(1 - \cos t)$. Each term on the right side has value in the interval $[0, 2]$, so we know that $x \in [0, 4]$. However, $\frac{13}{4} + \sqrt{10} > 3 + 3 = 6$ is way too big. So we must have $x = \frac{13}{4} - \sqrt{10}$ as our answer. $\square$

## EXERCISES

**1.6.1** Compute $\sin\frac{\pi}{12}$ and $\cos\frac{\pi}{12}$.

**1.6.2** Find formulas for $\sin\frac{\theta}{2}$ and $\cos\frac{\theta}{2}$ in terms of $\sin\theta$ and/or $\cos\theta$.

**1.6.3** Find a formula for $\tan(\alpha + \beta)$ in terms of $\tan\alpha$ and $\tan\beta$. **Hints:** 151

**1.6.4** Find formulas for $\tan 2\theta$ and $\tan\frac{\theta}{2}$.

## 1.7 EXPONENTIALS AND LOGARITHMS

At this point, we have several classes of functions to work with: polynomial functions, square roots, and trigonometric functions. But there's one more very important class of functions that we need.

From your algebra and precalculus courses, you are familiar with exponentials and their inverses, logarithms:

$$a^r = b \quad \Leftrightarrow \quad r = \log_a(b).$$

For calculus, we will need a deeper understanding of these sorts of functions. In order to gain this understanding, let's suppose that we were trying to construct an exponential function $f$ from scratch. What properties should it have? We can try to answer this question by looking at a common exponential function that we should be very familiar with:

$$f(x) = 2^x.$$

What properties does this have?

**Problem 1.27:** Let $f(x) = 2^x$.

(a) What is $f(0)$? What is $f(1)$?

(b) Write $f(a + b)$ in terms of $f(a)$ and $f(b)$.

(c) Write $f(-a)$ in terms of $f(a)$.

(d) Sketch a graph of $f$. What are the domain and range of $f$?

*Solution for Problem 1.27:*

(a) $f(0) = 2^0 = 1$ and $f(1) = 2^1 = 2$.

(b) This is a basic property of exponentials:

$$f(a + b) = 2^{a+b} = 2^a 2^b = f(a)f(b).$$

(c) We have

$$f(-a) = 2^{-a} = \frac{1}{2^a} = \frac{1}{f(a)} = f(a)^{-1}.$$

We can also use the fact from part (b). We know that $f(a + (-a)) = f(0) = 1$, but on the other hand $f(a + (-a)) = f(a)f(-a)$. So $f(a)f(-a) = 1$, and thus $f(-a) = 1/f(a)$.

(d) We sketch the graph of $y = 2^x$ at right. Note that from part (a), we know that the graph must pass through the points $(0, 1)$ and $(1, 2)$.

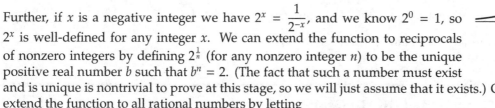

This graph seems to imply that the domain of $f$ is all of $\mathbb{R}$ and that the range of $f$ is the positive real numbers, but are these statements really true? Certainly there's no problem describing $2^x$ if $x$ is a positive integer:

$$2^x = \underbrace{2 \cdot 2 \cdot \cdots \cdot 2}_{x \text{ terms}}.$$

Further, if $x$ is a negative integer we have $2^x = \frac{1}{2^{-x}}$, and we know $2^0 = 1$, so $2^x$ is well-defined for any integer $x$. We can extend the function to reciprocals of nonzero integers by defining $2^{\frac{1}{n}}$ (for any nonzero integer $n$) to be the unique positive real number $b$ such that $b^n = 2$. (The fact that such a number must exist and is unique is nontrivial to prove at this stage, so we will just assume that it exists.) Going further, we can extend the function to all rational numbers by letting

$$2^{\frac{m}{n}} = (2^m)^{\frac{1}{n}},$$

for all integers $m$ and positive integers $n$. But what, for example, is $2^\pi$? How do we define this?

So, at this point, although we may believe that the domain of $2^x$ is $\mathbb{R}$ and the range is positive real numbers, all we can definitively say is that the domain of $2^x$ contains $\mathbb{Q}$.

$\square$

Notice that there's nothing special about the "2" in our above discussion—we could just have easily worked with $f(x) = a^x$ for any positive real number $a$. The issue is that although it's straightforward to define $a^x$ when $x$ is rational, it's not obvious what to do when $x$ is irrational, and we'd like to have a function $a^x$ whose domain is all of $\mathbb{R}$.

Let's focus on what should be the properties of the function $a^x$. To simplify things a little bit, let's assume that $a > 1$. Then we want to have:

- $f(x) = a^x$ has domain $\mathbb{R}$ and range $(0, +\infty)$.

- $f(x) = a^x$ is **strictly increasing**: if $m < n$ then $a^m < a^n$.

- $a^{m+n} = a^m a^n$ for any real numbers $m$ and $n$.

---

**Problem 1.28:** How do we need to alter the above list if $a = 1$ or $0 < a < 1$?

---

*Solution for Problem 1.28:* If $a = 1$, then the function is just the constant function $f(x) = 1^x = 1$. So the range is just the point $\{1\}$, and the function is constant, not increasing.

If $a < 1$, then the function should be **strictly decreasing** instead of strictly increasing: that is, if $m < n$, then $a^m > a^n$. The domain is still $\mathbb{R}$ and the range is still $(0, +\infty)$. This also follows from the fact that $a^x = \frac{1}{a^{-x}} = \left(\frac{1}{a}\right)^{-x}$ for all $x \in \mathbb{R}$, so the function $a^x$ is decreasing if and only if $\left(\frac{1}{a}\right)^x$ is increasing.

In any case, the function should satisfy $a^{m+n} = a^m a^n$. $\square$

Using these properties, we can make an abstract definition of an "exponential" function:

---

**Definition:** Let $f$ be a strictly increasing, strictly decreasing, or constant function with domain $\mathbb{R}$ that takes positive values. We say that $f$ is **exponential** if $f(x + y) = f(x)f(y)$ for all $x, y \in \mathbb{R}$.

---

We know that $a^0 = 1$ for any positive $a$, so we hope that our abstract exponential functions have this property too:

---

**Problem 1.29: Suppose** that $f$ is an exponential function.
(a)   Show that $f(0) = 1$.
(b)   Let $a = f(1)$. Show that $f(n) = a^n$ for any integer $n$.

---

*Solution for Problem 1.29:* We use a common technique:

---

**Concept:**   When dealing with a functional equation, it often helps to plug in simple values to the equation, such as 0 or 1.

---

(a)   Set $y = 0$ in the functional equation $f(x + y) = f(x)f(y)$. This gives us $f(x) = f(x)f(0)$. Since $f$ takes positive values, $f(x)$ is nonzero, so we can divide by it to get $1 = f(0)$.

(b)   We prove $f(n) = a^n$ for positive $n$ by induction. Note that $f(1) = a^1 = a$ by definition, and if $f(k) = a^k$ for any positive integer $k$, then

$$f(k + 1) = f(k)f(1) = (a^k)(a) = a^{k+1}.$$

Thus $f(n) = a^n$ for all positive integers $n$. By part (a), $f(0) = 1 = a^0$. Finally, for negative integers $n$, we have $f(n)f(-n) = f(0) = 1$, so

$$f(n) = \frac{1}{f(-n)} = \frac{1}{a^{-n}} = a^n.$$

$\square$

We can extend Problem 1.29, by essentially repeating the arguments from Problem 1.27(d), to show that $f(x) = a^x$ for all *rational* $x$. However, this does not prove that $f(x) = a^x$ for values of $x$ that are irrational. In fact, we haven't even defined $a^x$ when $x$ is irrational. But $f$, by definition, has domain $\mathbb{R}$, so what we do is *define* $a^x$ to equal $f(x)$ for the exponential function $f$ such that $f(1) = a$.

---

There is one more fundamental exponential property that we will need, and that is

$$a^{rs} = (a^r)^s$$

for all $r, s \in \mathbb{R}$. Unfortunately, this is quite difficult to prove using our current notion of exponential, so we will have to take it on faith (for now) that this is true, and defer the proof until Section 5.A.

> **Concept:** The point of this discussion is that, for any positive $a$, we can consider $f(x) = a^x$ as a function whose domain is all of $\mathbb{R}$, and that this function has all of the nice properties that we expect exponentials to have.
>
> In Chapter 5, we will be able to define very precisely an exponential function, and prove all of these properties. However, we introduce the exponential function now, because we'd really like to be able to use it in examples throughout Chapters 2-4, even if we have to assume certain facts about the function that we cannot prove right now.

There is one very special exponential function that we use throughout calculus. In fact, it is so special that it is usually called *the* **exponential function**. It is the exponential with the special base $e$. The number $e$ can be defined as

$$e = 1 + \frac{1}{1!} + \frac{1}{2!} + \frac{1}{3!} + \frac{1}{4!} + \cdots.$$

There are several issues with this "definition." First of all, it's not at all clear how to define rigorously the above infinite sum, but we will discuss such matters in Chapter 7. Second, even if we assume that the above number exists—and it does, it is approximately 2.71828—what's so special about $e$? Unfortunately, we can't say too much right now. You can see a little bit about why $e$ is special in Section 1.A, but the real power of $e$ will have to wait until Chapter 3.

> **Definition:** The **exponential function**, denoted $\exp(x)$, is the exponential with base $e$:
>
> $$\exp(x) = e^x,$$
>
> for all $x \in \mathbb{R}$.

Again, recall that this means that exp is the strictly increasing, positive-valued function satisfying $\exp(1) = e$ and $\exp(a + b) = \exp(a) \exp(b)$ for all $a, b \in \mathbb{R}$. We usually write it to look like an exponential, so we would write the above properties as $e^1 = e$ and $e^{a+b} = e^a e^b$.

Right now, this is mostly a tease. We'll see why exp is a really nice function in Chapter 3, but we won't be able to make the definition rigorous, or to prove facts about the exponential function, until Chapter 5.

Exponential functions have inverses, called **logarithms**. For example,

$$2^4 = 16 \quad \Leftrightarrow \quad \log_2 16 = 4.$$

More generally, if $a$ is any positive real number and $x \in \mathbb{R}$, then

$$a^x = y \quad \Leftrightarrow \quad \log_a y = x.$$

And if we let $a$ be our special number $e$, then we have

$$e^x = y \quad \Leftrightarrow \quad \log_e y = x.$$

More abstractly, we defined the exponential function to be a strictly increasing function with domain $\mathbb{R}$ and range $(0, +\infty)$. Because it is strictly increasing, it has an inverse (you will explain why as an exercise). This allows us to define our "natural" logarithm function.

---

**Definition:** The **natural logarithm** function $\log : (0, +\infty) \to \mathbb{R}$ is the inverse of the exponential function; that is, for any $x \in (0, +\infty)$ and $y \in \mathbb{R}$, we have

$$\log(x) = y \quad \Leftrightarrow \quad x = e^y.$$

---

Note that we think of log as being $\log_e$; that is, a logarithm with "base" $e$.

---

**WARNING!!**     Most calculus textbooks (and the AP Calculus Examination), and most calculators, use the notation ln for the natural logarithm function. But most mathematicians use log, thus so shall we.

---

Let's verify that the log function has the properties that a good logarithm should have.

---

**Problem 1.30:**

(a) What is $\log(1)$?

(b) Show that, if $a, b \in (0, +\infty)$, then $\log(ab) = \log(a) + \log(b)$.

(c) If $r \in \mathbb{R}$, then what is $\log(a^r)$?

---

*Solution for Problem 1.30:*

(a) Since $\exp(0) = 1$, we have $\log(1) = 0$.

(b) Let $A = \log(a)$ and $B = \log(b)$. Then $\exp(A) = a$ and $\exp(B) = b$, so $\exp(A+B) = (\exp A)(\exp B) = ab$. Therefore,

$$\log(ab) = A + B = \log(a) + \log(b).$$

(c) Let $A = \log(a)$. Then $\exp(A) = a$, so $\exp(rA) = e^{rA} = (e^A)^r = (\exp(A))^r = a^r$. Therefore, $\log(a^r) = rA = r\log(a)$.

$\square$

So our log function behaves like a logarithm should.

## EXERCISES

**1.7.1** For practice, simplify the following. (The goal is for these computations to become nearly automatic.)

(a) $\log(e^5)$     (b) $\log(\sqrt{e})$     (c) $e^{2\log 3}$     (d) $(e^{-(\log 4)})^2$

**1.7.2**

(a) Write $\log_3(7)$ as an expression in terms of the natural log function.

(b) Assume $a$ and $b$ are positive and $a \neq 1$. How do we write $\log_a b$ in terms of natural log?

**1.7.3** Explain why if $f$ is a strictly increasing function, then $f$ must have an inverse function.

## REVIEW PROBLEMS

**1.31** Show that if $A$ and $B$ are two sets, then we cannot have both $A \subset B$ and $B \subset A$.

**1.32** The **symmetric difference** of two sets $A$ and $B$ is

$$A \ominus B = \{x \mid x \text{ is in exactly one of } A \text{ or } B\}.$$

(a) Show that symmetric difference is commutative: $A \ominus B = B \ominus A$

(b) Show that symmetric difference is associative: $(A \ominus B) \ominus C = A \ominus (B \ominus C)$

(c) What is $A \ominus \emptyset$?

(d) Describe, in words, the set $A \ominus B \ominus C \ominus D$, and why it is valid to write this without parentheses.

**1.33** Suppose $a < b < c < d$ are real numbers. Write each of the following as an interval if possible. If it is not an interval, explain why not.

(a) $(a, b) \cup (c, d)$     (b) $(a, b) \cap (c, d)$

(c) $(a, c) \cup (b, d)$     (d) $(a, c) \cap (b, d)$

**1.34** Find the domain and range of $f(x) = \sqrt{2 - x - x^2}$.

**1.35** Suppose that a function $f$ has domain $(-2, 2)$ and range $(-3, 5)$. Find the domain and range (if possible) of:

(a) $f(2x)$     (b) $f(\sqrt{x})$     (c) $f^{-1}(x)$ (assuming it exists)

**1.36** Evaluate the following. (The goal is for these computations to become nearly automatic.)

(a) $\tan \frac{\pi}{4}$     (b) $\cos \frac{7\pi}{4}$     (c) $\sin \frac{5\pi}{3}$     (d) $\csc \frac{3\pi}{4}$

(e) $\cot \frac{21\pi}{4}$     (f) $\sin\left(\pi \sin\left(\frac{\pi}{6}\right)\right)$     (g) $\tan 21\pi$     (h) $\sec\left(-\frac{7\pi}{2}\right)$

**1.37** Find the following quantities in terms of $\sin \theta$ or $\cos \theta$:

(a) $\cos(\pi - \theta)$     (b) $\sin\left(\frac{\pi}{2} - \theta\right)$     (c) $\sin\left(\frac{3\pi}{2} + \theta\right)$

**1.38** Compute $\sin \frac{5\pi}{12}$, $\cos \frac{5\pi}{12}$ and $\tan \frac{5\pi}{12}$. **Hints:** 39

**1.39** Find the smallest positive $\theta$ such that $\sin 3\theta = \cos 7\theta$. **Hints:** 87

**1.40** Find $\arctan\left(\tan \frac{47\pi}{9}\right)$.

**1.41** If $x \in [-1, 1]$, write $\cos(\sin^{-1} x)$ more simply in terms of $x$. **Hints:** 267, 89

**1.42** Solve the following equations:

(a) $\log_5(25^{3x}) = 10$

(b) $\log_2(x^2) + \log_2(3x) = 16$

(c) $e^{2x} - 3e^x - 4 = 0$

## CHALLENGE PROBLEMS

**1.43**

(a) If $A \cup B = A$, what is the relationship (if any) between $A$ and $B$?

(b) If $A \cap B = A$, what is the relationship (if any) between $A$ and $B$?

**Hints:** 132

**1.44** Let $f(x) = \dfrac{ax + b}{cx + d}$ for some real numbers $a, b, c, d$ with $ad \neq bc$.

(a) Find the domain and range of $f$.

(b) Find the inverse of $f$ if it exists.

(c) Why is the condition that $ad \neq bc$ important? What happens if $ad = bc$?

**1.45** Determine all $\theta$ such that $0 \leq \theta \leq \frac{\pi}{2}$ and $\sin^5 \theta + \cos^5 \theta = 1$. **Hints:** 280, 174

**1.46** Compute $\sin(\arctan 3)$. **Hints:** 232

**1.47** If $\sin 2x = \dfrac{21}{25}$ and $\cos x > \sin x$, then compute $\cos x - \sin x$. **Hints:** 60

**1.48** Compute $\tan^{-1} \frac{1}{2} + \tan^{-1} \frac{1}{3}$. **Hints:** 118, 237

**1.49** The following are the **hyperbolic trig functions**:

$$\sinh x = \frac{e^x - e^{-x}}{2},$$
$$\cosh x = \frac{e^x + e^{-x}}{2}.$$

(a) Prove that $\cosh^2 x - \sinh^2 x = 1$ for all $x \in \mathbb{R}$.

(b) Find a formula for $\sinh(x + y)$ in terms of $\sinh x$, $\sinh y$, $\cosh x$, and $\cosh y$. Do the same for $\cosh(x + y)$.

(c) Can you suggest why we use the name *hyperbolic* for these functions? **Hints:** 216

**1.50★** There's an interesting phenomenon called **Russell's paradox** that occurs with sets: Let $C$ be the set whose elements are sets that do not contain themselves as an element. Is $C \in C$? Can you explain what's going on? **Hints:** 6

## 1.A  RELATIONSHIP BETWEEN TRIGONOMETRIC FUNCTIONS AND EXPONENTIALS

Two of the types of functions that we looked at in this chapter—trig functions and exponentials—are connected using complex numbers. Although we will not be using complex numbers in our study of calculus in this book, we will briefly discuss how complex numbers connect trig functions to exponentials.

The set of **complex numbers**, denoted $\mathbb{C}$, is the set

$$\mathbb{C} = \{a + bi \mid a, b \in \mathbb{R}\}.$$

The **imaginary number** $i$ is defined to have the property that $i^2 = -1$. In the complex number $a + bi$, the real number $a$ is called the **real part** and the real number $b$ is called the **imaginary part**.

Complex numbers are added and multiplied as follows:

$$(a + bi) + (c + di) = (a + c) + (bi + di)$$
$$= (a + c) + (b + d)i,$$
$$(a + bi)(c + di) = ac + bci + adi + bdi^2$$
$$= (ac - bd) + (ad + bc)i.$$

It turns out that trig functions are related to exponentials of complex numbers via one of the most important equations of analysis:

> **Important:**   **Euler's Formula:**
> $$e^{i\theta} = \cos\theta + i\sin\theta.$$

For example, letting $\theta = \pi$ in Euler's Formula gives

$$e^{\pi i} = \cos\pi + i\sin\pi = -1 + i(0) = -1.$$

This is often rewritten as

$$e^{\pi i} + 1 = 0,$$

and is considered by many to be the most elegant equation in all of mathematics, as it combines what are arguably the five most fundamental constants in math: $0, 1, \pi, e,$ and $i$.

A less trivial example is

$$e^{\frac{\pi i}{3}} = \cos\left(\frac{\pi}{3}\right) + i\sin\left(\frac{\pi}{3}\right) = \frac{1}{2} + \frac{\sqrt{3}}{2}i.$$

Notice that the left side cubed is

$$(e^{\frac{\pi i}{3}})^3 = e^{\pi i} = -1,$$

and we see that this is true when we cube the right side as well:

$$\left(\frac{1}{2} + \frac{\sqrt{3}}{2}i\right)^3 = \left(\frac{1}{2}\right)^3 + 3\left(\frac{1}{2}\right)^2\left(\frac{\sqrt{3}}{2}i\right) + 3\left(\frac{1}{2}\right)\left(\frac{\sqrt{3}}{2}i\right)^2 + \left(\frac{\sqrt{3}}{2}i\right)^3$$

$$= \frac{1}{8} + \frac{3\sqrt{3}}{8}i + \frac{9}{8}i^2 + \frac{3\sqrt{3}}{8}i^3$$

$$= \frac{1}{8} + \frac{3\sqrt{3}}{8}i - \frac{9}{8} - \frac{3\sqrt{3}}{8}i$$

$$= -1.$$

One of the many wonderful things about Euler's Formula is that it encapsulates the sine and cosine angle-addition formulas. If $\alpha, \beta \in \mathbb{R}$, then we have

$$e^{i(\alpha+\beta)} = \cos(\alpha + \beta) + i\sin(\alpha + \beta),$$

but on the other hand

$$e^{i(\alpha+\beta)} = (e^{i\alpha})(e^{i\beta})$$

$$= (\cos\alpha + i\sin\alpha)(\cos\beta + i\sin\beta)$$

$$= (\cos\alpha\cos\beta - \sin\alpha\sin\beta) + i(\sin\alpha\cos\beta + \cos\alpha\sin\beta).$$

Comparing the real and imaginary parts of this with the Euler's Formula expansion of $e^{i(\alpha+\beta)}$ from above gives us the angle-addition formulas:

$$\cos(\alpha + \beta) = \cos\alpha\cos\beta - \sin\alpha\sin\beta,$$
$$\sin(\alpha + \beta) = \sin\alpha\cos\beta + \cos\alpha\sin\beta.$$

So if you remember Euler's Formula, you don't have to memorize the angle-addition formulas, since they are very easily reconstituted via the above calculation.

Right now, this is magic. In Chapter 7, we'll see more clearly why Euler's Formula is true.

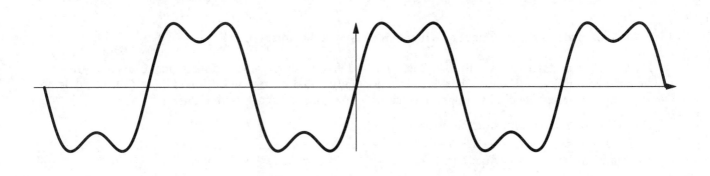

# CHAPTER 2

## LIMITS AND CONTINUITY

### 2.1 LIMITS

**Limit** is probably the calculus concept that students initially find the most confusing. Intuitively, a limit describes what happens as a function "approaches" a point in ℝ. We can get some idea of what a limit is by looking at an example.

> **Problem 2.1:** Consider the functions $f(x) = x + 1$ and $g(x) = \dfrac{x^2 - 1}{x - 1}$.
>
> (a) Determine $\text{Dom}(f)$ and $\text{Dom}(g)$.
>
> (b) Sketch the graphs of $f$ and $g$. How do they differ?

*Solution for Problem 2.1:*

(a) It is clear that $\text{Dom}(f) = \mathbb{R}$. However, $1 \notin \text{Dom}(g)$ since that would make the denominator equal to 0; otherwise, $g$ is defined. So $\text{Dom}(g) = \mathbb{R} \setminus \{1\} = (-\infty, 1) \cup (1, +\infty)$.

(b) The graph of $f$ is the line $y = x + 1$, as in the figure on the left. The graph of $g$ is also this line for all $x \neq 1$, because if $x \neq 1$ then $\dfrac{x^2 - 1}{x - 1} = x + 1$. However, 1 is not in the domain of $g$. Thus, there is a "hole" in the graph of $g$ at $(1, 2)$, as in the figure on the right.

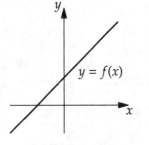
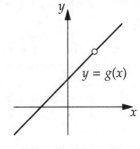

□

On the other hand, looking at the graph of $g$ from Problem 2.1, it is "obvious" that the graph of $g$ "approaches" the point $(1, 2)$. Slightly more precisely (though still pretty informally), the graph of $g$ gets "arbitrarily close" to the point $(1, 2)$. Mathematically, we write this as $\lim_{x \to 1} g(x) = 2$. This should be read as "the **limit** of $g(x)$ as $x$ approaches

1 is 2." We could also write it without referring to the name of the function, as $\lim_{x \to 1} \dfrac{x^2 - 1}{x - 1} = 2$.

There are lots of different ways that we could try to define this precisely, and mathematicians over the years tried some different ideas. The idea that stuck is colloquially called the **δ-ε definition** of limit. (The Greek letters $\delta$ (delta) and $\epsilon$ (epsilon) are used throughout calculus in this context, so get used to them.)

The definition is a bit confusing the first time you see it:

---

**Definition:** Let $f$ be a real-valued function. We say that the **limit** of $f(x)$ as $x$ approaches $a$ is $L$, or

$$\lim_{x \to a} f(x) = L,$$

if, for all $\epsilon > 0$, there exists $\delta > 0$ such that if $x$ is within $\delta$ of $a$ (with $x \neq a$), then $f(x)$ is within $\epsilon$ of $L$. We write this more precisely as

$$0 < |x - a| < \delta \quad \Rightarrow \quad |f(x) - L| < \epsilon,$$

where the "$\Rightarrow$" symbol means "implies":

$$\text{If } 0 < |x - a| < \delta, \text{ then } |f(x) - L| < \epsilon.$$

---

This definition is much easier to understand by looking at the picture to the right. Intuitively, we think of $\lim_{x \to a} f(x) = L$ as meaning that the graph of $f$ comes arbitrarily close to the point $(a, L)$. What this means is: suppose someone tells you that you need to have $f(x)$ within $\epsilon$ of $L$. In other words, someone gives you a value of $\epsilon$ and insists that $|f(x) - L| < \epsilon$. Then, you have to be able to come up with a value of $\delta$ such that all values of $x$ within $\delta$ of $a$—except possibly $a$ itself—have $f(x)$ within $\epsilon$ of $L$. This means you must choose $\delta$ such that

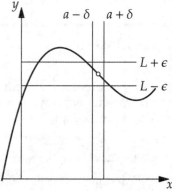

$$0 < |x - a| < \delta \quad \Rightarrow \quad |f(x) - L| < \epsilon.$$

To put it another way, the entire graph of $f$ on the (horizontal) interval $(a-\delta, a+\delta)$—*except possibly at $a$ itself*—must lie within the (vertical) interval $(L - \epsilon, L + \epsilon)$.

In other words, you are given the width of the vertical region centered at $L$ that we require the graph of the function to be contained in, and you have to determine a width of a horizontal region centered at $a$ so that the graph of the function is contained entirely within the box near $(a, L)$. For example, the diagram on the right below shows a smaller value of $\epsilon$ than the diagram above; the value of $\delta$ is also decreased to "trap" the function inside the box near $(a, L)$.

There are a couple of things slightly tricky about this definition. First, it has to work for any positive value of $\epsilon$, but once $\epsilon$ is given, we get to choose the value of $\delta$ that works. (Some sources even use the functional notation $\delta(\epsilon)$, to emphasize the fact that the value of $\delta$ depends on the value of $\epsilon$.) Second, the value $f(a)$ doesn't enter into this at all—in fact, $a$ need not even be in the domain of $f$. Limit is a concept that describes what happens as $x$ *approaches $a$*, not what happens *at $a$*.

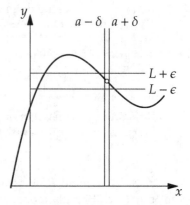

---

**Concept:** The definition of limit is a tricky concept. Don't be discouraged if it doesn't make sense right away. Hopefully, as we progress through the next several examples, the concept will become more clear.

---

Let's practice with this definition by going back to our original example:

**Problem 2.2:** Consider the function $g(x) = \frac{x^2-1}{x-1}$. We wish to prove that $\lim_{x \to 1} g(x) = 2$.

(a) If $\epsilon = 0.2$ is given, what value of $\delta$ can we choose to satisfy the definition?

(b) If $\epsilon = 0.05$ is given, what value of $\delta$ can we choose to satisfy the definition?

(c) Prove that $\lim_{x \to 1} g(x) = 2$.

*Solution for Problem 2.2:* We first note that $g(x) = x + 1$ for all values $x \in \mathbb{R} \setminus \{1\}$. Note that the definition of our limit does not concern itself with what happens when $x = 1$, because we only examine values of $x$ such that $0 < |x - 1| < \delta$ for some $\delta > 0$, and in particular we don't have to worry about $x = 1$. Thus, we can replace $g(x)$ with $x + 1$ when trying to prove the condition in the definition of limit, so $g(x) = x + 1$ for all values of $x$ that we will be considering.

**Concept:** The definition of $\lim_{x \to a} f(x)$ does not concern itself with what happens *at* $x = a$, only with what happens *near* $x = a$.

With this idea, let's proceed to the specific calculations:

(a) We need to choose $\delta$ such that
$$0 < |x - 1| < \delta \quad \Rightarrow \quad |g(x) - 2| < 0.2.$$
But since $x \neq 1$, the condition on the right side of the implication above is equivalent to
$$|(x + 1) - 2| < 0.2,$$
or $|x - 1| < 0.2$. Thus, letting $\delta = 0.2$ will satisfy the condition. In other words, if $x \neq 1$ is within 0.2 (that is, $\delta$) of 1, then $f(x)$ will be within 0.2 (that is, $\epsilon$) of 2.

(b) We need to choose $\delta$ such that
$$0 < |x - 1| < \delta \quad \Rightarrow \quad |g(x) - 2| < 0.05.$$
But since $x \neq 1$, the condition on the right side of the implication above is equal to
$$|(x + 1) - 2| < 0.05,$$
or $|x - 1| < 0.05$. Thus, letting $\delta = 0.05$ will satisfy the condition.

(c) Our solutions to parts (a) and (b) were exactly the same argument with just the value of $\epsilon$ changed, so this argument should work for any value of $\epsilon$. Specifically, we need to choose $\delta$ such that
$$0 < |x - 1| < \delta \quad \Rightarrow \quad |g(x) - 2| < \epsilon.$$
But since $x \neq 1$, the condition on the right side of the implication above is equal to
$$|(x + 1) - 2| < \epsilon,$$
or $|x - 1| < \epsilon$. Thus, letting $\delta = \epsilon$ will satisfy the condition.

$\square$

It just so happened in Problem 2.2 that $\delta = \epsilon$ worked. This will not usually be the case, as in the next example:

**Problem 2.3:** Determine $\lim_{x \to 2} 3x^2$. Prove your answer is correct using the $\delta$-$\epsilon$ definition of limit.

*Solution for Problem 2.3:* Let $f(x) = 3x^2$. Since the graph of $f$ is "smooth" and has no holes or skips, we expect that $f(x)$ approaches $f(2)$ as $x$ approaches 2; in other words, we strongly suspect that

$$\lim_{x \to 2} 3x^2 = f(2) = 12.$$

(Later in this chapter, we'll make this intuition more precise.) Let's prove this limit using the $\delta$-$\epsilon$ definition.

We are given some $\epsilon > 0$, and we need to find $\delta$ such that

$$0 < |x - 2| < \delta \quad \Rightarrow \quad |3x^2 - 12| < \epsilon.$$

The inequality $|3x^2 - 12| < \epsilon$ will be more useful if it is in terms of $x - 2$ rather than $x$, since the inequality $0 < |x - 2| < \delta$ is in terms of $x - 2$. For simplicity, let $z = x - 2$. Then we wish to find $\delta$ such that

$$0 < |z| < \delta \quad \Rightarrow \quad |3(z + 2)^2 - 12| < \epsilon.$$

We can simplify this to

$$0 < |z| < \delta \quad \Rightarrow \quad |3z^2 + 12z| < \epsilon.$$

However, we know that $|3z^2 + 12z| \le |3z^2| + |12z| = 3z^2 + 12|z|$. So it suffices to find $\delta$ such that

$$0 < |z| < \delta \quad \Rightarrow \quad 3z^2 + 12|z| < \epsilon.$$

If $0 < |z| < \delta$, then $3z^2 + 12|z| < 3\delta^2 + 12\delta = 3\delta(4 + \delta)$. Thus it suffices to choose $\delta$ such that

$$3\delta(4 + \delta) \le \epsilon.$$

The $4 + \delta$ term is somewhat annoying. We can make it much simpler by assuming that $\delta \le 1$.

> **Concept:** All we have to do is find *any* $\delta$ that works for our given $\epsilon$. So we can always make $\delta$ smaller than it needs to be.

If we assume that $\delta \le 1$, then $4 + \delta \le 5$, and the inequality that we need becomes

$$3\delta(4 + \delta) \le 15\delta \le \epsilon.$$

To force this to be true, we select $\delta = \frac{\epsilon}{15}$. (In the unlikely event that $\epsilon > 15$, we can just take $\delta = 1$.) We then conclude that

$$0 < |z| < \delta \quad \Rightarrow \quad |3z^2 + 12z| < 3\delta(4 + \delta) \le 15\delta = \epsilon.$$

Thus, for any $\epsilon < 15$, we have found that $\delta = \frac{\epsilon}{15}$ satisfies the $\delta$-$\epsilon$ condition:

$$0 < |x - 2| < \delta \quad \Rightarrow \quad |3x^2 - 12| < \epsilon,$$

and hence we have established that $\lim_{x \to 2} 3x^2 = 12$. $\square$

While performing the sort of calculation that we did in Problem 2.3 is useful to do once or twice in your life, in practice it's not how we usually think about computing limits. We'll have other, more useful techniques to compute limits that we'll develop later in this chapter and at other points in the book.

Once again, we stress that the limit of $f(x)$ as $x$ approaches $a$ does not depend at all on $f(a)$. Let's look at an extreme example of this:

---

**Problem 2.4:** Consider the function

$$f(x) = \begin{cases} x & \text{if } x \neq 0, \\ 2 & \text{if } x = 0. \end{cases}$$

What is the value of $\lim_{x \to 0} f(x)$?

---

*Solution for Problem 2.4:* Looking at the graph of this function, we see that this is just the graph of $y = x$, except the point $(0,0)$ on the graph is replaced by the point $(0,2)$. But as the function approaches $x = 0$, it is clear that the function approaches the point $(0,0)$. Therefore, we should have $\lim\limits_{x \to 0} f(x) = 0$, since the function gets "arbitrarily close" to $(0,0)$ as $x$ approaches 0.

Another way to look at this is to compare $f$ to the function $g(x) = x$. These functions are equal at all of $\mathbb{R}$ except for 0. Thus, since the limit doesn't depend on what happens at $x = 0$, but only depends on what happens *near* $x = 0$, we have

$$\lim_{x \to 0} f(x) = \lim_{x \to 0} g(x) = \lim_{x \to 0} x = 0.$$

Yet another way to see this is to appeal to the $\delta$-$\epsilon$ definition. For any $\epsilon > 0$, we can choose $0 < \delta < \epsilon$, since

$$0 < |x - 0| < \delta \quad \Rightarrow \quad |f(x) - 0| = |x - 0| < \delta < \epsilon.$$

$\square$

Once again, the important concept to take from Problem 2.4 is

**Important:** When determining $\lim\limits_{x \to a} f(x)$, the value of $f(a)$ is irrelevant.

In fact, $f(a)$ doesn't even have to be defined, as in Problem 2.2, where we computed $\lim\limits_{x \to 1} \dfrac{x^2 - 1}{x - 1} = 2$, even though 1 is not in the domain of this function.

It may not immediately be clear that our definition gives us a unique limit. In other words, we need to check the following:

**Problem 2.5:** Suppose $\lim\limits_{x \to a} f(x) = L$ and $\lim\limits_{x \to a} f(x) = L'$. Prove that $L = L'$.

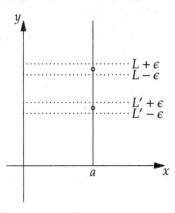

*Solution for Problem 2.5:* Intuitively, if we had two different limits $L$ and $L'$, there's no way that the function could "approach" both points $(a, L)$ and $(a, L')$ simultaneously.

The picture to the right gives us the idea of the proof. We want to pick $\epsilon$ small enough so that the shown horizontal bands for the two limits don't intersect. We can pick any $\epsilon$ such that $0 < \epsilon < \dfrac{|L - L'|}{2}$, which is possible because by assumption $L \ne L'$. The picture clearly shows that, no matter how close $x$ is to $a$, we cannot have $f(x)$ within $\epsilon$ of both $L$ and $L'$, because the horizontal bands in the picture don't overlap. A picture, however, is not a proof, so let us prove this rigorously using the $\delta$-$\epsilon$ definition of limit.

**Concept:** A picture may give you intuition, but it is never a substitute for a rigorous proof.

We'll now prove the result rigorously using the definition of limit. We suppose that $L \ne L'$ and try to derive a contradiction. As above, let $\epsilon$ be such that $0 < \epsilon < \dfrac{|L - L'|}{2}$. Since $L$ is a limit, we can find $\delta$ such that

$$0 < |x - a| < \delta \quad \Rightarrow \quad |f(x) - L| < \epsilon.$$

But since $L'$ is also a limit, we can find $\delta'$ such that

$$0 < |x - a| < \delta' \quad \Rightarrow \quad |f(x) - L'| < \epsilon.$$

This means if we pick $x$ close enough to $a$, then both $|f(x) - L| < \epsilon$ and $|f(x) - L'| < \epsilon$ will be simultaneously satisfied; that is,

$$0 < |x - a| < \min\{\delta, \delta'\} \quad \Rightarrow \quad |f(x) - L| < \epsilon \text{ and } |f(x) - L'| < \epsilon.$$

We write the first inequality on the right as $|L - f(x)| < \epsilon$, and add the two inequalities on the right. We get

$$|L - f(x)| + |f(x) - L'| < 2\epsilon.$$

Then, applying the Triangle Inequality (which states that $|y + z| \le |y| + |z|$ for all $y, z \in \mathbb{R}$) gives us

$$|L - L'| = |(L - f(x)) + (f(x) - L')| \le |L - f(x)| + |f(x) - L'| < 2\epsilon,$$

so $\dfrac{|L - L'|}{2} < \epsilon$. But this contradicts our original choice of $\epsilon < \dfrac{|L - L'|}{2}$, so we have our contradiction, and thus the limit must be unique. $\square$

When they are defined, limits have very nice properties. We'll prove one, and then list a bunch of others that are similar (some of which you will prove as exercises).

---

**Problem 2.6:** Let $f$ and $g$ be functions and $a \in \mathbb{R}$. If $\lim\limits_{x \to a} f(x) = L$ and $\lim\limits_{x \to a} g(x) = M$, compute $\lim\limits_{x \to a}(f + g)(x)$.

---

*Solution for Problem 2.6:* We would be shocked if the answer were not $L + M$. Let's prove that it is $L + M$. As usual when trying to rigorously prove facts about limits, we appeal to the $\delta$-$\epsilon$ definition.

We want to show that if given any $\epsilon > 0$, we can find $\delta > 0$ such that

$$0 < |x - a| < \delta \quad \Rightarrow \quad |(f + g)(x) - (L + M)| < \epsilon.$$

This suggests constructing the similar inequalities for $f$ and $g$ separately using $\frac{\epsilon}{2}$, and adding them together, as we shall see.

Specifically, because we have $\lim\limits_{x \to a} f(x) = L$, we can choose $\delta_f$ such that

$$0 < |x - a| < \delta_f \quad \Rightarrow \quad |f(x) - L| < \frac{\epsilon}{2}.$$

Similarly, because we have $\lim\limits_{x \to a} g(x) = M$, we can choose $\delta_g$ such that

$$0 < |x - a| < \delta_g \quad \Rightarrow \quad |g(x) - M| < \frac{\epsilon}{2}.$$

So if we let $\delta = \min\{\delta_f, \delta_g\}$, then when $0 < |x - a| < \delta$, both $|f(x) - L| < \frac{\epsilon}{2}$ and $|g(x) - M| < \frac{\epsilon}{2}$ above are satisfied, so we have

$$0 < |x - a| < \delta \quad \Rightarrow \quad |f(x) - L| < \frac{\epsilon}{2} \text{ and } |g(x) - M| < \frac{\epsilon}{2}.$$

When we add the two inequalities on the right side and apply the Triangle Inequality, we get

$$|(f + g)(x) - (L + M)| \le |f(x) - L| + |g(x) - M| < \frac{\epsilon}{2} + \frac{\epsilon}{2} = \epsilon.$$

Thus we have satisfied the $\delta$-$\epsilon$ definition for $\lim\limits_{x \to a}(f + g)(x) = L + M$. $\square$

There are other similar properties; we will leave the proofs as exercises.

---

> **Important:** Let $f$ and $g$ be functions with $\lim\limits_{x\to a} f(x) = L$ and $\lim\limits_{x\to a} g(x) = M$. Then:
>
> 1. $\lim\limits_{x\to a}(f + g)(x) = L + M$
>
> 2. $\lim\limits_{x\to a}(fg)(x) = LM$
>
> 3. If $c \in \mathbb{R}$, then $\lim\limits_{x\to a}(cf)(x) = cL$
>
> 4. If $M \neq 0$, then $\lim\limits_{x\to a}(f/g)(x) = L/M$

Now we see that we can easily determine the limit of many "nice" functions by breaking them up into their constituent parts. For example, revisiting Problem 2.3, we quickly see that:

$$\lim_{x\to 2} 3x^2 = 3\left(\lim_{x\to 2} x^2\right)$$
$$= 3\left(\lim_{x\to 2} x\right)^2$$
$$= 3(2)^2 = 12.$$

---

**Problem 2.7:**

(a) Suppose that $f$ is a real-valued function such that $f(x) \geq 0$ for all $x \in \mathrm{Dom}(f)$, and suppose that $\lim\limits_{x\to a} f(x) = L$ for some $a \in \mathbb{R}$. Show that $L \geq 0$.

(b) In part (a), now suppose that $f(x) > 0$. Can we conclude that $L > 0$?

(c) Suppose that $f$ and $g$ are real-valued functions such that $f(x) \leq g(x)$ for all $x \in \mathbb{R}$. Show that

$$\lim_{x\to a} f(x) \leq \lim_{x\to a} g(x),$$

provided both limits are defined.

---

*Solution for Problem 2.7:*

(a) To prove this, we proceed by contradiction and assume that $L < 0$. Pick $\epsilon > 0$ sufficiently small so that $L + \epsilon < 0$ (for example, we could take $\epsilon = -L/2$). Then, by the definition of limit, there must exist $\delta$ such that

$$0 < |x - a| < \delta \quad \Rightarrow \quad |f(x) - L| < \epsilon.$$

But $|f(x) - L| < \epsilon$ means $f(x) \in (L - \epsilon, L + \epsilon)$, which, by our choice of $\epsilon$, means $f(x) < 0$, a contradiction. So we must have $L \geq 0$.

(b) A function that is strictly positive can still approach a value of 0; that is, we might have $f(x) > 0$ for all $x \in \mathbb{R}$ and yet have some value of $a$ such that $\lim\limits_{x\to a} f(x) = 0$. A simple example is $f(x) = |x|$ for all $x \in \mathbb{R} \setminus \{0\}$. Note that we are explicitly excluding 0 from the domain of $f$, so that $f(x) > 0$ for all $x \in \mathrm{Dom}(f)$. But clearly $\lim\limits_{x\to 0} |x| = 0$, so we only have $L \geq 0$, not $L > 0$. We could also construct an example with $\mathrm{Dom}(f) = \mathbb{R}$; for example,

$$f(x) = \begin{cases} |x|, & x \neq 0, \\ 1, & x = 0. \end{cases}$$

Note that $f(x) > 0$ for all $x \in \mathbb{R}$, but $\lim\limits_{x\to 0} f(x) = 0$.

(c) Consider the function $g - f$, so that $(g - f)(x) \geq 0$ for all $x \in \mathbb{R}$, and use part (a). That is,

$$0 \leq \lim_{x\to a}(g - f)(x) = \lim_{x\to a} g(x) - \lim_{x\to a} f(x),$$

so we conclude that $\lim\limits_{x \to a} f(x) \le \lim\limits_{x \to a} g(x)$.

$\square$

Along the lines of Problem 2.7 is an important result called the **Squeeze Theorem**:

> **Important:** The **Squeeze Theorem**: Let $a \in \mathbb{R}$ and let $f, g, h$ be real-valued functions such that $f(x) \le g(x) \le h(x)$ for all $x$ in an open interval containing $a$ (but not necessarily at $a$ itself). If
>
> $$\lim\limits_{x \to a} f(x) = \lim\limits_{x \to a} h(x) = L,$$
>
> then $\lim\limits_{x \to a} g(x) = L$ as well.

We can see what's going on in the picture to the right. The function $g$ is trapped between the function $f$ below and the function $h$ above. Since $f$ and $h$ both approach the point $(a, L)$, and the function $g$ is "squeezed" between them, we conclude that the function $g$ must approach $(a, L)$ as well. Note that the Squeeze Theorem tells us both that the limit must exist and that it must equal $L$. The proof of the Squeeze Theorem uses the result from Problem 2.7; we will leave the details of the proof as an exercise.

We'll continue our initial exploration of limits with a classic nontrivial example that is quite important for calculus:

**Problem 2.8:** Compute $\lim\limits_{\theta \to 0} \dfrac{\sin \theta}{\theta}$.

*Solution for Problem 2.8:* Of course, the function is undefined at $\theta = 0$. You can make a guess of the limit by computing (via calculator) $\frac{\sin \theta}{\theta}$ for values of $\theta$ close to 0. You can also make a guess by using your graphing calculator to graph $y = \frac{\sin x}{x}$ and observing where the graph appears to cross the $y$-axis. Doing either of these should convince you that the limit should be 1.

We can see geometrically what's going on by looking at the picture to the right. Shown is a unit circle with a central angle $\theta$ drawn. By definition, the length of the bold arc is $\theta$ and the length of the vertical line segment is $\sin \theta$. As $\theta$ decreases towards 0, the lengths of these two curves grow closer together, as in the bottom picture. It is geometrically "obvious" that the ratio $(\sin \theta)/\theta$ is approaching 1 as the angle $\theta$ approaches 0.

To prove rigorously that $\lim\limits_{\theta \to 0} \dfrac{\sin \theta}{\theta} = 1$, we will use the Squeeze Theorem. Specifically, we are looking for functions $f(\theta)$ and $h(\theta)$, both with limits of 1 as $\theta \to 0$, such that

$$f(\theta) \le \frac{\sin \theta}{\theta} \le h(\theta).$$

To do this, we'll extend our unit circle diagram a bit, and look at the areas of the shaded regions in the pictures below:

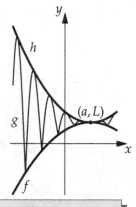

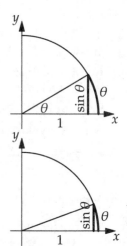

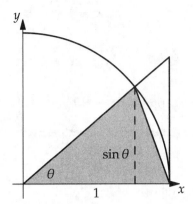 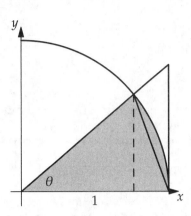 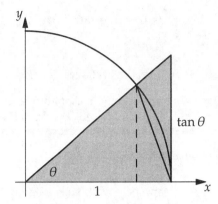

The shaded region in the left picture is a triangle with base 1 and height $\sin\theta$, so its area is $(\sin\theta)/2$. The shaded region in the middle picture is a sector of a circle of radius 1 with central angle $\theta$, so its area is $\theta/2$. The shaded region in the right picture is a triangle with base 1 and height $\tan\theta$, so its area is $(\tan\theta)/2$. Thus, comparing the areas, we have

$$\frac{\sin\theta}{2} < \frac{\theta}{2} < \frac{\tan\theta}{2},$$

or more simply,

$$\sin\theta < \theta < \tan\theta.$$

Taking reciprocals (which we can do since we are only considering small $\theta > 0$) reverses the direction of the inequalities, so we have

$$\frac{1}{\tan\theta} < \frac{1}{\theta} < \frac{1}{\sin\theta}.$$

Then, multiplying by $\sin\theta$ (which is positive), and noting that $\frac{\sin\theta}{\tan\theta} = \cos\theta$, gives us

$$\cos\theta < \frac{\sin\theta}{\theta} < 1.$$

Our calculation only establishes this inequality chain for $0 < \theta < \frac{\pi}{2}$, but since all the terms are the same when we replace $\theta$ with $-\theta$, it is true for all nonzero $\theta \in \left(-\frac{\pi}{2}, \frac{\pi}{2}\right)$. Furthermore, our above argument shows that

$$-\theta < \sin\theta < \theta$$

for values of $\theta$ close to 0, and hence

$$\cos\theta = \sqrt{1 - \sin^2\theta} > \sqrt{1 - \theta^2} > 1 - \theta^2,$$

so we have

$$1 - \theta^2 < \cos\theta < \frac{\sin\theta}{\theta} < 1$$

for values of $\theta$ sufficiently close to 0. Thus, by the Squeeze Theorem, since $\lim_{\theta\to 0}(1 - \theta^2) = \lim_{\theta\to 0} 1 = 1$, we conclude that $\lim_{\theta\to 0} \frac{\sin\theta}{\theta} = 1$. $\square$

Often, when considering $\lim_{x\to a} f(x)$ for some function $f$, it is useful to look only as $x$ approaches $a$ from one side—that is, we only look at the behavior for $x < a$ or for $x > a$. We illustrate the basic idea with the following example:

**Problem 2.9:** Consider the function
$$f(x) = \begin{cases} x \text{ if } x \leq 0, \\ x+1 \text{ if } x > 0. \end{cases}$$

(a) Show that $\lim_{x \to 0} f(x)$ does not exist.

(b) What would be a reasonable answer to the question "what is the limit as $f(x)$ approaches $x = 0$ *from the left*?" What if we replace "from the left" with "from the right"?

*Solution for Problem 2.9:*

(a) The graph of $y = f(x)$ has a "jump" at $x = 0$. It certainly does not appear that a limit exists at $x = 0$. To prove this, suppose that $\lim_{x \to 0} f(x) = L$, and we will attempt to show a contradiction. If the limit exists, then for any $\epsilon > 0$, there must exist some $\delta > 0$ such that

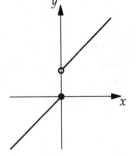

$$0 < |x| < \delta \quad \Rightarrow \quad |f(x) - L| < \epsilon.$$

Choose some $x$ such that $0 < x < \delta$. Then, since $f(x) = x + 1$ and $f(-x) = -x$, we must have

$$|x + 1 - L| < \epsilon \quad \text{and} \quad |L + x| = |-x - L| < \epsilon.$$

Adding these and applying the Triangle Inequality gives

$$|1 + 2x| < 2\epsilon \quad \Rightarrow \quad 1 < 2\epsilon.$$

But this must be true for *any* value of $\epsilon$, and clearly it cannot be true for $\epsilon < \frac{1}{2}$. This is our contradiction, so the limit cannot exist.

(b) When we look at values of $x$ to the left of 0, and ignore the values of $x$ to the right of 0, we see that the graph of the function $f(x)$ approaches the point $(0, 0)$. So it makes sense to say "the limit of $f(x)$ as $x$ approaches 0 from the left is 0."

Similarly, when we look at values of $x$ to the right of 0, and ignore the values of $x$ to the left of 0, we see that the graph of the function $f(x)$ approaches the point $(0, 1)$. So it makes sense to say "the limit of $f(x)$ as $x$ approaches 0 from the right is 1."

$\square$

We'll denote the so-called **one-sided limits** from Problem 2.9 with the notations

$$\lim_{x \to 0^-} f(x) = 0 \quad \text{and} \quad \lim_{x \to 0^+} f(x) = 1.$$

The superscript "$-$" in $0^-$ means to consider only values to the left of 0 (that is, less than 0), and the superscript "$+$" in $0^+$ means to consider only values to the right of 0 (that is, greater than 0).

To make a formal $\delta$-$\epsilon$ definition of one-sided limits, we restrict the values of $x$ under consideration to those on one side or the other:

**Definition:**

(a) We say that $f(x)$ has limit $L$ as $x$ approaches $a$ from the left, denoted

$$\lim_{x \to a^-} f(x) = L,$$

if, for every $\epsilon > 0$, there exists $\delta > 0$ such that

$$0 < a - x < \delta \quad \Rightarrow \quad |f(x) - L| < \epsilon.$$

(b) We say that $f(x)$ has limit $L$ as $x$ approaches $a$ from the right, denoted

$$\lim_{x \to a^+} f(x) = L,$$

if, for every $\epsilon > 0$, there exists $\delta > 0$ such that

$$0 < x - a < \delta \quad \Rightarrow \quad |f(x) - L| < \epsilon.$$

Note that all we've changed are the values of $x$ that we have to consider. When we approach from the left, we only consider $x$ such that $0 < a - x$; that is, $x < a$. When we approach from the right, we only consider $x$ such that $0 < x - a$; that is, $x > a$.

Let's verify that these are weaker conditions than the regular definition of limit.

**Problem 2.10:** Let $f$ be a real-valued function. Show that

$$\lim_{x \to a^-} f(x) = \lim_{x \to a^+} f(x) = L$$

if and only if $\lim_{x \to a} f(x) = L$. (In other words, if the two one-sided limits agree at a point $a$, then the limit at $a$ exists and is equal to the one-sided limits, and vice versa.)

*Solution for Problem 2.10:* This is primarily a matter of chasing the definitions. Suppose the two one-sided limits each equal $L$. Then, by definition, for any $\epsilon > 0$, we can find $\delta_-$ such that

$$0 < a - x < \delta_- \quad \Rightarrow \quad |f(x) - L| < \epsilon,$$

and we can find $\delta_+$ such that

$$0 < x - a < \delta_+ \quad \Rightarrow \quad |f(x) - L| < \epsilon.$$

We can satisfy these simultaneously by letting $\delta = \min\{\delta_-, \delta_+\}$. Then the two statements combine into one:

$$0 < |x - a| < \delta \quad \Rightarrow \quad |f(x) - L| < \epsilon.$$

This is the definition of $\lim_{x \to a} f(x) = L$, so we have finished the proof in this direction.

We will leave the proof of the other direction—that the existence of the limit implies the existence of the two one-sided limits—as an exercise. $\square$

## EXERCISES

**2.1.1** Give an example of a function $f$ in which $0 \in \text{Dom}(f)$ but where $\lim_{x \to 0} f(x)$ is undefined.

**2.1.2** Show, using the $\delta$-$\epsilon$ definition, that for any $a \in \mathbb{R}$, $\lim_{x \to a} x = a$. **Hints:** 288

**2.1.3** Prove that if $\lim_{x \to a} f(x) = L$ and $c \in \mathbb{R}$, then $\lim_{x \to a} (cf)(x) = cL$.

**2.1.4** The **greatest integer function**, denoted $f(x) = \lfloor x \rfloor$, is the function in which $f(x)$ equals the greatest integer less than or equal to $x$. Show that

$$\lim_{x \to 2^-} \lfloor x \rfloor = 1 \text{ and } \lim_{x \to 2^+} \lfloor x \rfloor = 2.$$

**2.1.5** Prove that if $\lim_{x \to a} f(x) = L$, then

$$\lim_{x \to a^-} f(x) = \lim_{x \to a^+} f(x) = L.$$

**2.1.6★** Show that $\lim_{x \to a}(fg)(x) = \left(\lim_{x \to a} f(x)\right)\left(\lim_{x \to a} g(x)\right)$, assuming all terms are defined. (Caution: this is harder than it looks.) **Hints:** 298, 51

**2.1.7★** Prove the Squeeze Theorem. **Hints:** 277, 62

## 2.2 CONTINUITY

Intuitively, a function is **continuous** if its graph can be drawn without lifting your pen from the paper. What this means is that the graph has no holes or jumps. Naturally, in order to rigorously use the notion of continuity, we'll need a more precise definition than "no holes or jumps." At first, it seems somewhat tricky to state exactly what "no holes or jumps" means. But it's actually pretty easy: we use limits. Continuity means that if the graph of a function approaches a point, then the graph actually hits that point; it doesn't skip it or jump away at the last minute.

---

**Definition:** Let $f$ be a real-valued function. We say that $f$ is **continuous** at a point $a \in \text{Dom}(f)$ if

$$\lim_{x \to a} f(x) = f(a).$$

If $f$ is continuous at every point in its domain, we say that $f$ is **continuous everywhere** (or simply $f$ is **continuous**).

---

However, we need to modify this definition slightly if $a$ is on the boundary of $\text{Dom}(f)$. In this case, instead of the limit, we only need use a suitable one-sided limit. For instance, if $\text{Dom}(f) = [a, b]$, then we say that $f$ is continuous at $a$ if $\lim_{x \to a^+} f(x) = f(a)$—since the function isn't defined to the left of $a$, we just use the one-sided limit as $f$ approaches $a$ from the right. Similarly, we say that $f$ is continuous at $b$ if $\lim_{x \to b^-} f(x) = f(b)$, since we only care what happens as $f$ approaches $b$ from the left.

We'll start with some simple examples to show that continuity is not quite as mysterious as it may seem.

---

**Problem 2.11:**
(a) Prove that $f(x) = c$, where $c \in \mathbb{R}$ is a constant, is continuous.
(b) Prove that $f(x) = x$ is continuous.

---

*Solution for Problem 2.11:*

(a) Let $a \in \mathbb{R}$. We wish to show that $\lim_{x \to a} f(x) = f(a) = c$. So, using the definition of limit, we let $\epsilon > 0$ be given. We need to choose $\delta$ so that

$$0 < |x - a| < \delta \quad \Rightarrow \quad |f(x) - f(a)| < \epsilon.$$

But since $f(x) = f(a) = c$ for all $x$, the inequality on the right is just $0 < \epsilon$, which is true for *any* value of $\delta$. So the constant function is continuous.

(b)  Let $a \in \mathbb{R}$. We wish to show that $\lim_{x \to a} f(x) = f(a) = a$. Again, we let $\epsilon > 0$ be given, and we need to choose $\delta > 0$ so that

$$0 < |x - a| < \delta \quad \Rightarrow \quad |f(x) - f(a)| < \epsilon.$$

But the inequality on the right is just $|x - a| < \epsilon$, so choosing $\delta = \epsilon$ does the trick. Thus $\lim_{x \to a} f(x) = a$ and the function is continuous.

$\square$

One thing to note about continuity is that it is a **local** property. What this means is that, for any $a \in \mathbb{R}$, if two functions $f$ and $g$ are equal on an open interval containing $a$, then either both $f$ and $g$ are continuous at $a$ or both are discontinuous at $a$. This is because they have the same value at $a$ and the same limit at $a$ (if these exist). If $I$ is an interval, we write $f|_I = g|_I$ to mean that $f$ and $g$ agree on $I$; that is, $f(x) = g(x)$ for all $x \in I$. (The notation $f|_I$ is read "$f$ restricted to $I$.")

This localness property saves us some time when dealing with some more complicated functions, as in the next problem.

> **Problem 2.12:**  Consider the function $f(x) = \lfloor x \rfloor$, where $\lfloor x \rfloor$ is the greatest integer less than or equal to $x$. At what points is $f$ continuous?

*Solution for Problem 2.12:* The graph of $y = \lfloor x \rfloor$ is shown at right. Just by observing the graph, we see that it "jumps" at every integer, so we suspect that the function is continuous at all non-integer values and discontinuous at the integers. Let's try to prove this.

If $a \in \mathbb{R}$ is not an integer, then the function $f(x) = \lfloor x \rfloor$ equals the constant function $g(x) = \lfloor a \rfloor$ on a sufficiently small open interval centered at $a$. Since $g$ is continuous at $a$ (because it is a constant function), so is $f$.

On the other hand, if $a \in \mathbb{Z}$, then $f(a) = a$, but the limit of $f(x)$ as $x$ approaches $a$ does not exist, since

$$\lim_{x \to a^-} f(x) = a - 1 \quad \text{but} \quad \lim_{x \to a^+} f(x) = a.$$

Since the two one-sided limits are not equal, the limit cannot exist. $\square$

Next, let's state an important basic observation about continuous functions:

> **Important:**  Suppose that $f$ and $g$ are continuous at $a$, and $c \in \mathbb{R}$. Then $f + g$, $fg$, and $cf$ are all continuous at $a$. Further, if $g(a) \neq 0$, then $f/g$ is continuous at $a$.

All of these facts follow from the equivalent facts for limits. For instance, if $f$ and $g$ are continuous at $a$, then

$$\lim_{x \to a}(f + g)(x) = \left( \lim_{x \to a} f(x) \right) + \left( \lim_{x \to a} g(x) \right) = f(a) + g(a) = (f + g)(a),$$

so $f + g$ is continuous at $a$. In particular, this means that, in light of Problem 2.11, all polynomial functions are continuous on all of $\mathbb{R}$, and all rational functions (quotients of polynomials) are continuous at all points in their domains. It is also true, but harder to prove, that the trigonometric, exponential, and natural logarithm functions are continuous. (We will prove that sine and cosine are continuous as an exercise.)

The most important feature of a continuous function is the property explored in the following problem:

**Problem 2.13:** Suppose that $f$ is continuous on all of $\mathbb{R}$ and that $f(0) = 0$ and $f(2) = 3$.

(a)   Must there be a point $c \in (0, 2)$ such that $f(c) = 1$? Explain briefly why or why not (don't expect to be able to prove this rigorously).

(b)   Must there be a point $c \in (0, 2)$ such that $f(c) = 4$? Explain briefly why or why not.

(c)   As generally as you can, describe $f([0, 2])$.

(d)   Why is the assumption that $f$ is continuous necessary?

*Solution for Problem 2.13:*

(a)   At right we sketch the graph of a continuous function $f$ that contains the points $(0, 0)$ and $(2, 3)$. The line $y = 1$ is dashed horizontally. We can see, intuitively, that there's no way for the graph to go from $(0, 0)$ to $(2, 3)$ without crossing the line $y = 1$ at least once. At a point $(c, 1)$ where the graph crosses that line, we have $f(c) = 1$.

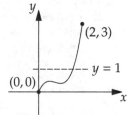

   Of course, this is not a rigorous proof, but we'll get to that in a moment.

(b)   We can do the same sketch as in part (a), but with the line $y = 4$ dashed horizontally. Now it's clear that we can draw a graph from $(0, 0)$ to $(2, 3)$ without hitting $y = 4$. Indeed, the most simple example is where $f(x) = \frac{3}{2}x$; in this case, the graph is a straight line and does not intersect $y = 4$ at a point with $x \in (0, 2)$.

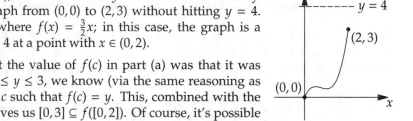

(c)   The only thing that was special about the value of $f(c)$ in part (a) was that it was between 0 and 3. In other words, if $0 \le y \le 3$, we know (via the same reasoning as in part (a)) that there is some value of $c$ such that $f(c) = y$. This, combined with the values of $f$ at the endpoints 0 and 2, gives us $[0, 3] \subseteq f([0, 2])$. Of course, it's possible that $f([0, 2])$ might be strictly larger that $[0, 3]$. In fact, the most general thing that we can say is that $f([0, 2])$ is a closed interval that contains $[0, 3]$, but the proof is rather technical and we will get to it a bit later.

(d)   If $f$ is not continuous, as in the picture at right, then $f$ can have all sorts of gaps and jumps, and there's no guarantee that any particular value will be in the range. To take an extreme example, we might have

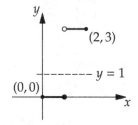

$$f(x) = \begin{cases} 0 \text{ if } x \le 1, \\ 3 \text{ if } x > 1. \end{cases}$$

Note that this function (shown at right) is discontinuous only at a single point, $x = 1$, but that $f([0, 2])$ only contains the two points 0 and 3; that is, $f([0, 2]) = \{0, 3\}$.

□

   As we saw in our exploration of Problem 2.13, the key feature of a continuous function is that it doesn't skip any points. This is more formally stated as:

> **Important:** The **Intermediate Value Theorem**: If $f$ is a continuous, real-valued function defined on an interval $[a, b]$, with $f(a) \ne f(b)$, and $y$ is a real number between $f(a)$ and $f(b)$, then there exists some $c \in (a, b)$ such that $f(c) = y$.

   Intuitively, the Intermediate Value Theorem means that every real number between $f(a)$ and $f(b)$ (so-called "intermediate values") must be the image of some real number between $a$ and $b$. In other words, $f$ can't "skip" any values. As we saw in Problem 2.13(d), it is vital that $f$ be continuous in order to apply the Intermediate Value Theorem.

We will defer the proof of the Intermediate Value Theorem to Section 2.A. It is possibly the most technically difficult proof of all of the calculus topics that we will study in this book.

There is another result that is closely related to the Intermediate Value Theorem, but to prove it, we first must establish the following theorem, which is interesting in its own right. This result states that continuous functions are bounded on closed intervals.

> **Important:** The **Boundedness Theorem**: Suppose $f$ is continuous on a closed interval $[a, b]$. Then there exists some value $M \in \mathbb{R}$ such that $f(c) \leq M$ for all $c \in [a, b]$. (That is, $M$ is an upper bound for $f$ on the interval $[a, b]$.)

> **WARNING!!** This result is not true for *open* intervals $(a, b)$. For example, consider the function $f(x) = \frac{1}{x}$ on the interval $(0, 1)$. This function is continuous on $(0, 1)$ but gets arbitrarily large as $x$ is close to $0$, and thus does not have a maximum on $(0, 1)$.

We can intuitively see why the Boundedness Theorem must be true: if we try to draw a graph in which $f$ is continuous yet grows without bound in $[a, b]$, starting at $x = a$, then we can't "go off to infinity" and yet still reach $x = b$. Of course, this is hardly a convincing argument. Unfortunately, the proof is quite technical, and we will defer it to Section 2.A as well.

> **Concept:**  Understanding (in a general sense) *why* the Intermediate Value Theorem and the Boundedness Theorem are natural consequences of continuity is vastly more important for calculus than learning the nuts and bolts of the proofs. So you should not worry if you skip Section 2.A or if you don't really follow all the details in that section. This is a part of calculus where seeing "the big picture" is a lot more important than worrying about all the gory details.

The Boundedness Theorem allows us to prove the following important fact about continuous functions on closed intervals:

> **Problem 2.14:** The **Extreme Value Theorem**: Suppose $f$ is continuous on a closed interval $[a, b]$. Show that $f$ attains a maximum on $[a, b]$; that is, there exists a real number $c \in [a, b]$ such that $f(c) \geq f(x)$ for any $x \in [a, b]$.

*Solution for Problem 2.14:* By the Boundedness Theorem, we know that $f([a, b])$ has an upper bound, and thus, by the completeness property of $\mathbb{R}$, it has a least upper bound. Call this least upper bound $M$. We need to show that $M$ is the image of some point $c \in [a, b]$. We will prove this by contradiction, so assume that $M$ is not in the image of $f([a, b])$. Then the function $g(x) = M - f(x)$ is continuous and strictly positive on all of $[a, b]$. But more than that: because $M$ is the *least* upper bound, we know that $g^{-1}((0, \epsilon)) \neq \emptyset$ for all $\epsilon > 0$, because otherwise $M - \epsilon$ would be an upper bound for $f([a, b])$.

Since $g(x) \neq 0$ on $[a, b]$, the function $h(x) = 1/g(x)$ is a continuous function on $[a, b]$. However, $h(x)$ is unbounded, since for all $\epsilon > 0$, there is some $x$ such that $g(x) < \epsilon$, and hence $\frac{1}{\epsilon}$ is not an upper bound for $h$. But the unboundedness of $h$ contradicts the Boundedness Theorem. Therefore, $M$ must be in $f([a, b])$, as desired. $\square$

Naturally, the Boundedness Theorem and the Extreme Value Theorem work just as well for lower bounds and minimums—we can simply replace $f$ with $-f$, since a lower bound for $f$ is $-1$ times an upper bound of $-f$, and vice versa.

---

**Sidenote:**  It's possible to construct a function that's not continuous anywhere on its domain. For example, consider the function

$$f(x) = \begin{cases} 1 \text{ if } x \in \mathbb{Q}, \\ 0 \text{ if } x \notin \mathbb{Q}. \end{cases}$$

Since the value of the function changes "infinitely frequently" between 0 and 1, we suspect that the function does not have any limits. Indeed, for a limit at a point $a$ to exist, then for any $\epsilon > 0$ we must be able to find $\delta > 0$ such that

$$0 < |x - a| < \delta \quad \Rightarrow \quad |f(x) - L| < \epsilon.$$

But no matter how small we choose $\delta$, there will be both rational and irrational values of $x$ such that $|x - a| < \delta$. Thus, we must simultaneously satisfy

$$|0 - L| < \epsilon \quad \text{and} \quad |1 - L| < \epsilon.$$

Adding these means $1 < 2\epsilon$, so if $\epsilon < \frac{1}{2}$, we cannot possibly satisfy these inequalities simultaneously. Therefore, $\lim\limits_{x \to a} f(x)$ does not exist at any $a \in \mathbb{R}$, and hence $f$ is discontinuous at all points of $\mathbb{R}$.

---

## EXERCISES

**2.2.1**  Show that $f(x) = |x|$ is continuous.

**2.2.2**  Construct a function with domain $\mathbb{R}$ that is continuous at all points in $\mathbb{R}$ except 0 and 2.

**2.2.3**  Prove that if $f$ and $g$ are continuous at $a$, then so is $fg$. What about $f/g$?

**2.2.4**  Show that if $f$ is continuous on $[a, b]$, then $f$ attains a minimum on $[a, b]$.

**2.2.5★**  Suppose that $f$ is continuous on $[a, b]$ and $f([a, b]) \subseteq \mathbb{Q}$. What can we conclude about $f$? **Hints:** 227

**2.2.6★**  We prove that sine and cosine are continuous as follows:

(a)  Use the fact that $\lim\limits_{x \to 0} \dfrac{\sin x}{x} = 1$ to show that $\sin x$ is continuous at $x = 0$. **Hints:** 90

(b)  Use the fact that $\sin^2 x + \cos^2 x = 1$ and part (a) to show that $\cos x$ is continuous at $x = 0$. **Hints:** 26, 295

(c)  Use the angle-addition formulas to show that sine and cosine are continuous, by showing that

$$\lim_{h \to 0} \sin(x + h) = \sin(x) \quad \text{and} \quad \lim_{h \to 0} \cos(x + h) = \cos(x).$$

**2.2.7★**  Show that every polynomial of odd degree has at least one real root. Is there an analogous statement for polynomials of even degree? **Hints:** 65

---

**Sidenote:**  The **Fundamental Theorem of Algebra** states that a polynomial of degree $n$ has at most $n$ real roots. This is not that hard to prove—try to prove it yourself! The more general version of the Fundamental Theorem of Algebra states that a polynomial of degree $n$ has exactly $n$ complex roots, counting multiplicity. However, this is quite difficult to prove.

---

## REVIEW PROBLEMS

**2.15** Use the $\delta$-$\epsilon$ definition of limit to prove that $\lim\limits_{x \to 2} x^3 = 8$.

**2.16** Compute the following:

(a) $\lim\limits_{x \to 1} \dfrac{x^3 - 1}{x - 1}$

(b) $\lim\limits_{x \to 0} \dfrac{(x + 2)^2 - 4}{x}$

(c) $\lim\limits_{x \to 1} \dfrac{1 - \sqrt{x}}{1 - x}$

(d) $\lim\limits_{x \to 0} \sqrt{x^2}$

(e) $\lim\limits_{x \to 1^+} (x - \lfloor x \rfloor)$

(f) $\lim\limits_{x \to 1^-} (x - \lfloor x \rfloor)$

**2.17** Find an example of a function $f(x)$ with domain $\mathbb{R}$ for which $\lim\limits_{x \to 0^+} f(x)$ exists but $\lim\limits_{x \to 0^-} f(x)$ does not exist.

**2.18** Suppose that $f$ has domain $\mathbb{R}$ and is continuous. Prove or disprove: if the range of $f$ contains both positive and negative numbers, then it must contain 0.

**2.19** Find a function $f$ with domain $\mathbb{R}$ that is continuous on all of $\mathbb{R}$ except $-1, 0$, and 1.

**2.20**

(a) Let $f$ be a function such that $\lim\limits_{x \to 0} f(x) = L$. Prove that $\lim\limits_{x \to 0} f(cx) = L$ for any nonzero constant $c$.

(b) Use part (a) to compute $\lim\limits_{x \to 0} \dfrac{\sin ax}{x}$, where $a$ is a nonzero real number.

(c) Use part (b) to compute $\lim\limits_{x \to 0} \dfrac{\sin ax}{\sin bx}$, where $a$ and $b$ are nonzero real numbers.

**2.21** Show that $f$ is continuous if and only if for all $a \in \text{Dom}(f)$ and all $\epsilon > 0$, there exists $\delta > 0$ such that

$$|x - a| < \delta \quad \Rightarrow \quad |f(x) - f(a)| < \epsilon.$$

## CHALLENGE PROBLEMS

**2.22** Suppose $f$ is a function with domain $\mathbb{R}$ such that $|f(x)| \le |x|$ for all $x \in \mathbb{R}$. Prove that $f$ is continuous at 0.

**2.23** Suppose we define $f(x) = \dfrac{\sin(x)}{x}$, but where $x$ is in *degrees*, not radians. Find $\lim\limits_{x \to 0} f(x)$.

**2.24**

(a) Assume that $\lim\limits_{x \to 0} f(x) = L$. Prove that $\lim\limits_{x \to 0} f(x^3) = L$.

(b) Find an example where $\lim\limits_{x \to 0} f(x^2)$ exists but $\lim\limits_{x \to 0} f(x)$ does not exist.

**2.25** Suppose that $f$ is a continuous function.

(a) Show that if $I$ is an interval with $I \subseteq \text{Dom}(f)$, then $f(I)$ is an interval.

(b) Show that if $I$ is a closed interval with $I \subseteq \text{Dom}(f)$, then $f(I)$ is a closed interval.

(c) Find examples of noncontinuous functions such that (a) and (b) are not true.

**2.26** Let $f$ be a continuous function with domain $[0, 1]$ and range $[0, 1]$. Prove that $f$ must have a **fixed point**: that is, there exists some $a \in [0, 1]$ such that $f(a) = a$. Is the result still true if the domain and range are $(0, 1)$?
**Hints:** 278

**2.27★**  Let $f$ and $g$ be functions with domain $\mathbb{R}$. Suppose

$$\lim_{x \to a} f(x) = b \quad \text{and} \quad \lim_{x \to b} g(x) = c.$$

Prove or disprove that we must have $\lim_{x \to a}(g \circ f)(x) = c$. (If true, explain why, with a rigorous proof if possible; if false, give an example.) **Hints:** 23, 170

**2.28★**  Consider the function

$$f(x) = \begin{cases} 0 \text{ if } x \notin \mathbb{Q}, \\ \frac{1}{q} \text{ if } x = \frac{p}{q} \in \mathbb{Q}, \text{ with } p, q \in \mathbb{Z}, q > 0, \text{ and } p, q \text{ relatively prime.} \end{cases}$$

Show that $f$ is continuous at every irrational point and discontinuous at every rational point in $\mathbb{R}$. **Hints:** 163, 185

---

## 2.A  PROOFS OF SOME CONTINUITY RESULTS

We prove two important but technical results about continuous functions defined on closed intervals.

> **Important:**  The **Intermediate Value Theorem**: If $f$ is a continuous, real-valued function defined on an interval $[a, b]$, with $f(a) \neq f(b)$, and $y$ is a real number between $f(a)$ and $f(b)$, then there exists some $c \in (a, b)$ such that $f(c) = y$.

We prove the theorem in the case that $f(a) < f(b)$. (The proof in the case with $f(a) > f(b)$ is nearly identical.)

Let $y$ be given with $f(a) < y < f(b)$. We want to find some $c \in (a, b)$ such that $f(c) = y$. Define

$$U = \{x \in [a, b] \mid f(x) \le y\}.$$

In other words, $U$ is the subset of $[a, b]$ that $f$ maps to values less than or equal to $y$. Since $U$ is a nonempty bounded subset of $\mathbb{R}$ (it's nonempty since $a \in U$), it has a least upper bound. Let $c = \sup U$. We will prove that $f(c) = y$.

First, we show that $c \neq a$. Choose $\epsilon$ such that $f(a) < y - \epsilon < y$. (For example, we could take $\epsilon = (y - f(a))/2$, since $f(a) < y$.) Then, since $f$ is continuous at $a$, we can choose $\delta > 0$ such that

$$0 < x - a < \delta \quad \Rightarrow \quad |f(a) - f(x)| < \epsilon.$$

But then $f(x) < f(a) + \epsilon < y$, so $x \in U$, and thus $[a, a + \delta) \subseteq U$. This means than any upper bound, and in particular the least upper bound, must be at least $a + \delta$; specifically, $c \ge a + \delta$, and in particular $c > a$.

Next, we show that $c \neq b$, using a similar argument. Choose $\epsilon$ such that $y < y + \epsilon < f(b)$. (For example, we could take $\epsilon = (f(b) - y)/2$, since $y < f(b)$.) Then, since $f$ is continuous at $b$, we can choose $\delta > 0$ such that

$$0 < b - x < \delta \quad \Rightarrow \quad |f(x) - f(b)| < \epsilon.$$

But then $f(x) > f(b) - \epsilon > y$, so $x \notin U$, and thus $(b - \delta, b] \cap U = \emptyset$. But this means that $b - \delta$ is an upper bound of $U$, and hence $c < b$.

Recall our goal is to show that $f(c) = y$, where $c = \sup U$. Let $z = f(c)$; we will show that $z = y$ by showing that both $z < y$ and $z > y$ lead to contradictions.

If $f(c) = z < y$, then pick any $\epsilon$ such that $z < z + \epsilon < y$. Since $f$ is continuous, we have $\lim_{x \to c} f(x) = z$, so there is some $\delta$ such that

$$0 < |x - c| < \delta \quad \Rightarrow \quad |f(x) - z| < \epsilon.$$

Pick $\delta$ satisfying the above to be small enough so that $c + \delta < b$. (We can do this since we've already proved that $c < b$.) Let $c'$ be any real number such that $c < c' < c + \delta$. Then $|f(c') - z| < \epsilon$, so $f(c') < z + \epsilon < y$. This means that $c' \in U$, which contradicts the fact that $c$ is an upper bound for $U$.

On the other hand, if $f(c) = z > y$, then pick any $\epsilon$ such that $y < z - \epsilon < z$. Since $f$ is continuous, we have $\lim_{x \to c} f(x) = z$, so there is some $\delta$ such that

$$0 < |x - c| < \delta \quad \Rightarrow \quad |f(x) - z| < \epsilon.$$

Pick $\delta$ small enough so that $a < c - \delta$, and let $c'$ be any real number such that $c - \delta < c' < c$. Then $|f(c') - z| < \epsilon$, giving $f(c') > z - \epsilon > y$. But then $c'$ is an upper bound for $U$ as well, contradicting the fact that $c$ was the least upper bound.

Thus we must have $f(c) = y$, proving the theorem.

> **Important:** The **Boundedness Theorem**: suppose $f$ is continuous on a closed interval $[a, b]$. Then there exists some value $M \in \mathbb{R}$ such that $f(c) \le M$ for all $c \in [a, b]$. (That is, $M$ is an upper bound for $f$ on the interval $[a, b]$.)

Let's try to isolate the point where $f$ might first become unbounded. In particular, let's start at the point $x = a$ and move slowly rightward, and try to figure out exactly where the function might become unbounded.

Clearly $f$ is bounded on the interval $[a, a]$ (which is just the point $a$), since $f(a)$ is an upper bound. We move to the right, and keep track of where the function stays bounded. Specifically, let

$$D = \{x \in [a, b] \mid f([a, x]) \text{ is bounded}\}.$$

Clearly $D$ is a bounded set (it's a subset of $[a, b]$), and by our basic properties of $\mathbb{R}$, we know that $D$ must have a least upper bound. Let $d = \sup D$. Note that for any $c$ such that $a \le c < d$, the set $f([a, c])$ is bounded.

First, we prove that $d > a$. By assumption, $f$ is continuous at $a$, thus for any $\epsilon > 0$ we can choose $\delta > 0$ such that $f((a, a + \delta)) \subseteq (f(a) - \epsilon, f(a) + \epsilon)$. In particular, this implies that $(a + \delta) \in D$, so $d \ge a + \delta > a$.

We next consider the possibility that $d \ne b$. Since $f$ is continuous at $d$, we have $\lim_{x \to d} f(x) = f(d)$. Thus, given $\epsilon > 0$, we can find $\delta > 0$ such that

$$0 \le |x - d| < \delta \quad \Rightarrow \quad |f(x) - f(d)| < \epsilon.$$

Choose $\delta$ small enough so that $(d - \delta, d + \delta) \subseteq (a, b)$. Then

$$f([a, d + \delta)) = f([a, d - \delta]) \cup f((d - \delta, d + \delta)).$$

The first term on the right is bounded since $d - \delta < d$, and the second term is bounded since it lies entirely within the interval $(f(d) - \epsilon, f(d) + \epsilon)$. Thus we see that $[a, d + \delta) \subseteq D$, but this contradicts the fact that $d = \sup D$.

Thus, we have shown that $d = b$. Since $f$ is continuous at $b$, we have $\lim_{x \to b^-} f(x) = f(b)$. Thus, given $\epsilon > 0$ we can find $\delta > 0$ such that

$$0 \le b - x < \delta \quad \Rightarrow \quad |f(x) - f(b)| < \epsilon.$$

Choose $\delta$ small enough so that $a < b - \delta$. Then

$$f([a, b]) = f([a, b - \delta]) \cup f((b - \delta, b]).$$

The first set on the right is bounded since $\sup D = b$, and the second set is bounded since it lies entirely within the interval $(f(b) - \epsilon, f(b) + \epsilon)$. Thus we see that $f([a, b])$ is bounded, as desired.

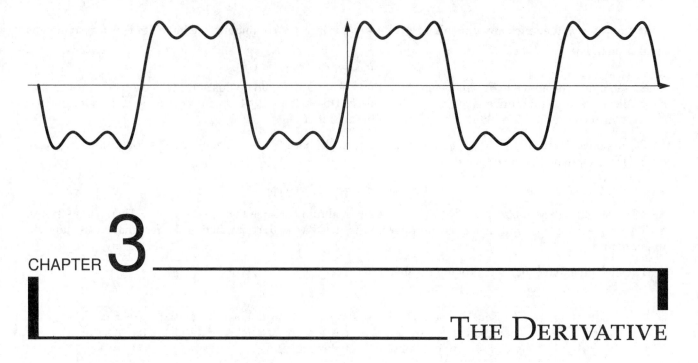

CHAPTER 3

THE DERIVATIVE

Calculus provides the answers to two natural geometric questions regarding the graph $y = f(x)$ of a function $f$.

**Question 1:** Given a real number $a$ in the domain of a function $f$, what is the slope of the line that is tangent to the graph $y = f(x)$ at the point $(a, f(a))$?

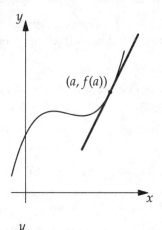

**Question 2:** Given real numbers $a \leq b$ such that the interval $[a, b]$ is a subset of the domain of a function $f$, what is the area of the region bounded by the graph $y = f(x)$, the lines $x = a$ and $x = b$, and the $x$-axis?

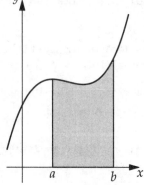

We'll defer our discussion of Question 2 until Chapter 5, when we will have some more tools at our disposal.

Our immediate goal is to try to answer Question 1. The answer to Question 1 is the fundamental calculus concept known as the **derivative**.

## 3.1 INTUITIVE INTRODUCTION

Our first task is to decide what we mean by "tangent." We can think back to plane geometry: given a circle $C$ and a point $P$ on $C$, there is a unique line $\ell$ through $P$ that does not intersect $C$ at another point. This is called the **tangent line** to $C$ at $P$. Every other line through $P$ will also intersect the circle at some other point; such lines are called **secant lines**.

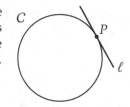

Let's provisionally use this as our definition of a tangent line to the graph of a function:

> **Provisional Definition #1**: A **tangent line** to the graph of $y = f(x)$ at the point $(a, f(a))$, where $a$ is in the domain of $f$, is a line $\ell$ passing through $(a, f(a))$ that does not intersect the graph at any other point.

Let's try this provisional definition with a simple function:

> **Problem 3.1:** Let $f(x) = x^2$. Find a "tangent line" (under our provisional definition above) to the graph $y = f(x)$ at the point $(1, 1)$.

*Solution for Problem 3.1:* Any line (other than a vertical line) through $(1, 1)$ will satisfy the equation $(y-1) = m(x-1)$, where $m$ is the slope of the line. So $y = mx + (1 - m)$. We want to find $m$ such that the point $(1, 1)$ is the only intersection of $y = x^2$ and $y = mx + (1 - m)$. This means that $(x, y) = (1, 1)$ is the only solution to the system of equations

$$y = x^2,$$
$$y = mx + (1 - m).$$

Eliminating $y$ gives us $x^2 - mx + (m - 1) = 0$, which is a quadratic equation in $x$. Clearly $x = 1$ is a solution to this equation (as we already know), but it will have another solution if the discriminant is positive. So for $x = 1$ to be the only solution, we must have $m^2 - 4(m - 1) = 0$. This simplifies to $(m - 2)^2 = 0$, so $m = 2$. (Note that for all other values of $m$, the discriminant is positive, so there are two solutions.) Therefore, the slope of the tangent line is $m = 2$, and the equation of the line is $y = 2x - 1$. $\square$

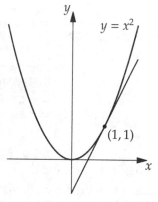

We can sketch a picture of this, as shown to the right, to convince ourselves that we did the right thing. It does indeed look like the correct tangent line. This all looks fine, but it seems like a lot of trouble to go through just to find a tangent line. Another issue is that there is another line that intersects $y = x^2$ only at the point $(1, 1)$, and that is the line $x = 1$. We didn't get that line in our solution above because its slope is undefined. (Remember our "other than a vertical line" qualifier in the first sentence of our solution to Problem 3.1.)

Moreover, we can see that in any graph $y = f(x)$, the line $x = a$ will intersect the graph in only one point, namely $(a, f(a))$. This is the Vertical Line Test for graphs of functions: there is only one $y$-value for each possible $x$-value in the domain.

We can revise our provisional definition to exclude vertical tangent lines:

**Provisional Definition #2:** A **tangent line** to the graph of $y = f(x)$ at the point $(a, f(a))$, where $a$ is in the domain of $f$, is a line $\ell$, not parallel to the $y$-axis, passing through $(a, f(a))$ that does not intersect the graph at any other point.

But there's a more significant flaw, as we'll see with a slightly more complicated example:

**Problem 3.2:** Find the equation of the tangent line to the graph of $y = x^3 + x$ at the point $(1, 2)$.

*Solution for Problem 3.2:* A non-vertical line through $(1, 2)$ has the equation $(y - 2) = m(x - 1)$. So we are looking for a value of $m$ that gives only the solution $(x, y) = (1, 2)$ to the system

$$y = x^3 + x,$$
$$y = mx + (2 - m).$$

Setting the two equations equal gives $x^3 + (1 - m)x + (m - 2) = 0$. We know that $x = 1$ is always a solution, so we can factor the equation and get $(x - 1)(x^2 + x - (m - 2)) = 0$. We need the cubic to have no other roots, so either the quadratic has the double root $x = 1$, or the quadratic has no roots (since we want $x = 1$ to be the only root of the original cubic). The only monic quadratic with double root $x = 1$ is $x^2 - 2x + 1$, which clearly does not match our quadratic, so the only possibility is for the quadratic to have no root.

Thus, we need the discriminant of the quadratic to be negative. The discriminant is $1 + 4(m - 2)$, which is negative when $m < \frac{7}{4}$. So any line with slope less than $\frac{7}{4}$ through $(1, 2)$ intersects the graph of $y = x^3 + x$ only at the point $(1, 2)$. $\square$

This is a bad state of affairs. We have a whole range of "tangent" lines. Worse, none of these lines really look like good candidates for a tangent line, as they all "cross" the graph, as shown in the diagram to the right. If we think back to our original circle example, the tangent line through a point on a circle just "touches" the circle without "crossing" it. We'd like that property to be true of more general tangents to graphs.

We can see a little bit of what's really going on here if we look at the value of $m$ that makes our quadratic $x^2 + x - (m - 2)$ also have a root of $x = 1$. Plugging in $x = 1$ gives $2 - (m - 2) = 0$, so $m = 4$. If we draw the line with slope 4 through the point $(1, 2)$, which is the line $y = 4x - 2$, then we get the picture at left below. This looks like what we should have as our "tangent line" to $y = x^3 + x$ at $(1, 2)$: it just "touches" the curve at $(1, 2)$, but doesn't cross it. However, this line has the unfortunate property that it intersects the curve at another point, namely $(-2, -10)$, as shown in the picture to the left below. Should we be worried about this?

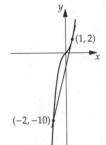

The number of words that appear inside quotation marks in the last two paragraphs is a sign that we're being too vague. So we'll try to define precisely what a tangent line is, but as we've seen, this is not easy.

However, what *is* easy to define is a secant line:

**Definition:** A **secant line** of the graph $y = f(x)$ is any line that intersects the graph in at least two distinct points.

So given two points $P = (a, f(a))$ and $Q = (b, f(b))$ on the graph of $y = f(x)$, with $a \neq b$, the line $\overleftrightarrow{PQ}$ is a secant line. Unless the graph of $y = f(x)$ is a line—that is, unless $f(x)$ is a linear polynomial or a constant—we expect that there will be infinitely many secant lines through $P$. However, if $Q$ is very close to $P$, then the secant line $\overleftrightarrow{PQ}$ is very close to what we want to be the tangent line at $P$. In fact, as $Q$ approaches $P$, then the secant line approaches the tangent line:

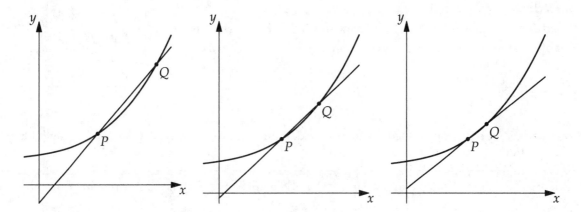

"Approaches"... this sounds like a job for a limit!

## 3.2  DEFINITION OF THE DERIVATIVE

Let's take our informal discussion from the end of the previous section and try to make it rigorous.

**Problem 3.3:**  Let $P = (a, f(a))$ be a point on the graph of $y = f(x)$. We wish to compute the slope of the tangent line to the curve at the point $P$.

(a)  Let $Q = (b, f(b))$ be another point on the curve (so that $b \neq a$). Compute the slope of the secant line $\overleftrightarrow{PQ}$.

(b)  Redo part (a) where we let $b = a + h$ for some $h \neq 0$, so that $Q = (a + h, f(a + h))$. Write the slope in terms of $a$ and $h$.

(c)  In terms of a limit, what does it mean for $Q$ to "approach" $P$?

(d)  Write an expression (using a limit) for the slope of the tangent line at $P$.

*Solution for Problem 3.3:*

(a)  We start with a secant $\overleftrightarrow{PQ}$ where $Q = (b, f(b))$ is some point other than $P$. The slope of $\overleftrightarrow{PQ}$ is, as usual, the difference in the $y$-coordinates divided by the difference in the $x$-coordinates:

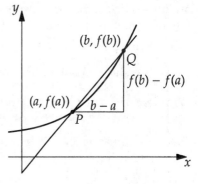

$$\text{slope of } \overleftrightarrow{PQ} = \frac{f(b) - f(a)}{b - a}.$$

(b)  Instead of writing $Q$ in terms of a "new" $x$-coordinate $b$, let's write it relative to $P$; that is, let's set $b = a + h$ for some nonzero real number $h$, so that $Q = (a + h, f(a + h))$. Our expression for the slope then becomes:

$$\text{slope of } \overleftrightarrow{PQ} = \frac{f(a + h) - f(a)}{(a + h) - a} = \frac{f(a + h) - f(a)}{h}.$$

(c) As $Q$ approaches $P$, the number $h$ approaches 0, and the secant line $\overleftrightarrow{PQ}$ "approaches" the tangent line at $P$. This last clause—the secant line "approaching" the tangent line—is not well-defined, but the part about $h$ approaching 0 is: it's a limit!

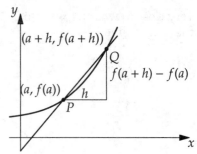

(d) We can *define* the tangent line at $P$ as the line through $P$ whose slope is the limit of the slope of the secant $\overleftrightarrow{PQ}$ as $Q$ approaches $P$. This gives us:

$$\text{slope of tangent line at } P = \lim_{h \to 0} \frac{f(a+h) - f(a)}{h}.$$

☐

To summarize, we have constructed the following definition (non-provisional at last!) of a tangent line to the graph of a function:

> **Definition:** The **tangent line** to the curve $y = f(x)$ at the point $P = (a, f(a))$ is the line passing through $P$ with slope
> $$\lim_{h \to 0} \frac{f(a+h) - f(a)}{h},$$
> provided that this limit is defined.

The quantity described by the above limit is so fundamental to calculus that it has a name:

> **Definition:** The **derivative** of the function $f$ at $a$, denoted $f'(a)$, is
> $$f'(a) = \lim_{h \to 0} \frac{f(a+h) - f(a)}{h},$$
> provided this limit exists. If the limit exists, we say that $f$ is **differentiable at** $a$. We say that $f$ is **differentiable** if it is differentiable at every point in its domain.

We see that the derivative $f'(a)$, *by definition*, is the slope of the tangent line at $(a, f(a))$, provided both are defined.

Note that we could have instead defined

$$f'(a) = \lim_{b \to a} \frac{f(b) - f(a)}{b - a},$$

and this is in fact the exact same quantity as our definition of derivative, but it is usually easier to compute limits when something is approaching 0, as in $\lim_{h \to 0}$. There are other minor variations in the form of the definition of the derivative; you will explore some of these as some exercises.

Let's go back to our earlier example:

> **Problem 3.4:** Let $f(x) = x^2$. Find the tangent line to the graph $y = f(x)$ at the point $(1, 1)$.

*Solution for Problem 3.4:* By definition, this line has slope $f'(1)$, so we compute:

$$f'(1) = \lim_{h \to 0} \frac{f(1+h) - f(1)}{h} = \lim_{h \to 0} \frac{(h+1)^2 - 1}{h}.$$

We can simplify the expression for $h \neq 0$:

$$\frac{(h+1)^2 - 1}{h} = \frac{h^2 + 2h}{h} = h + 2,$$

and therefore

$$f'(1) = \lim_{h \to 0}(h + 2) = 2.$$

Thus the tangent line has slope 2 and passes through $(1, 1)$. Therefore, it is the graph of $y = 2x - 1$. $\square$

Rather than just consider the derivative point-by-point, we often think of the derivative of $f$ as a function:

---

**Definition:** The **derivative** of a function $f$ is a function $f'$ such that

$$f'(x) = \lim_{h \to 0} \frac{f(x + h) - f(x)}{h}$$

at every $x$ in the domain of $f$ where the limit is defined.

---

Let's go back to another of our earlier examples:

**Problem 3.5:** Find the derivative of $f(x) = x^3 + x$.

*Solution for Problem 3.5:* We write the limit:

$$\begin{aligned}
f'(x) &= \lim_{h \to 0} \frac{f(x + h) - f(x)}{h} \\
&= \lim_{h \to 0} \frac{((x + h)^3 + (x + h)) - (x^3 + x)}{h} \\
&= \lim_{h \to 0} \frac{(x^3 + 3x^2h + 3xh^2 + h^3 + x + h) - (x^3 + x)}{h} \\
&= \lim_{h \to 0} \frac{3x^2h + 3xh^2 + h^3 + h}{h} \\
&= \lim_{h \to 0}(3x^2 + 3xh + h^2 + 1) \\
&= 3x^2 + 1.
\end{aligned}$$

$\square$

Now, going back to Problem 3.2, we can immediately see that the slope of the tangent line to the graph of $f(x) = x^3 + x$ at $(1, 2)$ is $f'(1) = 3(1)^2 + 1 = 4$, and thus the tangent line at $(1, 2)$ is $y = 4x - 2$.

The derivative of $f(x)$ has many different notations:

$$f'(x) \qquad Df(x) \qquad \dot{f}(x) \qquad \frac{df}{dx} \qquad \frac{d}{dx}f(x)$$

We'll usually use the first notation. The second notation is called **operator notation**, but we will not use it anywhere in this book. The third notation (the function with a dot over it) is commonly used in physics, but will also not appear elsewhere in this book. The last two notations in the above list are called **differential notation** and we'll see more of these later in the chapter. The notations can be used both with functions that are explicitly named and functions that are not; for example, if $f(x) = \sin x + x^3$, we could write any of

$$f'(x), \ (\sin x + x^3)', \ \frac{df}{dx}, \ \frac{d}{dx}f(x), \ \frac{d}{dx}(\sin x + x^3)$$

to indicate the derivative of $f$.

Just because we have a useable definition of the derivative, this doesn't mean that the derivative is always defined. There are basically three different circumstances in which the derivative $f'(a)$ might be undefined for a function $f$ and a real number $a$ in the domain of $f$. We'll explore these circumstances in the next 3 problems.

**Problem 3.6:** Suppose $f$ is a function such that $f$ is differentiable at $a$ (recall that this means that $f'(a)$ is defined). Compute $\lim_{h \to 0} f(a + h)$ in terms of $f(a)$ and $f'(a)$, and explain why this means that $f$ must be continuous at $a$.

*Solution for Problem 3.6:* We start with $\lim_{h \to 0} f(a + h)$, and do some algebra to get the definition of $f'(a)$ into the picture:

$$\lim_{h \to 0} f(a + h) = \lim_{h \to 0} (f(a + h) - f(a) + f(a))$$

$$= \lim_{h \to 0} \left( \frac{f(a + h) - f(a)}{h} \cdot h + f(a) \right)$$

$$= \lim_{h \to 0} \left( \frac{f(a + h) - f(a)}{h} \right) \cdot \lim_{h \to 0} h + \lim_{h \to 0} f(a).$$

The first term in the last line above is just the definition of $f'(a)$, which exists since we are assuming that $f$ is differentiable at $a$. Evaluating the other limits in the above expression, we have

$$\lim_{h \to 0} f(a + h) = f'(a) \cdot 0 + f(a) = f(a).$$

Thus, $\lim_{h \to 0} f(a + h) = f(a)$. But this is exactly the same thing as saying that $\lim_{x \to a} f(x) = f(a)$, and hence $f$ is continuous at $a$. $\square$

So Problem 3.6 tells us the following fundamental fact:

**Concept:** Differentiability implies continuity. That is, $f'(a)$ is defined only if $f$ is continuous at $a$. If $f$ is not continuous at $a$, then $f'(a)$ is undefined.

**Important:** Continuity does not imply differentiability.

Indeed, the next problem is an example of a continuous function that is not everywhere differentiable:

**Problem 3.7:** Let $f(x) = |x|$ be the absolute value function.
(a) What is $f'(x)$ if $x > 0$?
(b) What is $f'(x)$ if $x < 0$?
(c) Attempt to compute $f'(0)$, and verify that is undefined.
(d) Explain, in terms of the graph of $f$, why $f'(0)$ is undefined.

*Solution for Problem 3.7:*

(a) If $x > 0$, then $f(x) = |x| = x$. So, if we restrict ourselves to $h$ sufficiently close to 0 so that $x + h > 0$, we can write

$$f'(x) = \lim_{h \to 0} \frac{f(x + h) - f(x)}{h} = \lim_{h \to 0} \frac{|x + h| - |x|}{h} = \lim_{h \to 0} \frac{(x + h) - x}{h} = \lim_{h \to 0} \frac{h}{h} = 1.$$

So $f'(x) = 1$ for all $x > 0$.

(b)  If $x < 0$, then $f(x) = |x| = -x$. As in part (a), if we restrict ourselves to $h$ sufficiently close to 0 so that $x + h < 0$, we can write

$$f'(x) = \lim_{h \to 0} \frac{f(x + h) - f(x)}{h} = \lim_{h \to 0} \frac{|x + h| - |x|}{h} = \lim_{h \to 0} \frac{-(x + h) - (-x)}{h} = \lim_{h \to 0} \frac{-h}{h} = -1.$$

So $f'(x) = -1$ for all $x < 0$.

(c)  We compute:

$$f'(0) = \lim_{h \to 0} \frac{f(h) - f(0)}{h} = \lim_{h \to 0} \frac{|h|}{h}.$$

But we see a problem with this limit. The function $\dfrac{|h|}{h}$ is not continuous at 0, since

$$\frac{|h|}{h} = \begin{cases} 1 & \text{if } h > 0, \\ -1 & \text{if } h < 0. \end{cases}$$

The graph of $|h|/h$ is shown at right, and we can see that it is not continuous at 0. More specifically, we see that

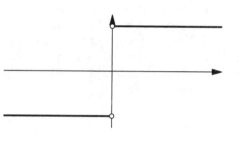

$$\lim_{h \to 0^+} \frac{|h|}{h} = 1 \quad \text{and} \quad \lim_{h \to 0^-} \frac{|h|}{h} = -1.$$

Since the left-sided limit and the right-sided limit are different, we conclude that $\lim_{h \to 0} \dfrac{|h|}{h}$ does not exist. Thus, $f'(0)$ is undefined.

(d)  We sketch the graph of $f(x) = |x|$ below:

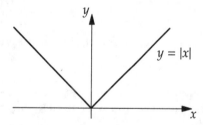

The $x > 0$ portion of the graph suggests that the slope of the tangent line at $x = 0$ should be 1. But the $x < 0$ portion of the graph suggests that the slope of the tangent line at $x = 0$ should be $-1$. This comes about because there is a sharp corner in the graph at the point $(0, 0)$, so we can't have a uniquely defined tangent line at that point.

$\square$

---

**Concept:**  If the graph of $y = f(x)$ has a "sharp corner" at $(a, f(a))$, then the derivative $f'(a)$ is undefined.

---

**Sidenote:**  Rather bizarrely, it turns out that there are functions that are continuous everywhere on $\mathbb{R}$ but are differentiable at no points of $\mathbb{R}$. However, it is very difficult to write down the description of such a function (and virtually impossible to draw its graph).

---

**Problem 3.8:** Let $f(x) = \sqrt[3]{x}$.

(a) Explain why $f'(0)$ is undefined using the definition of derivative.

(b) Explain why $f'(0)$ is undefined in terms of the graph of $f$.

*Solution for Problem 3.8:*

(a) We can try to compute $f'(0)$ using the definition of derivative:

$$f'(0) = \lim_{h \to 0} \frac{f(h) - f(0)}{h} = \lim_{h \to 0} \frac{\sqrt[3]{h}}{h} = \lim_{h \to 0} \frac{1}{\sqrt[3]{h^2}}.$$

But this limit does not exist: the denominator grows arbitrarily small as $h \to 0$, so the fraction grows arbitrarily large. (We may say that $\lim_{h \to 0} \dfrac{1}{\sqrt[3]{h^2}} = +\infty$, as we will explore further in Chapter 6.)

(b) Shown at right is the graph of $y = \sqrt[3]{x}$, with a "tangent line" drawn in at the point $(0,0)$. We see that, geometrically, the natural choice for the tangent line is the vertical line $x = 0$. However, recall that vertical lines are not allowed as tangent lines, since by definition $f'(x)$ is the slope of the tangent line at $x$, and a vertical line has undefined slope. Thus, $f'(0)$ is undefined.

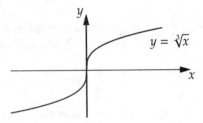

$\Box$

> **Concept:** If the graph of $y = f(x)$ has a vertical "tangent line" at $(a, f(a))$, then $f'(a)$ is undefined.

We summarize the non-differentiability criteria explored in the previous three problems:

> **Important:** Given a function $f$ and a number $a \in \text{Dom } f$, there are essentially three reasons why the derivative $f'(a)$ might be undefined:
>
> - $f$ is not continuous at $a$
> - The graph of $f$ has a sharp corner at $(a, f(a))$
> - The graph of $f$ has a vertical tangent line at $(a, f(a))$

There are occasionally more exotic reasons why $f'(a)$ might be undefined, but virtually all of the examples that you will commonly encounter fall into one of the above three categories.

## EXERCISES

**3.2.1** Use the limit definition of derivative to compute the derivatives of the following functions:

(a) $f(x) = c$ where $c$ is any real number

(b) $f(x) = 2x$

(c) $f(x) = x^2 - 3x$

(d) $f(x) = (x - 1)^3$

(e) $f(x) = \dfrac{1}{2x}$

**3.2.2** Find the equation of the tangent line to the curve $y = x^4 + 3$ at the point $(1, 4)$.

**3.2.3**  Find the equation of the tangent line to the graph $f(x) = \dfrac{x^2}{2}$ at the point $(2, 2)$.

**3.2.4**  Find a function $f$, with domain $\mathbb{R}$, that is continuous on all of $\mathbb{R}$ but that is not differentiable at $x = 0$ and $x = 1$.

**3.2.5★**  Suppose we had defined the derivative as

$$f'(a) = \lim_{h \to 0} \frac{f(a) - f(a - h)}{h}.$$

Is this equivalent to our previous definition? Why or why not? **Hints:** 93, 282

## 3.3  BASIC DERIVATIVE COMPUTATIONS

In this section, we'll start to explore some of the basic algebraic properties of the derivative. Our goal is to develop a catalog of derivatives of common functions (such as polynomials, trig functions, and exponentials), and a series of algebraic rules to compute derivatives of more complicated functions. Hopefully, by the end of this chapter, you'll find that calculating derivatives is a very routine process.

We'll start with a basic algebraic property of the derivative:

**Problem 3.9:** Let $f$ and $g$ be differentiable functions. Show that $(f + g)' = f' + g'$.

*Solution for Problem 3.9:*  This property is true for limits, and since the derivative is defined as a limit, we shouldn't be too surprised that this property is true for derivatives as well. The proof is a straightforward application of the corresponding rules for limits:

$$
\begin{aligned}
(f + g)'(x) &= \lim_{h \to 0} \frac{(f + g)(x + h) - (f + g)(x)}{h} \\
&= \lim_{h \to 0} \frac{f(x + h) + g(x + h) - f(x) - g(x)}{h} \\
&= \lim_{h \to 0} \left( \frac{f(x + h) - f(x)}{h} + \frac{g(x + h) - g(x)}{h} \right) \\
&= \lim_{h \to 0} \left( \frac{f(x + h) - f(x)}{h} \right) + \lim_{h \to 0} \left( \frac{g(x + h) - g(x)}{h} \right) \\
&= f'(x) + g'(x).
\end{aligned}
$$

□

It is also true that:

> **Important:**  Let $f$ be a differentiable function, and $c \in \mathbb{R}$. Then $(cf)' = c(f')$.

The proof is very similar to the solution to Problem 3.9, and we will leave the details as an exercise.

> **Concept:**  The previous results mean that the derivative is **linear**. The derivative of a sum of functions is just the sum of the derivatives of the functions, and we can "factor out" a constant factor from a derivative.

The limit definition of derivative is somewhat cumbersome to use. We'd like to build a catalog of common derivatives. So let's start with some simple functions.

**Problem 3.10:** Let $f(x) = x^n$, where $n$ is an integer. Find $f'(x)$.

*Solution for Problem 3.10:* First, let's look at the case where $n$ is a positive integer. We just plug $x^n$ into our limit definition of derivative:

$$f'(x) = \lim_{h \to 0} \frac{f(x+h) - f(x)}{h} = \lim_{h \to 0} \frac{(x+h)^n - x^n}{h}.$$

We can expand the $(x+h)^n$ term in the numerator using the Binomial Theorem:

$$f'(x) = \lim_{h \to 0} \frac{\left(x^n + \binom{n}{1}x^{n-1}h + \binom{n}{2}x^{n-2}h^2 + \cdots + h^n\right) - x^n}{h}.$$

Now we want to simplify. Notice that the $x^n$ terms cancel in the numerator. Then, every remaining term has at least one factor of $h$, so we can divide by the $h$ in the denominator:

$$f'(x) = \lim_{h \to 0} \left( \binom{n}{1}x^{n-1} + \binom{n}{2}x^{n-2}h + \cdots + h^{n-1} \right).$$

Every term except for the first term has a factor of $h$, so when we take the limit as $h$ approaches 0, these terms are all 0. Thus we're just left with the first term, and since $\binom{n}{1} = n$, we have

$$f'(x) = nx^{n-1}.$$

We'll state this result using differential notation:

**Important:** If $n$ is a positive integer, then

$$\frac{d}{dx}x^n = nx^{n-1}.$$

Notice that when $n = 1$, we get $\frac{d}{dx}x = 1$. This makes perfect sense when we think about the graph of $y = x$: the graph is just a line with slope 1, so the tangent line to this graph should have slope 1 everywhere.

When $n = 0$, the function is just the constant function $f(x) = x^0 = 1$. We can again use the limit definition of derivative:

$$f'(x) = \lim_{h \to 0} \frac{f(x+h) - f(x)}{h}$$
$$= \lim_{h \to 0} \frac{1 - 1}{h}$$
$$= \lim_{h \to 0} 0 = 0.$$

So $\frac{d}{dx}1 = 0$. This also make graphical sense: the graph of $y = 1$ is a horizontal line, which has slope 0 at every point. Note also that this function satisfies our earlier formula (for $x \neq 0$):

$$\frac{d}{dx}1 = \frac{d}{dx}x^0 = 0x^{-1} = 0.$$

Finally, we consider the function $f(x) = x^{-m}$ where $m$ is a positive integer. We again try to use our limit definition:

$$f'(x) = \lim_{h \to 0} \frac{f(x+h) - f(x)}{h} = \lim_{h \to 0} \frac{\frac{1}{(x+h)^m} - \frac{1}{x^m}}{h}.$$

We can simplify the numerator by subtracting the fractions:

$$f'(x) = \lim_{h \to 0} \frac{\frac{x^m - (x+h)^m}{(x(x+h))^m}}{h} = \lim_{h \to 0} \frac{x^m - (x+h)^m}{h(x(x+h))^m}.$$

As we did before, we use the Binomial Theorem to expand the numerator, cancel the $x^m$ term, and divide the rest of the terms by $h$. This leaves:

$$f'(x) = \lim_{h \to 0} \frac{-\left(\binom{m}{1}x^{m-1} + \binom{m}{2}x^{m-2}h + \cdots + h^{m-1}\right)}{(x(x+h))^m}.$$

If we now plug in $h = 0$, all of the terms except for the first disappear from the numerator, and the denominator becomes $x^{2m}$. So we have:

$$f'(x) = \frac{-mx^{m-1}}{x^{2m}} = -\frac{m}{x^{m+1}} = -mx^{-m-1}.$$

Notice that this is the same formula that we got for positive integer exponents! □

---

**Important:**  If $n$ is an integer, then

$$\frac{d}{dx}x^n = nx^{n-1}.$$

We can think of this as "moving the exponent to the front as a constant, and then decreasing the exponent by 1."

---

We can now combine the results of the previous two problems to instantly compute the derivative of any polynomial function, even a "polynomial" with negative powers.

---

**Problem 3.11:** Compute the derivatives of the following functions:

(a) $f(x) = x^3 - 2x^2 + 6x - 9$

(b) $f(x) = 3x^{11} - 5x^9 + 188x$

(c) $f(x) = \frac{5}{x^7} - \frac{2}{x} + 3 - 8x^4$

(d) $f(x) = (2x + 3)^3$

---

*Solution for Problem 3.11:*

(a) We'll work out all the steps of this one, just so it's clear what we're allowed to do.

$$
\begin{aligned}
f'(x) &= (x^3 - 2x^2 + 6x - 9)' \\
&= (x^3)' + (-2x^2)' + (6x)' + (-9)' &&\text{(by Problem 3.9)} \\
&= (x^3)' - 2(x^2)' + 6(x)' - 9(1)' &&\text{(by the box after Problem 3.9)} \\
&= 3x^2 - 2(2x) + 6(1) - 9(0) &&\text{(by Problem 3.10)} \\
&= 3x^2 - 4x + 6.
\end{aligned}
$$

Once you've mastered the process, there's no need to be so pedantic. Just immediately write:

$$(x^3 - 2x^2 + 6x - 9)' = 3x^2 - 4x + 6.$$

(b)  This time, we'll omit most of the intermediate steps:

$$(3x^{11} - 5x^9 + 188x)' = 3(11x^{10}) - 5(9x^8) + 188(1) = 33x^{10} - 45x^8 + 188.$$

(c)  Negative exponents are no problem: we just use the same rule.

$$(5x^{-7} - 2x^{-1} + 3 - 8x^4)' = -35x^{-8} + 2x^{-2} - 32x^3.$$

> **WARNING!!**    A very common mistake, particularly with negative exponents, is increasing the exponent when you should be decreasing it. For example:
>
> $$(5x^{-7})' \neq -35x^{-6}.$$
>
> Make sure that you *decrease* the exponent by 1—in this example, from −7 to −8:
>
> $$(5x^{-7})' = -35x^{-8}.$$

(d)  Be careful! It's tempting to do this:

> **Bogus Solution:**
>
> $$\frac{d}{dx}(2x + 3)^3 = 3(2x + 3)^2.$$

But we don't have a rule (yet) for taking the derivative of things like $(2x + 3)^3$. We can only take derivative of monomial terms like $cx^n$. So we need to first expand $(2x + 3)^3$ into a sum of monomial terms, using the Binomial Theorem:

$$(2x + 3)^3 = (2x)^3 + 3(2x)^2(3) + 3(2x)(3)^2 + 3^3 = 8x^3 + 36x^2 + 54x + 27.$$

Now we can take the derivative:

$$f'(x) = (8x^3 + 36x^2 + 54x + 27)' = 24x^2 + 72x + 54.$$

Note that this is *not* equal to $3(2x + 3)^2 = 3(4x^2 + 12x + 9) = 12x^2 + 36x + 27$. But the derivative is exactly twice $3(2x + 3)^2$. We'll see more of this interesting property in the next section.

□

We know how to take derivatives of sums of functions and of constant multiples of functions. What about derivatives of products of functions?

**Problem 3.12:** Let $f$ and $g$ be differentiable functions. Find a formula for $(fg)'$ in terms of $f$, $g$, $f'$, and $g'$.

*Solution for Problem 3.12:* Many people are tempted to say:

> **Bogus Solution:**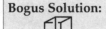
>
> $$(fg)' = (f')(g').$$

Sorry, but it's not that simple. In the vast majority of examples, the above "formula" is not true. For example, let $f(x) = x^2$ and $g(x) = x^3$. Then $(fg)' = (x^5)' = 5x^4$, but $(f')(g') = (x^2)'(x^3)' = (2x)(3x^2) = 6x^3$, so clearly $(fg)' \neq (f')(g')$.

What do we do instead? We go back to our limit definition!

$$(fg)'(x) = \lim_{h \to 0} \frac{(fg)(x + h) - (fg)(x)}{h} = \lim_{h \to 0} \frac{f(x + h)g(x + h) - f(x)g(x)}{h}.$$

Uh-oh. There doesn't seem to be any nice way to simplify this.

We'll have to use some algebraic slight-of-hand. We want to force into our expression some terms that look more like the terms in the definition of derivative, so let's insert a couple of carefully-chosen expressions into the numerator:

$$(fg)'(x) = \lim_{h \to 0} \frac{f(x+h)g(x+h) - f(x)g(x)}{h} = \lim_{h \to 0} \frac{f(x+h)g(x+h) - f(x+h)g(x) + f(x+h)g(x) - f(x)g(x)}{h}.$$

This allows us to conveniently group the terms:

$$(fg)'(x) = \lim_{h \to 0} \frac{f(x+h)g(x+h) - f(x+h)g(x) + f(x+h)g(x) - f(x)g(x)}{h}$$

$$= \lim_{h \to 0} \left( \frac{f(x+h)(g(x+h) - g(x))}{h} + \frac{g(x)(f(x+h) - f(x))}{h} \right).$$

It's even more clear what's going on if we break it up further:

$$(fg)'(x) = \lim_{h \to 0} f(x+h) \frac{g(x+h) - g(x)}{h} + \lim_{h \to 0} g(x) \frac{f(x+h) - f(x)}{h}.$$

Now we see that the limits of the fraction above are just the derivatives of $f$ and $g$! And since $\lim_{h \to 0} f(x+h) = f(x)$ (remember, $f$ must be continuous, since it is differentiable), we conclude that

$$(fg)'(x) = f(x)g'(x) + g(x)f'(x).$$

□

> **Important:** The **Product Rule** for derivatives: if $f$ and $g$ are differentiable functions, then
>
> $$(fg)' = f'g + fg'.$$

We can quickly check this with our bogus example from earlier. If $f(x) = x^2$ and $g(x) = x^3$, then $(fg)(x) = x^5$, so $(fg)'(x) = 5x^4$. On the other hand, the Product Rule gives:

$$(fg)'(x) = f'(x)g(x) + f(x)g'(x) = (2x)(x^3) + (x^2)(3x^2) = 2x^4 + 3x^4 = 5x^4.$$

There is a similar (but, alas, somewhat uglier) formula for the derivative of a quotient:

> **Important:** The **Quotient Rule** for derivatives: if $f$ and $g$ are differentiable functions, then
>
> $$\left( \frac{f}{g} \right)' = \frac{f'g - fg'}{g^2}.$$

We will leave the proof of this formula as an exercise.

Let's continue building our library of derivatives. Next up is trig functions:

**Problem 3.13:** Compute $\frac{d}{dx}(\sin x)$.

*Solution for Problem 3.13:* Let $f(x) = \sin x$. Again, we'll use the limit definition:

$$f'(x) = \lim_{h \to 0} \frac{\sin(x + h) - \sin(x)}{h}.$$

At first, this looks intractable, but we can break up $\sin(x + h)$ using the sine angle-addition formula. This gives us:

$$f'(x) = \lim_{h \to 0} \frac{\sin x \cos h + \sin h \cos x - \sin x}{h}.$$

This is easier to work with when we factor out the $\sin x$ and $\cos x$ terms:

$$f'(x) = \sin x \left( \lim_{h \to 0} \frac{\cos h - 1}{h} \right) + \cos x \left( \lim_{h \to 0} \frac{\sin h}{h} \right).$$

Fortunately, we know those trig limits. Recall from Problem 2.8 that $\lim\limits_{h \to 0} \dfrac{\sin h}{h} = 1$. A similar method can be used to show that $\lim\limits_{h \to 0} \dfrac{\cos h - 1}{h} = 0$ (we will leave the details for you to work out if you like). So, plugging these in, we have that $f'(x) = \cos x$. $\square$

A similar calculation will show that $\dfrac{d}{dx}(\cos x) = -\sin x$. (Note the minus sign!) We will leave this calculation as an exercise. Then, we can use the rules for derivatives of products and quotients to compute the derivatives of the other trig functions. We will do one as an example:

---

**Problem 3.14:** Compute $\dfrac{d}{dx} \tan x$.

---

*Solution for Problem 3.14:* This is a simple matter of writing tangent as a quotient and then applying the Quotient Rule:

$$\begin{aligned} \frac{d}{dx} \tan x &= \frac{d}{dx} \left( \frac{\sin x}{\cos x} \right) \\ &= \frac{(\sin x)'(\cos x) - (\sin x)(\cos x)'}{\cos^2 x} \\ &= \frac{\cos^2 x + \sin^2 x}{\cos^2 x} \\ &= \frac{1}{\cos^2 x} = \sec^2 x. \end{aligned}$$

$\square$

We can easily compute the derivatives of the remaining trig functions:

**Important:**

$$\frac{d}{dx}(\sin x) = \cos x \qquad \frac{d}{dx}(\sec x) = \sec x \tan x$$

$$\frac{d}{dx}(\cos x) = -\sin x \qquad \frac{d}{dx}(\csc x) = -\csc x \cot x$$

$$\frac{d}{dx}(\tan x) = \sec^2 x \qquad \frac{d}{dx}(\cot x) = -\csc^2 x$$

We will leave the computations of the derivatives of sec, csc, and cot as exercises.

There are a couple of other basic functions that we will want in our derivative catalog, namely exponentials and logarithms. Unfortunately, we don't yet have the tools to prove these derivatives, so for now we will just have to tell you what they are; later in the book we will be able to prove them.

One derivative hints at a large part of the reason why the number $e$ is special:

$$\frac{d}{dx}e^x = e^x.$$

That is, $e^x$ is its own derivative! In fact, $f(x) = ce^x$ (where $c$ is any constant) are the only functions for which $f' = f$, although this is hard to prove. We'll revisit this concept later in Chapter 9 when we study differential equations.

The flip side of $e$ being nice is that the natural logarithm function has a nice derivative too:

$$\frac{d}{dx}(\log x) = \frac{1}{x}.$$

In fact, one way that we can *define* the natural logarithm is as a function whose derivative is $1/x$. (We'll discuss this more in Chapter 5.)

---

**Sidenote:** In this discussion, we're seeing a bit of why calculus is a tough subject to learn. We want to have functions like exp and log because they create lots of interesting examples, but we're forced to assume lots of facts about these functions that we can't rigorously prove until later. If we took a more strict approach and proved everything as we go, then we wouldn't be able to talk about exp, log, and trigonometric functions until much later in the book; we'd essentially be limited to polynomials at this stage, and we wouldn't have many interesting problems and examples to play with. So, in this book, we choose to "decree" certain facts for now, with the idea of re-examining them later in the book (specifically, in Chapter 5) when we have more tools in our calculus toolbox.

---

## EXERCISES

**3.3.1**  Prove that $(cf)' = c(f')$ for any differentiable function $f$ and real number $c$.

**3.3.2**  Compute the derivatives of the following:

(a)  $4x^3 + 3x - 8 - 2x^{-2}$    (b)  $(3x^2 + 2)^5$    (c)  $(x^2 + 1)\sin x$    (d)  $\cos 2x$

(e)  $e^{2x}$    (f)  $(5\log x)(1 + \tan x)$    (g)  $\log x^3$    (h)  $x^2 e^x (\sec x)$

**3.3.3**

(a)  Prove that if $g$ is a differentiable function, then

$$\frac{d}{dx}\left(\frac{1}{g(x)}\right) = -\frac{g'(x)}{(g(x))^2}$$

for any $x \in \text{Dom}(g)$ such that $g(x) \neq 0$.

(b)  Prove the Quotient Rule: if $f$ and $g$ are differentiable functions, and $g(x) \neq 0$, then:

$$\left(\frac{f}{g}\right)'(x) = \frac{g(x)f'(x) - f(x)g'(x)}{(g(x))^2}.$$

**Hints:** 276

**3.3.4**  Prove that $\frac{d}{dx}(\cos x) = -\sin x$.

**3.3.5**  Use the derivatives of sin and cos, together with the Product and Quotient Rules, to find the derivatives for the trigonometric functions sec, csc, and cot.

## 3.4  THE CHAIN RULE FOR DERIVATIVES

In Problem 3.11(d), we saw that

$$\frac{d}{dx}(2x+3)^3 = 6(2x+3)^2,$$

although computing this required us first to expand $(2x+3)^3$ using the Binomial Theorem and then take the derivative of each monomial. We'd like a quicker way to compute such a derivative.

Let's look at another example:

> **Problem 3.15:** Our goal is to find an easy way to compute
>
> $$\frac{d}{dx}(x^2+1)^5$$
>
> *without* applying the Binomial Theorem.
> (a)  First compute it the long way, by expanding $(x^2+1)^5$ using the Binomial Theorem and then taking the derivative.
> (b)  Does your answer from part (a) factor nicely?
> (c)  Let $f(x) = (x^2+1)$ and $g(x) = x^5$. Write the function $(x^2+1)^5$ as a composition of $f$ and $g$.
> (d)  Can you algebraically manipulate the derivative of the composition to write it in terms of $f$, $f'$, $g$, and $g'$?

*Solution for Problem 3.15:*  Before we begin, note the following incorrect solution:

> **Bogus Solution:**
>
> $$\frac{d}{dx}(x^2+1)^5 = 5(x^2+1)^4.$$

This is not correct; we cannot take our $\frac{d}{dx}x^5 = 5x^4$ rule and directly apply it to more complicated expressions raised to a power.

(a)  Consider the function $h(x) = (x^2+1)^5$. We can certainly compute its derivative by expanding it into a polynomial using the Binomial Theorem:

$$h(x) = x^{10} + 5x^8 + 10x^6 + 10x^4 + 5x^2 + 1,$$

and hence

$$h'(x) = 10x^9 + 40x^7 + 60x^5 + 40x^3 + 10x.$$

(b)  Our answer from part (a) is somewhat ugly, especially compared to the relatively nice expression that we started with. But, if you're observant, you might notice that the above polynomial factors quite nicely:

$$h'(x) = 10x(x^8 + 4x^6 + 6x^4 + 4x^2 + 1) = 10x(x^2+1)^4.$$

That's a lot nicer, and it seems related to our original $h(x) = (x^2+1)^5$.

(c)  If we set $f(x) = (x^2 + 1)$ and $g(x) = x^5$, then $h(x) = (g \circ f)(x) = g(f(x)) = (x^2 + 1)^5$; that is, $h$ is the composition of $g$ and $f$.

(d)  At the beginning, if we had been naive and treated $(x^2 + 1)^5$ as if it were $x^5$, then we might have made the bogus conclusion that its derivative is $5(x^2 + 1)^4$. As we saw, this is incorrect, by a factor of $2x$, as the actual derivative is

$$h'(x) = 10x(x^2 + 1)^4.$$

Where did the extra factor of $2x$ come from? Hmmm... if we look at what's inside the parenthesis, we see the interesting coincidence that

$$\frac{d}{dx}(x^2 + 1) = 2x.$$

That's no coincidence! We can break up $h'(x)$ as follows:

$$h'(x) = 10x(x^2 + 1)^4 = (2x)(5(x^2 + 1)^4).$$

We see that the first term is just $f'(x)$. The second term is $g'(f(x))$: we plug $f(x) = (x^2 + 1)$ into $g'(x) = 5x^4$ to get $g'(f(x)) = 5(x^2 + 1)^4$.

□

Based on our work on Problem 3.15, our conjecture is:

> **Important:** If $f$ and $g$ are differentiable functions, and if $(g \circ f)$ exists, then
>
> $$(g \circ f)'(x) = g'(f(x))f'(x).$$
>
> This is known as the **Chain Rule**.

We can get some idea of why the Chain Rule is true by looking at the limit definition of the derivative of $(g \circ f)$:

$$(g \circ f)'(x) = \lim_{h \to 0} \frac{g(f(x + h)) - g(f(x))}{h}.$$

Since we know that we want an $f'(x)$ term to appear, we expect that we'll need to have $f(x + h) - f(x)$ in the numerator somewhere. So let's multiply the above limit by $\dfrac{f(x + h) - f(x)}{f(x + h) - f(x)}$. Of course, this is only valid if $f(x + h) - f(x) \neq 0$, so for the moment assume that $f(x + h) \neq f(x)$ for sufficiently small nonzero $h$. Then we have

$$(g \circ f)'(x) = \lim_{h \to 0} \left( \frac{g(f(x + h)) - g(f(x))}{f(x + h) - f(x)} \cdot \frac{f(x + h) - f(x)}{h} \right)$$
$$= \left( \lim_{h \to 0} \frac{g(f(x + h)) - g(f(x))}{f(x + h) - f(x)} \right) \cdot \left( \lim_{h \to 0} \frac{f(x + h) - f(x)}{h} \right).$$

This second term is just the definition of $f'(x)$, so we have

$$(g \circ f)'(x) = \left( \lim_{h \to 0} \frac{g(f(x + h)) - g(f(x))}{f(x + h) - f(x)} \right) f'(x).$$

So all we have left to do to establish the Chain Rule is to show that

$$\lim_{h \to 0} \frac{g(f(x + h)) - g(f(x))}{f(x + h) - f(x)} = g'(f(x)). \qquad (\star)$$

This seems plausible: as $f(x + h)$ approaches $f(x)$, the fraction on the left side of $(\star)$ is the slope of the secant line from $(f(x), g(f(x)))$ to $(f(x+h), g(f(x+h)))$, so its limit as $h$ approaches 0 should be the derivative of $g$ at $f(x)$, which is $g'(f(x))$.

In fact, $(\star)$ is true provided we make the assumption that $f(x+h) \neq f(x)$ for sufficiently small nonzero $h$, but the proof is a somewhat tedious $\delta$-$\epsilon$ argument. We also have not addressed the issue of what happens if $f(x+h) = f(x)$ for values of $h$ arbitrarily close to 0. We can fix these issues and get a rigorous proof of the Chain Rule, but the proof is rather technical, so we will defer the proof to Section 3.A.

It is often easier to remember the Chain Rule using differential notation. To do so, we write $g(f(x)) = g(u)$, so that $u = f(x)$. Then the Chain Rule is

$$\frac{dg}{dx} = \frac{dg}{du} \cdot \frac{du}{dx}.$$

For example, consider the function in Problem 3.15, $(x^2 + 1)^5$. We'll write this as $g(u) = u^5$, where $u = x^2 + 1$. Then, applying the Chain Rule, we have

$$\frac{dg}{dx} = \frac{dg}{du} \cdot \frac{du}{dx} = \frac{d}{du}(u^5) \cdot \frac{d}{dx}(x^2 + 1)$$
$$= 5u^4 \cdot 2x$$
$$= 5(x^2 + 1)^4 \cdot 2x = 10x(x^2 + 1)^4.$$

Note especially the final step: we want our final answer to be solely in terms of $x$ and not have any $u$ terms. The advantage of thinking of the Chain Rule using this notation is that we can informally remember the Chain Rule as "canceling the $du$ terms" when we multiply the "fractions" $dg/du$ and $du/dx$.

> **WARNING!!**  $dg/du$ and $du/dx$ are not really fractions. It's just a notation that happens to be very convenient for keeping track of the Chain Rule.

In practice, we usually won't go to all the trouble to write out $dg/dx$ or $(g \circ f)'$ or anything like that. Once you become adept with the Chain Rule, you'll just write the whole calculation out on one line, like so:

$$((x^2 + 1)^5)' = 5(x^2 + 1)^4(x^2 + 1)' = 5(x^2 + 1)^4(2x) = 10x(x^2 + 1)^4.$$

---

**Problem 3.16:** Compute the following derivatives:

(a) $\dfrac{d}{dx}(2x^2 - 5x)^3$

(b) $\dfrac{d}{dx}\dfrac{1}{(1 - x^4)^2}$

(c) $\dfrac{d}{dx}((x^3 - 1)^2 + 9x)^6$

---

*Solution for Problem 3.16:* All of these are straightforward applications of the Chain Rule.

(a) Let $f(x) = 2x^2 - 5x$ and $g(x) = x^3$. Then our function is $g(f(x))$, so by the Chain Rule, we have:

$$\frac{d}{dx}(2x^2 - 5x)^3 = g'(f(x))f'(x) = 3(2x^2 - 5x)^2(4x - 5).$$

(b) Write the function as $(1 - x^4)^{-2}$. Then apply the Chain Rule:

$$((1 - x^4)^{-2})' = -2(1 - x^4)^{-3}(-4x^3) = \frac{8x^3}{(1 - x^4)^3}.$$

(c)   We apply the Chain Rule twice:

$$(((x^3 - 1)^2 + 9x)^6)' = 6((x^3 - 1)^2 + 9x)^5((x^3 - 1)^2 + 9x)'$$
$$= 6((x^3 - 1)^2 + 9x)^5(2(x^3 - 1)(x^3 - 1)' + 9)$$
$$= 6((x^3 - 1)^2 + 9x)^5(2(x^3 - 1)(3x^2) + 9)$$
$$= 6((x^3 - 1)^2 + 9x)^5(6x^2(x^3 - 1) + 9).$$

☐

The Chain Rule works equally well with "special" functions too. As part of the next problem, we will use the "$u$" notation for the Chain Rule computation.

---

**Problem 3.17:**   Compute the derivatives of the following functions:
(a)   $\cos(4x)$
(b)   $e^{x^3}$
(c)   $\log(\sin x)$

---

*Solution for Problem 3.17:*

(a)   Write the function as $\cos(u)$, where $u = 4x$. Then the derivative is

$$(\cos(u))' \cdot \frac{du}{dx} = (-\sin(u)) \cdot \frac{d}{dx}(4x) = -4\sin(u) = -4\sin(4x).$$

Note the importance of the final step: make sure that the final answer is in terms of the original variable, and does not contain any temporary variable or function that we introduced to help our Chain Rule calculation. Eventually you will get proficient at this type of computation, and you won't need all the intermediate steps—you can just write

$$\frac{d}{dx}(\cos(4x)) = -4\sin(4x).$$

(b)   Write as $e^u$ where $u = x^3$. Then

$$(e^{x^3})' = (e^u)' = e^u \cdot \frac{du}{dx} = e^u \cdot 3x^2 = 3x^2 e^{x^3}.$$

(c)   We'll consolidate the steps without using $u$:

$$\frac{d}{dx}\log(\sin x) = \frac{1}{\sin x} \cdot \frac{d}{dx}(\sin x) = \frac{\cos x}{\sin x} = \cot x.$$

☐

One neat application of the Chain Rule is the formula for the derivative of an inverse function.

---

**Problem 3.18:**   Find $(f^{-1}(x))'$, the derivative of the inverse function of $f$, and determine where it is defined.

---

*Solution for Problem 3.18:*   Of course, we know that $f(f^{-1}(x)) = x$, by definition, so

$$\frac{d}{dx}f(f^{-1}(x)) = \frac{d}{dx}(x) = 1.$$

But by the Chain Rule,

$$1 = \frac{d}{dx}f(f^{-1}(x)) = f'(f^{-1}(x))(f^{-1}(x))'.$$

Thus, assuming that $f'$ is nonzero, we have

$$(f^{-1}(x))' = \frac{1}{f'(f^{-1}(x))}.$$

☐

> **Important:** The **Inverse Function Rule**: if $f$ is a function with inverse $f^{-1}$, then
>
> $$(f^{-1}(x))' = \frac{1}{f'(f^{-1}(x))}$$
>
> wherever $f'(f^{-1}(x)) \neq 0$.

This result opens up a lot more derivative computations for us. A particularly important one (whose importance we will see in Chapter 5) is:

**Problem 3.19:** Compute $\dfrac{d}{dx}(\sin^{-1} x)$.

*Solution for Problem 3.19:* By the Inverse Function Rule, and since $\dfrac{d}{dx}(\sin x) = \cos x$, we have

$$\frac{d}{dx}(\sin^{-1} x) = \frac{1}{\cos(\sin^{-1} x)}.$$

But for any $x \in (-1, 1)$, we have $\cos(\sin^{-1} x) = \sqrt{1 - x^2}$, where we take the positive square root since $\sin^{-1} x \in \left(-\frac{\pi}{2}, \frac{\pi}{2}\right)$. Thus,

$$\frac{d}{dx}(\sin^{-1} x) = \frac{1}{\sqrt{1 - x^2}}.$$

☐

We will leave it as an exercise to compute

$$\frac{d}{dx}(\tan^{-1} x) = \frac{1}{1 + x^2},$$

the importance of which we will also see in Chapter 5.

**Problem 3.20:** Compute $\dfrac{d}{dx}\sqrt{x}$.

*Solution for Problem 3.20:* Think of $\sqrt{x}$ as the inverse function of $f(x) = x^2$ when $x$ is a positive real number. Therefore $f'(x) = 2x$, and we can use the Inverse Function Rule, giving:

$$\frac{d}{dx}\sqrt{x} = \frac{1}{2\sqrt{x}}.$$

Note that if we had written out initial function as $\sqrt{x} = x^{\frac{1}{2}}$, then this is consistent with our exponent derivative rule:

$$\frac{d}{dx}x^{\frac{1}{2}} = \frac{1}{2}x^{-\frac{1}{2}}.$$

☐

We can use the same general process, which we will leave as an exercise, to show:

**Important:** For any rational number $r$,

$$\frac{d}{dx}x^r = rx^{r-1}.$$

In fact, the result is true for any real number $r$, rational or irrational, as we can see with the following computation:

**Problem 3.21:**

(a) Recall that in Chapter 1, we assumed that $(e^a)^b = e^{ab}$ for any $a, b \in \mathbb{R}$. Using this, show that $x^r = \exp(r \log x)$ for any $x > 0$ and $r \in \mathbb{R}$.

(b) Use this to prove that $\frac{d}{dx}x^r = rx^{r-1}$.

*Solution for Problem 3.21:*

(a) We recall that $x = \exp(\log x)$, since exp and log are inverses. Thus

$$x^r = (e^{\log x})^r = e^{r \log x} = \exp(r \log x).$$

(b) By the Chain Rule, and the fact that $\frac{d}{dx}e^x = e^x$, we have

$$\begin{aligned}
\frac{d}{dx}x^r &= \frac{d}{dx}\exp(r \log x) \\
&= \exp(r \log x) \cdot (r \log x)' \\
&= \exp(r \log x) \cdot \frac{r}{x} \\
&= x^r \cdot \frac{r}{x} = rx^{r-1}.
\end{aligned}$$

$\square$

## EXERCISES

**3.4.1** Compute the derivatives of the following functions:

(a) $(3x^4 + x)^5$   (b) $\sqrt{x^2 - 1}$   (c) $\log(x^3 + \cos x)$   (d) $\sin \sqrt{x}$

(e) $e^{-2x^2}$   (f) $\sin^{-1} \theta^2$   (g) $\sqrt{1 + (x^2 + 1)^3}$   (h) $e^{e^x}$

**3.4.2** Assuming that $\frac{d}{dx}e^x = e^x$, prove that $\frac{d}{dx}(\log x) = \frac{1}{x}$.

**3.4.3**

(a) Let $n$ be a nonzero integer. Show that $\frac{d}{dx}x^{\frac{1}{n}} = \frac{1}{n}x^{\left(\frac{1}{n}-1\right)}$.

(b) Let $q$ be a nonzero rational number. Use part (a) to show that $\frac{d}{dx}x^q = qx^{q-1}$.

**3.4.4★** Compute $\frac{d}{dx}(\tan^{-1} x)$. Your final answer should not contain any trig functions.

**3.4.5★** The derivative of the derivative of $f$ is called the **second derivative** of $f$, denoted $f''$. A nonzero polynomial $f(x)$ with real coefficients has the property that $f(x) = f'(x)f''(x)$. What is the leading coefficient of $f(x)$? *(Source: HMMT)* **Hints:** 261

## 3.5   ROLLE'S THEOREM AND THE MEAN VALUE THEOREM

Consider a continuous function defined on a closed interval $[a, b]$. By our work in Chapter 2, we know that this function must attain a maximum at some point $c \in [a, b]$. What do we know about the derivative at this point? Looking at a sample sketch should give us some idea. We see that the graph tends to "flatten out" at its maximum, and thus the tangent line at the point $(c, f(c))$ is horizontal.

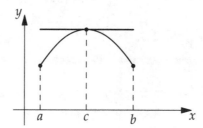

This gives us a conjecture:

**Problem 3.22:** Let $f$ be a continuous function on a closed interval $[a, b]$, and let $c \in (a, b)$ be a point at which $f$ attains its maximum on $[a, b]$. Show that if $f$ is differentiable at $c$, then $f'(c) = 0$.

Before we present the solution, note that there are a couple of subtle yet important conditions in this problem. First, $f$ might attain its maximum at one of the endpoints of $[a, b]$, and there's no reason to expect that $f' = 0$ at these points, as the diagram on the left below shows. Second, $f$ might not be differentiable at its maximum, as the diagram on the right below shows.

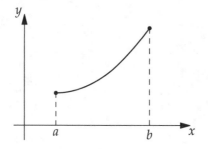 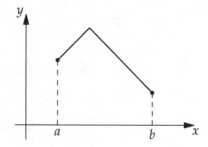

*Solution for Problem 3.22:*   Let $c \in (a, b)$ be the point where $f$ attains its maximum. We write the definition of the derivative $f'(c)$:

$$f'(c) = \lim_{h \to 0} \frac{f(c + h) - f(c)}{h}.$$

Assuming that $h$ is small enough so that $c + h \in [a, b]$, what do we know about the numerator of the above fraction? Since $f(c)$ is the maximum value that $f$ attains, we know that $f(c + h) \leq f(c)$; in other words, the numerator is negative or zero. But the denominator is positive for $h > 0$ and negative for $h < 0$. Thus, by considering only positive values of $h$, we see that $f'(c) \leq 0$, and by considering only negative $h$, we see that $f'(c) \geq 0$. Thus, the only possibility is $f'(c) = 0$. $\square$

Of course, essentially the same argument works for the minimum value of $f$ on $[a, b]$. We thus have the following theorem:

>
> **Important:** Let $f$ be a continuous function on $[a, b]$.
>
> - If $f$ attains its maximum at $c \in (a, b)$, and $f$ is differentiable at $c$, then $f'(c) = 0$.
>
> - If $f$ attains its minimum at $d \in (a, b)$, and $f$ is differentiable at $d$, then $f'(d) = 0$.

Once again, remember the important "exceptions" to the above theorem: $f$ might not be differentiable at its minimum or maximum, and the minimum or maximum might occur at one of the endpoints of the interval.

If we change the conditions slightly to remove these exceptions, we get a very useful theorem:

> **Problem 3.23:** Let $f$ be a function that is continuous on $[a, b]$ and differentiable on $(a, b)$, such that $f(a) = f(b)$. Show that there exists some $c \in (a, b)$ such that $f'(c) = 0$.

*Solution for Problem 3.23:* Suppose $c \in (a, b)$ is such that $f$ attains its maximum on $[a, b]$ at $c$. Then we can apply Problem 3.22 (since $f$ is differentiable at all points on $(a, b)$) and conclude that $f'(c) = 0$. Similarly, suppose $c \in (a, b)$ is such that $f$ attains its minimum on $[a, b]$ at $c$. Again we can conclude that $f'(c) = 0$. What is the only other possibility? That's if both the minimum and the maximum occur at the endpoints. But since $f(a) = f(b)$, this means that the function is constant on $[a, b]$, and thus $f' = 0$ everywhere!

So in all cases, $f'(c) = 0$ for some $c \in (a, b)$. $\square$

This result is known as:

>
> **Important:** **Rolle's Theorem**: If $f$ is continuous on $[a, b]$ and differentiable on $(a, b)$, and $f(a) = f(b)$, then there exists $c \in (a, b)$ such that $f'(c) = 0$.

Again, the easiest way to remember Rolle's Theorem is to keep the picture to the right in mind—if a continuous function on $[a, b]$ starts and ends at the same value $f(a) = f(b)$, then it must "flatten out" at some point $c$ with $f'(c) = 0$. It's a very nice theorem, but it's pretty specific: it only works if $f(a) = f(b)$. We'd like a more general version that works on any differentiable function on an interval.

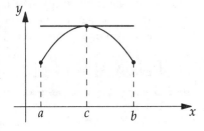

Let's consider an arbitrary function that's continuous on $[a, b]$ and differentiable on $(a, b)$, as shown at right. If we tilt our head and pretend that the $x$-axis runs through $(a, f(a))$ and $(b, f(b))$, we get the idea that we should be able to find a point $c \in (a, b)$ such that the tangent line through $(c, f(c))$ is parallel to our new "$x$-axis."

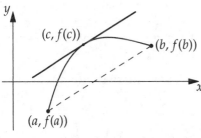

What does this really mean? It means that the tangent line through $(c, f(c))$ is parallel to the line through $(a, f(a))$ and $(b, f(b))$. And, of course, "parallel" means that the two lines have the same slope. If we put it all together, we have that

$$f'(c) = \text{slope of line through } (a, f(a)) \text{ and } (b, f(b)) = \frac{f(b) - f(a)}{b - a}.$$

We're now ready to state the theorem, which is one of the most important theorems in calculus.

> **Important:** **The Mean Value Theorem**: If $f$ is a continuous function on the closed interval $[a, b]$, with $a < b$, and $f$ is differentiable on $(a, b)$, then there exists some real number $c \in (a, b)$ such that
> $$f'(c) = \frac{f(b) - f(a)}{b - a}.$$

The Mean Value Theorem is arguably the most important theoretical result about the derivative. You should think about the Mean Value Theorem until its statement becomes intuitively obvious to you. The proof is a little bit tricky, so we'll defer it to Section 3.B. We'll see more of the significance of the Mean Value Theorem in Chapter 4.

## EXERCISES

**3.5.1** Suppose that $f$ is continuous on a closed interval $[a, b]$ and that $f'(c) = 0$ for all $c \in (a, b)$. What can you conclude about $f$? Prove your result. **Hints:** 207

**3.5.2** Suppose $f$ and $g$ are differentiable functions such that $f' = g'$. Show that $f - g$ is a constant function.

**3.5.3** Let $f$ be a degree $n$ polynomial with $n$ distinct real roots. Show that $f'$ has $n - 1$ distinct real roots. **Hints:** 262

**3.5.4** Suppose that $f$ is a differentiable function with domain $\mathbb{R}$ such that $f'(x) > 0$ for all $x \in \mathbb{R}$. Show that if $a, b \in \mathbb{R}$ with $a < b$, then $f(a) < f(b)$. **Hints:** 117

## 3.6  IMPLICIT DIFFERENTIATION

Many curves are not defined as the graph of a function, but instead are defined **implicitly** as the graph of an equation involving $x$ and $y$. For example, consider the circle with center $(0, 0)$ and radius 1. This circle is the set of all points $(x, y)$ satisfying the equation $x^2 + y^2 = 1$. Since it fails the Vertical Line Test, we know that this circle is not the graph of any function. This presents an issue with an example like the following:

> **Problem 3.24:** Find the slope of the tangent line to the circle $x^2 + y^2 = 1$ at the point $\left( \frac{\sqrt{2}}{2}, \frac{\sqrt{2}}{2} \right)$.

*Solution for Problem 3.24:* Of course, we know from our knowledge of geometry and trigonometry that the slope of this line is $-1$. However, for the sake of this exercise, let's compute this slope using calculus. Although the entire circle is not the graph of a function, the top half of the circle *is* the graph of a function, and we can compute the derivative of this function to get the slope of this line.

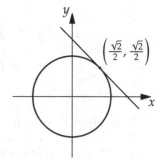

If we replace $y$ with $f(x)$ in our equation for the circle, we get

$$x^2 + (f(x))^2 = 1,$$

which we can solve to get

$$f(x) = \sqrt{1 - x^2},$$

the graph of which is the top half of the circle. If we instead had taken the negative square root, we would have $f(x) = -\sqrt{1 - x^2}$, whose graph is the bottom half of the circle.

We can now use the Chain Rule to take the derivative of $f(x) = (1 - x^2)^{\frac{1}{2}}$:

$$f'(x) = \frac{1}{2}(1 - x^2)^{-\frac{1}{2}}(-2x) = -\frac{x}{\sqrt{1 - x^2}}.$$

We now see that

$$f'\left(\frac{\sqrt{2}}{2}\right) = -\frac{\sqrt{2}/2}{\sqrt{1/2}} = -1,$$

so that the slope of the tangent line to the circle at the point $\left(\frac{\sqrt{2}}{2}, \frac{\sqrt{2}}{2}\right)$ is $-1$, as we expect. $\square$

But a simpler way of finding this derivative is to just take the derivative directly of the equation that implicitly defines the circle. Specifically, we start with

$$x^2 + (f(x))^2 = 1,$$

and we take the derivative of both sides:

$$\frac{d}{dx}\left(x^2 + (f(x))^2\right) = \frac{d}{dx}(1).$$

Since the derivative is linear, we can break up the left side into a sum of derivatives. We also note that $\frac{d}{dx}(x^2) = 2x$ and $\frac{d}{dx}(1) = 0$, so we have

$$2x + \frac{d}{dx}\left((f(x))^2\right) = 0.$$

How do we take the derivative of that remaining term? We can use the Chain Rule! This gives us

$$2x + 2(f(x))(f'(x)) = 0.$$

Now we solve for the derivative:

$$f'(x) = -\frac{2x}{2f(x)} = -\frac{x}{f(x)}.$$

Now we see, for example, that at the point $\left(\frac{\sqrt{2}}{2}, \frac{\sqrt{2}}{2}\right)$, the derivative is $-\frac{\sqrt{2}/2}{\sqrt{2}/2} = -1$, just as before.

More typically, equations that implicitly define functions are written in terms of $x$ and $y$. Thus, we would write the circle as

$$x^2 + y^2 = 1,$$

and implicitly differentiate to get $2x + 2yy' = 0$, from which we could solve to get $y' = -\frac{x}{y}$.

> **Concept:** The main thing to keep in mind when performing implicit differentiation is that taking the derivative (with respect to $x$) of any term containing a "$y$" is going to result in a $y'$ term being introduced. In other words, $\frac{d}{dx}y = y'$.

Here is a somewhat more complicated example:

**Problem 3.25:** Find the equation for the tangent line to the curve $3y^2 - 6xy + 2x^3 - 5y = 2$ at the point $(2, 1)$.

*Solution for Problem 3.25:* First, it's a good idea to verify that $(2, 1)$ is on the curve, which we can do by plugging $(x, y) = (2, 1)$ into the equation:

$$3(1)^2 - 6(2)(1) + 2(2)^3 - 5(1) = 3 - 12 + 16 - 5 = 2.$$

Next, we compute the derivative of the equation that implicitly defines the curve. Again, the idea is simple: whenever we have a term with a $y$ in it, we have to apply the Chain Rule to get a $y'$ term. Thus we get

$$6yy' - 6xy' - 6y + 6x^2 - 5y' = 0.$$

Don't forget to differentiate the constant on the right side as well (to get 0). We could solve this for $y'$ in terms of $x$ and $y$, but in this problem it's simpler to plug in $(x, y) = (2, 1)$ right away to get the slope of the tangent at $(2, 1)$:

$$6y' - 12y' - 6 + 24 - 5y' = 0,$$

so $y' = \frac{18}{11}$. Thus, in point-slope form, the equation of the tangent line is

$$y - 1 = \frac{18}{11}(x - 2).$$

$\square$

## Exercises

**3.6.1** Find the slope of the tangent line to the hyperbola $x^2 - y^2 = 1$ at the point $(2, \sqrt{3})$.

**3.6.2** Find the equation of the tangent line to the curve $y^3 - 3xy^2 + x^2 - xy = 6$ at the point $(-1, 1)$.

**3.6.3** Find $\dfrac{dy}{dx}$ if $x^2 + y = \log(y^2 - 1)$.

**3.6.4** Find the slope of the tangent line to the curve $x \sin(x + y) = y \cos(x - y)$ at the point $\left(0, \frac{\pi}{2}\right)$.

**3.6.5** Assume that $\dfrac{d}{d\theta} \sin \theta = \cos \theta$ and that $\dfrac{d}{d\theta} \cos \theta$ is continuous. Use implicit differentiation to prove that $\dfrac{d}{d\theta} \cos \theta = -\sin \theta$. **Hints: 258**

## 3.7 Summary of derivative computation

Here is a summary of derivative rules and the catalog of common derivatives that we developed in this chapter. You should learn all of the items below, and practice until computing a derivative is as easy as addition or multiplication.

**Definition**

$$f'(a) = \lim_{h \to 0} \frac{f(a + h) - f(a)}{h}$$

**Linearity**

$$(f + g)'(x) = f'(x) + g'(x)$$
$$(cf)'(x) = cf'(x)$$

**Product Rule**

$$(fg)'(x) = f'(x)g(x) + f(x)g'(x)$$

**Quotient Rule**

$$\left(\frac{f}{g}\right)'(x) = \frac{f'(x)g(x) - f(x)g'(x)}{(g(x))^2}$$

**Inverse Function Rule**

$$(f^{-1})'(x) = \frac{1}{f'(f^{-1}(x))}$$

**Monomials**

$$\frac{d}{dx}x^n = nx^{n-1}$$

**Trig Functions**

$$\frac{d}{dx}(\sin x) = \cos x \qquad \frac{d}{dx}(\cos x) = -\sin x$$

$$\frac{d}{dx}(\tan x) = \sec^2 x \qquad \frac{d}{dx}(\cot x) = -\csc^2 x$$

$$\frac{d}{dx}(\sec x) = \sec x \tan x \qquad \frac{d}{dx}(\csc x) = -\csc x \cot x$$

**Exponential and Natural Logarithm**

$$\frac{d}{dx}(e^x) = e^x \qquad \frac{d}{dx}(\log x) = \frac{1}{x}$$

**Chain Rule**

$$(g \circ f)'(x) = g'(f(x))f'(x)$$

**Mean Value Theorem**: If $f$ is continuous on $[a,b]$ and differentiable on $(a,b)$, then there exists $c \in (a,b)$ such that

$$f'(c) = \frac{f(b) - f(a)}{b - a}.$$

## REVIEW PROBLEMS

**3.26** Compute the derivatives of the following:

(a) $\dfrac{1}{(2x+3)^3}$  (b) $\sqrt{x^3 + e^x}$  (c) $\log(\sin x \cos x)$  (d) $\sqrt[3]{1 + \sqrt{x + \sqrt{e^x}}}$

(e) $axe^{-bx}$ where $a$ and $b$ are real  (f) $e^{-x^2}$  (g) $\sin^{-1} x^2$  (h) $\sin^3 x$

**3.27** Find the equation of the tangent line to the graph $y = (x-1)^3 + 2$ at the point $(3, 10)$.

**3.28** Let $f(x) = x^2 - 6x + 10$ with domain $[3, +\infty)$. Find $(f^{-1})'(2)$.

**3.29** Find the tangent line to the curve $y^2 = x^3 - 3x + 1$ at the point $(2, \sqrt{3})$.

**3.30** Define

$$f^{\#}(a) = \lim_{h \to 0} \frac{f(a+h) - f(a-h)}{2h}.$$

Show that if $f'(a)$ exists, then so does $f^{\#}(a)$, and $f^{\#}(a) = f'(a)$.

**3.31**

(a) Show that if $f, g, h$ are differentiable functions, then

$$(fgh)' = f'gh + fg'h + fgh'.$$

Hints: 191

83

(b)  Suppose $f_1, f_2, \ldots, f_k$ are differentiable functions. Find a formula for $(f_1 f_2 \cdots f_k)'$. **Hints:** 226

**3.32**  Find a continuous function $f$ for which the Mean Value Theorem fails. That is, find a continuous function $f$ and $a < b$ with $[a, b] \subseteq \mathrm{Dom}(f)$, such that there does not exist $c \in (a, b)$ satisfying

$$f'(c) = \frac{f(b) - f(a)}{b - a}.$$

**Hints:** 249

**3.33**  Let $f(x) = 1 + x + x^2 + \cdots + x^{100}$. Find $f'(1)$. *(Source: HMMT)* **Hints:** 208

## CHALLENGE PROBLEMS

**3.34**  Let $a$ be a positive real number. Find $\dfrac{d}{dx} a^x$ and $\dfrac{d}{dx} \log_a(x)$. **Hints:** 274

**3.35**  Let $f(x) = x^3 + ax + b$, with $a \neq b$, and suppose that the tangent lines to the graph of $f$ at $x = a$ and $x = b$ are parallel. Find $f(1)$. *(Source: HMMT)* **Hints:** 166, 42

**3.36**  Recall that a function $f$ is *even* if $f(-x) = f(x)$ and is *odd* if $f(-x) = -f(x)$. Prove that if $f$ is odd, then $f'$ is even, and that if $f$ is even, then $f'$ is odd.

**3.37**  Suppose the function $f(x) - f(2x)$ has derivative 5 at $x = 1$ and derivative 7 at $x = 2$. Find the derivative of $f(x) - f(4x)$ at $x = 1$. *(Source: HMMT)* **Hints:** 22, 213

**3.38**  We write $f^{(k)}(x)$ to mean taking the derivative of $f(x)$ $k$ times. Prove that if $f(x)$ is a degree $n$ polynomial, then $f^{(n)}(x) = c$ where $c$ is a nonzero constant. **Hints:** 140

**3.39**  A polynomial function $f(x)$ has a root $r$ with **multiplicity** $m$ if

$$f(x) = (x - r)^m h(x)$$

for some polynomial $h(x)$ with $h(r) \neq 0$.

(a)  Prove that if $f$ has root $r$ with multiplicity $m$, then $f'$ has root $r$ with multiplicity $m - 1$.

(b)  Prove that $f^{(k)}(r) = 0$ for all $1 \leq k < m$.

**3.40**  Suppose $f$ and $g$ are differentiable functions.

(a)  Show that

$$(fg)'' = f''g + 2f'g' + fg''.$$

(b)★  Generalize part (a) to show that for any positive integer $n$,

$$(fg)^{(n)} = \sum_{k=0}^{n} \binom{n}{k} f^{(k)} g^{(n-k)}.$$

This is called the **Leibniz Rule**. **Hints:** 33, 127

## 3.A  PROOF OF THE CHAIN RULE

**Problem 3.41:**  Prove that if $f$ and $g$ are differentiable functions, and if $a \in \mathbb{R}$ is such that $(g \circ f)(a)$ exists, then

$$(g \circ f)'(a) = g'(f(a))f'(a).$$

> **Sidenote:** The argument presented below is largely based on the argument in [**Sp**,Chapter 10]. There are other ways to prove this, but I find the argument in [**Sp**] to be the nicest I've seen.

*Solution for Problem 3.41:* We start as we did on page 73, with the limit definition of $(g \circ f)'(a)$:

$$(g \circ f)'(a) = \lim_{h \to 0} \frac{g(f(a+h)) - g(f(a))}{h}.$$

We want an $f'(a)$ term to appear on the right side of the above, thus it appears that we'll need to have $f(a+h) - f(a)$ in the numerator. So let's multiply by it. Of course, if we multiply by it, we have to divide by it too:

$$\frac{g(f(a+h)) - g(f(a))}{h} = \frac{g(f(a+h)) - g(f(a))}{f(a+h) - f(a)} \cdot \frac{f(a+h) - f(a)}{h}. \tag{3.1}$$

This is nice: the second fraction in (3.1) has limit $f'(a)$ as $h \to 0$. But we have a problem if some $h \neq 0$ satisfies $f(a+h) - f(a) = 0$. If this occurs, then the expression in (3.1) is not defined at that $h$, because the denominator of the first term is 0.

To be a little more precise about what the problem is here and how to fix it, suppose we define

$$r(h) = \frac{g(f(a+h)) - g(f(a))}{f(a+h) - f(a)}.$$

This is the first fraction on the right side of (3.1). We'd like to be able to show that $\lim_{h \to 0} r(h) = g'(f(a))$. The problem is that $r(h)$ is undefined wherever $f(a+h) = f(a)$. This is not an issue at $h = 0$, because we're taking a limit, but it is an issue if this happens at any $h \neq 0$. So what we'll do is use some "spackle" and fill in the "holes" in the definition of $r$ that occur where $f(a+h) = f(a)$. Specifically, we extend $r(h)$ to a new function $\rho(h)$ by:

$$\rho(h) = \begin{cases} \dfrac{g(f(a+h)) - g(f(a))}{f(a+h) - f(a)} & \text{if } f(a+h) \neq f(a), \\ g'(f(a)) & \text{if } f(a+h) = f(a). \end{cases}$$

Now $\rho$ doesn't have any holes, since we've filled the holes with the value $g'(f(a))$.

We now show that $\lim_{h \to 0} \rho(h) = g'(f(a))$. This means that for any $\epsilon > 0$, we need to be able to find $\delta > 0$ such that

$$0 < |h| < \delta \quad \Rightarrow \quad |\rho(h) - g'(f(a))| < \epsilon. \tag{3.2}$$

However, we know by definition that

$$\lim_{k \to 0} \frac{g(f(a) + k) - g(f(a))}{k} = g'(f(a)), \tag{3.3}$$

which means that we can choose $\zeta > 0$ such that

$$0 < |k| < \zeta \quad \Rightarrow \quad \left| \frac{g(f(a) + k) - g(f(a))}{k} - g'(f(a)) \right| < \epsilon, \tag{3.4}$$

and we know that $f$ is continuous at $a$, so we can choose $\delta > 0$ such that

$$0 < |x| < \delta \quad \Rightarrow \quad |f(a+x) - f(a)| < \zeta. \tag{3.5}$$

We claim that this is the $\delta$ that satisfies (3.2). To see why, let $h$ be given such that $0 < |h| < \delta$. If $f(a+h) = f(a)$, then by definition $\rho(h) = g'(f(a))$ (remember, this is the "spackle"), so clearly

$$|\rho(h) - g'(f(a))| = |g'(f(a)) - g'(f(a))| = 0 < \epsilon,$$

as needed. On the other hand, if $f(a + h) \neq f(a)$, then we use (3.5) to get $0 < |f(a + h) - f(a)| < \zeta$. Then, plugging $f(a + h) - f(a)$ in for $k$ in (3.4), we get

$$\left| \frac{g(f(a) + (f(a + h) - f(a))) - g(f(a))}{f(a + h) - f(a)} - g'(f(a)) \right| < \epsilon. \tag{3.6}$$

But that fraction in (3.6) is just $\rho(h)$:

$$\frac{g(f(a) + (f(a + h) - f(a))) - g(f(a))}{f(a + h) - f(a)} = \frac{g(f(a + h)) - g(f(a))}{f(a + h) - f(a)} = \rho(h).$$

Thus, (3.6) becomes

$$|\rho(h) - g'(f(a))| < \epsilon,$$

which is what we needed to establish in (3.2). Therefore, we have shown that $\lim_{h \to 0} \rho(h) = g'(f(a))$.

Now we can prove the Chain Rule. We modify (3.1) by observing that, for all $h \neq 0$, we have

$$\frac{g(f(a + h)) - g(f(a))}{h} = \left( \rho(h) \cdot \frac{f(a + h) - f(a)}{h} \right),$$

because if $f(a + h) \neq f(a)$, this is the same expression that we had in (3.1), and if $f(a + h) = f(a)$, then both sides of the above are 0. Thus, we can now finally complete the computation of the derivative of $g \circ f$:

$$\begin{aligned}
(g \circ f)'(a) &= \lim_{h \to 0} \frac{g(f(a + h)) - g(f(a))}{h} \\
&= \lim_{h \to 0} \left( \rho(h) \cdot \frac{f(a + h) - f(a)}{h} \right) \\
&= \left( \lim_{h \to 0} \rho(h) \right) \cdot \left( \lim_{h \to 0} \frac{f(a + h) - f(a)}{h} \right) \\
&= g'(f(a)) f'(a).
\end{aligned}$$

$\square$

## 3.B  PROOF OF THE MEAN VALUE THEOREM

> **Problem 3.42:** The **Mean Value Theorem**: Let $f$ be a continuous function on $[a, b]$ that is differentiable on $(a, b)$. Show that there exists a point $c \in (a, b)$ such that
> $$f'(c) = \frac{f(b) - f(a)}{b - a}.$$

*Solution for Problem 3.42:* Recall that the expression $\dfrac{f(b) - f(a)}{b - a}$ is the slope of the secant line between $(a, f(a))$ and $(b, f(b))$, shown by the dashed line in the picture to the right. The Mean Value Theorem asserts that there is a point $(c, f(c))$ on the graph of $y = f(x)$ such that the tangent line at $(c, f(c))$ is parallel to the secant line from $(a, f(a))$ to $(b, f(b))$, as in the picture at right. Also note that if $f(a) = f(b)$, then the Mean Value Theorem asserts that $f'(c) = 0$; in other words, we just have Rolle's Theorem.

We'd like to define a new function $g$ with $g(a) = g(b)$ in order to apply Rolle's Theorem. It's not immediately clear how we might do this. We might as well take $g(a) = f(a)$, and then we will aim for $g(b) = g(a) = f(a)$. A simple approach is to try to have some sort of linear "correction" of the form

$$g(x) = f(x) - (x - a)(\text{something}),$$

noting that $g(a) = f(a) + (a - a)(\text{something}) = f(a)$. Plugging in $x = b$ gives

$$g(b) = f(b) - (b - a)(\text{something}).$$

We want $g(b) = g(a) = f(a)$, so we need the "something" to be $\dfrac{f(b) - f(a)}{b - a}$, which happens to be the slope of the secant line from $(a, f(a))$ to $(b, f(b))$. Therefore, our new function is

$$g(x) = f(x) - \frac{f(b) - f(a)}{b - a}(x - a).$$

Notice that $g$ is continuous on $[a, b]$ (since it is a linear combination of the continuous functions $f(x)$ and $(x - a)$), and that

$$g'(x) = f'(x) - \frac{f(b) - f(a)}{b - a},$$

so $g$ is differentiable on $(a, b)$. Also we verify that $g(a) = f(a)$ and

$$g(b) = f(b) - \frac{f(b) - f(a)}{b - a}(b - a) = f(a),$$

so $g(a) = g(b)$. Thus, we may apply Rolle's Theorem to $g$ and find a point $c \in (a, b)$ such that $g'(c) = 0$. Finally,

$$f'(c) = g'(c) + \frac{f(b) - f(a)}{b - a} = \frac{f(b) - f(a)}{b - a},$$

as desired. $\square$

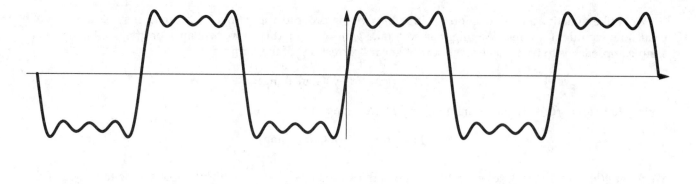

# APPLICATIONS OF THE DERIVATIVE

In Chapter 3 we introduced the concept of derivative in terms of geometry: the derivative of $f(x)$ at a point $(a, f(a))$ on the graph of $f$ is the slope of the tangent line to the curve at that point. However, if this is all that the derivative were good for, then calculus would be an interesting geometrical curiosity, and not the fundamental part of mathematics that it is today. Indeed, the derivative has many more applications than just finding slopes of tangent lines. We'll explore these applications in this chapter.

## 4.1 GRAPHICAL INTERPRETATION OF THE DERIVATIVE

We defined the derivative $f'(a)$ of a function $f$ at a point $a \in \mathrm{Dom}(f)$ to be the slope of the tangent line to the graph $y = f(x)$ at $(a, f(a))$. This right away gives us some pretty important qualitative information about the function's behavior at $x = a$. Let's start with some definitions:

> **Definition:** Let $f$ be a function.
>
> - $f$ is **increasing** on an interval $I$ if for all $a, b \in I$ with $a < b$, we have $f(a) \le f(b)$.
>
> - $f$ is **decreasing** on an interval $I$ if for all $a, b \in I$ with $a < b$, we have $f(a) \ge f(b)$.
>
> In either case we say that $f$ is **monotonic** on $I$. If $I$ is the entire domain of $f$, then we can simply say that $f$ is **increasing** (or **decreasing**).

Intuitively, the graph of an increasing function is "always rising" and the graph of a decreasing function is "always falling." In other words, the graph of an increasing function "moves upwards" as we move from left to right, and the graph of a decreasing function "moves downwards." However, because the inequalities in our definition above are not strict (that is, we used "$\le$" rather than "$<$" in the definition of increasing), the function might also "level off" at some point; indeed, under our definition, the constant function $f(x) = c$ is both increasing and decreasing.

We can modify our definition slightly:

> **Definition:** Let $f$ be a function.
>
> - $f$ is **strictly increasing** on an interval $I$ if for all $a, b \in I$ with $a < b$, we have $f(a) < f(b)$.
>
> - $f$ is **strictly decreasing** on an interval $I$ if for all $a, b \in I$ with $a < b$, we have $f(a) > f(b)$.
>
> In either case we say that $f$ is **strictly monotonic** on $I$. If $I$ is the entire domain of $f$, then we can simply say that $f$ is **strictly increasing** (or **strictly decreasing**).

The only difference between "increasing" and "strictly increasing" is that in the latter, we do not permit the function to "level off."

If the function is differentiable, then the derivative gives us a nice test for monotonicity.

> **Problem 4.1:** Let $f$ be a differentiable function.
> (a) Show that if $f'(x) > 0$ for all $x \in \mathrm{Dom}(f)$, then $f$ is strictly increasing.
> (b) Replace the ">" in the above expression with "<", "$\geq$", or "$\leq$" and determine what conclusion can be made.

*Solution for Problem 4.1:*

(a) Thinking of a picture gives us the idea: we can see that since the slope of any tangent line is **always positive**, the function is always "rising" as we move from left to right. Although this is a good intuitive way to think about what's going on, it is not a rigorous proof by any means. So how can we prove that the statement is true?

Let's use the definition of strictly increasing to set up a rigorous proof. We are given two values $a, b \in \mathrm{Dom}(f)$, with $a < b$, and we need to show that $f(a) < f(b)$. Hmmm... do we know any expressions that relate the quantities $a$, $b$, $f(a)$, $f(b)$, and $f'$?

> **Concept:** When trying to prove something about various quantities, think if you know any formulas, theorems, or previously-solved problems that involve these quantities.

The Mean Value Theorem does the trick! Recall that it states that there must be some $c \in (a, b)$ such that

$$f'(c) = \frac{f(b) - f(a)}{b - a}.$$

But we are given that $f'(c) > 0$, and we know that $b - a > 0$. So we must also have that $f(b) - f(a) > 0$, meaning that $f(a) < f(b)$, and thus we conclude that the function is strictly increasing.

(b) Replacing the inequality changes what we know about $f'(c)$ in our Mean Value Theorem expression, but the key fact is that since $b - a > 0$, then the sign of $f'(c)$ (whether it is positive, negative, or 0) will always match the sign of $f(b) - f(a)$. So we can make the following table:

| | | |
|---|---|---|
| $f'(c) > 0$ | $f(b) - f(a) > 0$ | $f$ is strictly increasing |
| $f'(c) \geq 0$ | $f(b) - f(a) \geq 0$ | $f$ is increasing |
| $f'(c) < 0$ | $f(b) - f(a) < 0$ | $f$ is strictly decreasing |
| $f'(c) \leq 0$ | $f(b) - f(a) \leq 0$ | $f$ is decreasing |

$\square$

More generally, looking at specific intervals (and not necessary the entire domain of $f$), we have the following result:

> **Important:** Let $f$ be a continuous differentiable function on an interval $[a, b]$.
>
> - If $f'(x) > 0$ for all $x \in (a, b)$, then $f$ is strictly increasing on $[a, b]$.
>
> - If $f'(x) \geq 0$ for all $x \in (a, b)$, then $f$ is increasing on $[a, b]$.
>
> - If $f'(x) < 0$ for all $x \in (a, b)$, then $f$ is strictly decreasing on $[a, b]$.
>
> - If $f'(x) \leq 0$ for all $x \in (a, b)$, then $f$ is decreasing on $[a, b]$.

This is our first look at how we can interpret the derivative as the *rate of change* of $f$. Basically, $f'$ is measuring the rate at which $f(x)$ changes as we increase $x$. If $f' > 0$, then the rate of change is positive, and the function is increasing. If $f' < 0$, then the rate of change is negative, and the function is decreasing.

> **Concept:** Thinking of the derivative as a rate of change is probably the most important application of the derivative. We will see this interpretation throughout this chapter, and indeed throughout calculus.

> **Problem 4.2:** Let $f$ be a differentiable function with $f'(x) = 0$ for all $x \in (a, b)$. What can we conclude about $f$?

*Solution for Problem 4.2:* Because $f' \geq 0$, the function is increasing on $[a, b]$. This means that $f(c) \leq f(d)$ for all $a \leq c \leq d \leq b$. On the other hand, because $f' \leq 0$, the function is decreasing on $[a, b]$. This means that $f(c) \geq f(d)$ for all $a \leq c \leq d \leq b$. The only way that we can have $f(c) \leq f(d)$ and simultaneously have $f(c) \geq f(d)$ is if $f(c) = f(d)$. But this is true for all $c, d \in [a, b]$. Hence, the function $f$ is constant on $[a, b]$. Also, this makes sense as a rate of change: if $f' = 0$, then the rate of change of $f$ is 0. That is, the function isn't changing at all! The only functions that don't change at all are constant functions. $\square$

> **Important:** If $f$ is differentiable and $f' = 0$ on an interval $I$, then $f$ is constant on $I$.

One immediate application of the sign of the derivative is that it lets us quickly make a rough sketch of the graph of an unfamiliar function. For example:

> **Problem 4.3:** Sketch the graph of $f(x) = x^3 - 3x^2 + 1$, and use this sketch to get information about the roots of the function.

*Solution for Problem 4.3:* We can start by finding a few "easy" points. One point is particularly easy: we plug in $x = 0$ to get $f(0) = 1$, so $(0, 1)$ must be on the graph. Also easy are $f(1) = -1$ and $f(-1) = -3$, so $(1, -1)$ and $(-1, -3)$ are also on the graph. We plot these points on the graph at right.

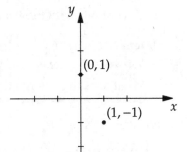

Our next step is to find where the function is increasing and where it is decreasing. For this, we compute the derivative:

$$f'(x) = 3x^2 - 6x.$$

The zeros of $3x^2 - 6x = 3x(x - 2)$ are at $x = 0$ and $x = 2$. Further, we can see that $f'(x) > 0$ on $(-\infty, 0)$ and on $(2, +\infty)$, and $f'(x) < 0$ on $(0, 2)$. We thus conclude that $f(x)$ is increasing from $-\infty$ up to $0$, then decreasing from $0$ to $2$, then increasing from $2$ to $+\infty$. Sometimes this information is represented as a **sign graph** for the derivative, as follows:

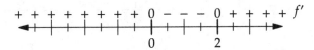

This little chart just indicates the sign of the derivative. Where it's "+", the function $f$ is strictly increasing, and where it's "−", the function $f$ is strictly decreasing.

Next, since the function changes from decreasing to increasing at $x = 2$, we probably want to calculate $f(2) = 8 - 12 + 1 = -3$. So the graph passes through $(2, -3)$.

Therefore, the graph increases up to $(0, 1)$ (passing through $(-1, -3)$ on the way), then decreases down to $(2, -3)$ (passing through $(0, 1)$ and $(1, -1)$ on the way), and then increases towards $+\infty$.

Putting all this information together, we get our sketch:

| Interval | $f'$ | $f$ |
|---|---|---|
| $(-\infty, 0)$ | $+$ | increasing |
| $0$ | $0$ | $f(0) = 1$ |
| $(0, 2)$ | $-$ | decreasing |
| $2$ | $0$ | $f(2) = -3$ |
| $(2, +\infty)$ | $+$ | increasing |

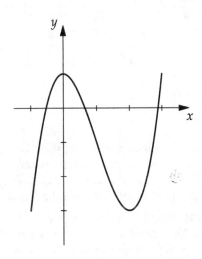

Finally, we can use this sketch to get information about the roots of the cubic. By the Intermediate Value Theorem, we know that one root is between $-1$ and $0$, one root is between $0$ and $2$, and one root is greater than $2$. □

We might ask a similar question about the derivative itself: when is it increasing or decreasing? To answer this, we start with the function $f'$, and we look at its derivative $(f')' = f''$. This is the **second derivative** of the original function $f$. (Analogously, we sometimes call $f'$ the **first derivative** of $f$.)

Let's continue with the example from Problem 4.3.

**Problem 4.4:** Let $f(x) = x^3 - 3x^2 + 1$.

(a)  Where is $f'$ increasing? Where is it decreasing?

(b)  What does this information say about the shape of the graph of $f$?

*Solution for Problem 4.4:*

(a)  We had $f'(x) = 3x^2 - 6x$, so $f''(x) = 6x - 6$. This is positive for $x > 1$, zero at $x = 1$, and negative for $x < 1$. So when $x < 1$, the derivative is decreasing, and when $x > 1$, the derivative is increasing. We can add this information to our sign chart:

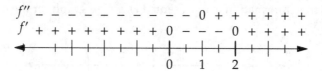

We notice that $f'$ starts positive, but is decreasing. At $x = 0$ we have $f'$ switching from positive to negative, and still decreasing. At $x = 1$ we see that $f'$ switches from decreasing to increasing; note $f'$ is still negative. At $x = 2$, while $f'$ is increasing, it switches from negative to positive, and continues to increase for $x > 2$.

(b)  We can see the effect of $f''$ on the graph of $f$:

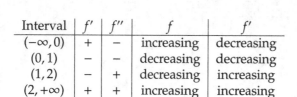

| Interval | $f'$ | $f''$ | $f$ | $f'$ |
|----------|------|-------|-----|------|
| $(-\infty, 0)$ | $+$ | $-$ | increasing | decreasing |
| $(0, 1)$ | $-$ | $-$ | decreasing | decreasing |
| $(1, 2)$ | $-$ | $+$ | decreasing | increasing |
| $(2, +\infty)$ | $+$ | $+$ | increasing | increasing |

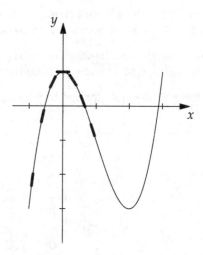

We have drawn some segments of the tangent lines as various points on the curve. We can see that as we move along the curve from left to right towards $x = 1$, the slopes of the tangent lines are decreasing, because $f'' < 0$. The fact that the derivative is decreasing means that the tangent lines to the curve are decreasing in slope, which means that they are rotating clockwise as we move along the curve.

Another way that you can think of this is that if you are a person walking along the curve in the increasing $x$ direction, then the curve is bending to the right as you walk along it. In our example, if we walk along the curve from $(-1, -3)$ through $(0, 1)$ and towards $(1, -1)$, the "path" provided by the curve is gradually bending to the right. (This is most noticeable in the big, sweeping right curve that we have to make near $x = 0$.) The curve bends to the right because the tangents are decreasing in slope, so their directions are rotating clockwise, which is towards the right of your direction of travel.

We say that the portion of the function where $f'' < 0$ is **concave down**. Basically, where $f$ is concave down, the graph of $f$ is "bending downwards" as it moves from left to right. This bending can happen whether the curve is increasing or decreasing, as we see in our example above: the function is increasing up to $x = 0$, then decreasing between $x = 0$ and $x = 1$, but the whole time it is concave down.

Conversely, if $f'' > 0$, then the derivative is increasing. This means that the tangent lines are increasing in slope, which means that they are rotating counterclockwise. In our example, this occurs when $x > 1$. We add more tangent line segments to our picture to illustrate this behavior:

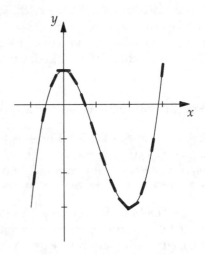

| Interval | $f'$ | $f''$ | $f$ | $f'$ |
|----------|------|-------|-----|------|
| $(-\infty, 0)$ | + | − | increasing | decreasing |
| $(0, 1)$ | − | − | decreasing | decreasing |
| $(1, 2)$ | − | + | decreasing | increasing |
| $(2, +\infty)$ | + | + | increasing | increasing |

We say that the function is **concave up** where $f'' > 0$: the graph is "bending upwards" as $x$ increases. Again, this bending can happen whether the function is increasing or decreasing.

Finally, the concavity of the graph may change (from up to down or vice versa) at points where $f''(x) = 0$. Any point at which the concavity of the graph changes is called an **inflection point**. In our $f(x) = x^3 - 3x^2 + 1$ example, we have $f''(1) = 0$, and the concavity of the graph changes from concave down (for $x < 1$) to concave up (for $x > 1$). Thus $(1, -1)$ is an inflection point; moreover, since it is the only value of $x$ such that $f''(x) = 0$, it is the only inflection point.

□

To summarize some of the definitions and concepts from Problem 4.4:

---

**Definition:** Let $f$ be a differentiable function.

- If $f''(x) > 0$ for all $x$ in some interval $I$, we say that $f$ is **concave up** on $I$.

- If $f''(x) < 0$ for all $x$ in some interval $I$, we say that $f$ is **concave down** on $I$.

- If the concavity of $f$ switches from up to down (or vice versa) at some point $x$, then we say $(x, f(x))$ is an **inflection point** of the graph of $f$.

---

**Problem 4.5:** Suppose $f$ is a twice-differentiable function and $f''$ is continuous.

(a) Prove that if $(a, f(a))$ is an inflection point, then $f''(a) = 0$.

(b) Find an example where $f''(a) = 0$ but $(a, f(a))$ is not an inflection point.

---

*Solution for Problem 4.5:*

(a) If $(a, f(a))$ is an inflection point, then we know that the concavity of the function changes from up to down (or from down to up) at $a$. Suppose it changes from up to down. Then we know that $f''(c) > 0$ for $c < a$ and $f''(c) < 0$ for $c > a$ (both of these statements assume that $c$ is sufficiently close to $a$). But since $f''$ is continuous, we can't skip from $f'' > 0$ to $f'' < 0$ without some point at which $f'' = 0$; this is the Intermediate Value Theorem. So we must have $f''(a) = 0$. The proof where the concavity of $f$ switches from down to up is essentially the same.

Note that we can get into some trouble if $f''$ is not continuous—we can have $f''$ jump directly from negative to positive (or vice versa) without attaining the value of 0. Such examples are a bit contrived, though; we will leave it as an exercise to try to construct one.

(b) The concavity doesn't have to change at $a$ just because $f''(a) = 0$. There are many examples of this. One simple example is $f(x) = x^4$ at $a = 0$. We see that $f'(x) = 4x^3$ and $f''(x) = 12x^2$. Since $f'' > 0$ for all nonzero $x$, we know that $f$ is concave up everywhere except at $x = 0$. Thus, even though $f''(0) = 0$, we don't have an inflection point at $(0, 0)$, since the function is concave up on both sides of $x = 0$.

$\square$

There are some other geometric ways to describe concavity.

> **Problem 4.6:** Let $f$ be a twice-differentiable function with continuous first and second derivatives, and suppose that $a \in \mathrm{Dom}(f)$ is such that $f'' > 0$ on some interval $I$ containing $a$. Show that the tangent line to the graph of $f$ at $(a, f(a))$ lies below the graph of $f$ along the interval $I$.

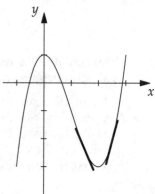

*Solution for Problem 4.6:* Sketching a picture gives us an idea. We can see from the picture that if the curve is concave up, then a segment of the tangent line should lie below the curve. But how do we prove this rigorously?

Suppose that $b$ is another point in $I$. Assume that $b > a$ (the proof for $b < a$ is essentially the same). We need to show that $f(b)$ is greater than the $y$-coordinate of the point on the tangent line with $x$-coordinate $b$. This point lies on the line through $(a, f(a))$ with slope $f'(a)$, and this line has equation $y - f(a) = f'(a)(x-a)$ in point-slope form. Therefore the point on this tangent line with $x$-coordinate $b$ has $y$-coordinate

$$f(a) + f'(a)(b - a).$$

Thus, in order to show that the graph lies above the tangent line when $x = b$, we have to show that $f(b) > f(a) + f'(a)(b - a)$. Let's rewrite this expression with all the terms on the same side:

$$\frac{f(b) - f(a)}{b - a} - f'(a) > 0.$$

That fraction on the left looks awfully familiar! It's once again the expression from the Mean Value Theorem. So we know that there is some $c$ between $a$ and $b$ (so that $a < c < b$) such that

$$f'(c) = \frac{f(b) - f(a)}{b - a}.$$

Now we just have to prove that $f'(c) - f'(a) > 0$, or $f'(c) > f'(a)$. But that's precisely the definition that $f'$ is strictly increasing, and we know $f'$ is strictly increasing since $f'' > 0$ on $I$. So we're done. $\square$

Not surprisingly, if a curve is concave down, then the tangent lines lie above the curve, as shown in the picture to the right. The proof is essentially the same as that of Problem 4.6, but with the inequalities reversed. We'll leave the details of the proof of this as an exercise.

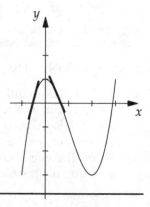

On the other hand, if $f$ is concave up between $a$ and $b$, what can we say about its *secant* lines? Looking at the picture on the next page, they appear to all lie above the graph. This is a reason why concave up portions of the graph of $f$ are also called **convex**: because the area of the plane above the graph contains all its secant lines, and is thus a convex region of the plane. Similarly, secant lines of concave down graphs lie below the graph. This is also shown in the picture on the next page.

We'll leave the proofs of these facts as exercises. They use a similar Mean Value Theorem argument as the proof in Problem 4.6.

We can summarize the features of concavity in the following chart:

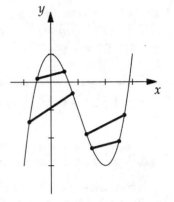

| Concave up | Concave down |
|---|---|
| $f'' > 0$ | $f'' < 0$ |
| $f'$ strictly increasing | $f'$ strictly decreasing |
| Tangent lines rotate counterclockwise as $x$ increases | Tangent lines rotate clockwise as $x$ increases |
| Person walking on the graph is turning left | Person walking on the graph is turning right |
| Tangent lines below curve | Tangent lines above curve |
| Secant lines above curve | Secant lines below curve |

**Concept:** Don't memorize the above table! Learn and understand the geometric features of the second derivative. Keeping a basic example like $f(x) = x^3 - x$ in mind is also very helpful.

## EXERCISES

**4.1.1** Sketch the graphs of the following functions. Find the intervals in which the functions are increasing or decreasing, the intervals in which the functions are concave up or down, and any inflection points.

(a) $3x^3 - 4x + 3$ (b) $\dfrac{x}{x^2 + 2}$ (c) $x + \sin x$ (d) $xe^{-x}$

**4.1.2** Below is the graph of a function $f$. Determine the sign (positive, negative, or zero) of $f'$ and $f''$ at each labeled point (or state that they are undefined).

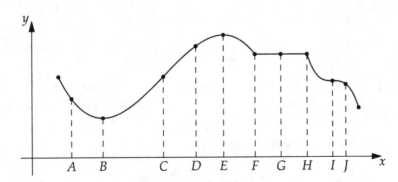

**4.1.3** Show that if $f$ is strictly monotonic, then $f$ has an inverse. Is the same true if $f$ is monotonic but not necessarily strictly monotonic?

**4.1.4** Prove the reverse of Problem 4.6: Let $f$ be a twice-differentiable function with continuous second derivative, and suppose that $a \in \text{Dom}(f)$ is such that $f'' < 0$ on some interval $I$ containing $a$. Show that the tangent line to the graph of $f$ at $(a, f(a))$ lies above the graph of $f$ along the interval $I$.

**4.1.5★**   Prove that if $f$ is concave up on some interval $I$, and $a, b \in I$, then the secant segment between $(a, f(a))$ and $(b, f(b))$ lies above the graph of $f$. Also prove that if we replace "concave up" with "concave down," then the secant segment lies below the graph of $f$. **Hints:** 147, 186, 99

## 4.2   EXTREMA AND OPTIMIZATION

Probably the most common use of derivatives (at least in an introductory calculus course) is to find minimum and/or maximum points of functions.

From what we've already seen in Chapter 2, we know that if $f$ is continuous on an interval $[a, b]$, then $f$ must attain a minimum and a maximum on $[a, b]$. These values are known as **extreme values** or more simply **extrema**. What we'd like to do is use the derivative to find the extrema. A sketch gives us a good idea of what's going on:

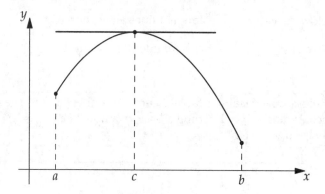

We've sketched a continuous function on $[a, b]$ with maximum value $f(c)$ on $[a, b]$, and drawn the tangent line to the graph at the point $(c, f(c))$. We can see pretty clearly that the tangent line is horizontal. Let's formally state this and prove it:

**Problem 4.7:**   Let $f$ be a function defined on $[a, b]$ and suppose that $c \in (a, b)$ is such that $f(c)$ is the maximum value of $f$ on $[a, b]$. Show that if $f$ is differentiable at $c$, then $f'(c) = 0$.

*Solution for Problem 4.7:*   We write the definition of the derivative $f'(c)$:

$$f'(c) = \lim_{h \to 0} \frac{f(c + h) - f(c)}{h}.$$

Assuming that $h$ is small enough so that $c + h \in [a, b]$, what do we know about $f(c + h) - f(c)$? Since $f(c)$ is the maximum value that $f$ attains, we know that $f(c + h) \le f(c)$; in other words, the numerator above is always negative (or zero). But the denominator is positive for $h > 0$ and negative for $h < 0$.

Using the properties of limits, this tells us that

$$\lim_{h \to 0^+} \frac{f(c + h) - f(c)}{h} \le 0$$

and

$$\lim_{h \to 0^-} \frac{f(c + h) - f(c)}{h} \ge 0.$$

But we know that both of these quantities exist and are equal to $f'(c)$. Thus, we have $f'(c) \le 0$ and $f'(c) \ge 0$, so the only possibility is $f'(c) = 0$. □

Of course, essentially the same argument works for the minimum value of $f$ on $[a, b]$. So we have:

> **Important:** Let $f$ be a function defined on $[a, b]$. If $c \in (a, b)$ is such that $f(c)$ is an extreme value (a maximum or minimum) of $f$ on $[a, b]$, and $f$ is differentiable at $c$, then $f'(c) = 0$.

Note that there are a couple of subtle yet very important conditions in this statement, as we will see in the next problem:

> **Problem 4.8:**
> (a) Consider $f(x) = x^2$ on the interval $[-1, 2]$. What is the maximum value of this function on $[-1, 2]$? Is $f' = 0$ at this point? Why or why not?
>
> (b) Consider $f(x) = |x|$ on the interval $[-1, 2]$. What is the minimum value of this function on $[-1, 2]$? Is $f' = 0$ at this point? Why or why not?

*Solution for Problem 4.8:*

(a) The function clearly has its maximum on $[-1, 2]$ at $f(2) = 4$. But $f'(x) = 2x$, so $f'(2) = 4 \neq 0$. We don't have $f' = 0$ at the maximum point, but this is because 2 is the endpoint of our interval $[-1, 2]$, and there's no reason to expect that $f'(2)$ should be 0.

(b) The function clearly has its minimum on $[-1, 2]$ at $f(0) = 0$. But $f'(0)$ is undefined for this function: the graph has a "sharp corner" at $(0, 0)$, and thus no uniquely-defined tangent line.

$\square$

As we saw in Problem 4.8, there are a couple of situations in which we might have an extreme value at $c$ but not have $f'(c) = 0$. First, $f$ might attain an extreme value at one of the endpoints of $[a, b]$, and there's no reason to expect that $f' = 0$ at these points, as in the picture on the left below.

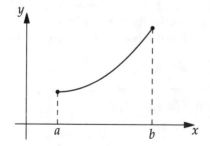 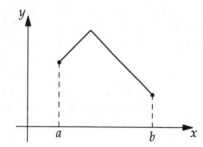

Second, $f$ might not be differentiable at an extreme value, as in the picture on the right above. Note that there is a "sharp corner" in the graph at the maximum point, so the tangent line there is not uniquely defined, and thus the function is not differentiable at that point.

So here is the final word on extrema of continuous functions on closed intervals:

> **Important:** Let $f$ be a continuous function on $[a, b]$ and suppose that $f(c)$ is an extreme value (maximum or minimum) of $f$ on $[a, b]$ for some $c \in [a, b]$. Then one of the following must be true:
>
> 1. $c \in (a, b)$ and $f'(c) = 0$
>
> 2. $c \in (a, b)$ and $f'(c)$ is undefined
>
> 3. $c = a$ or $c = b$

Points satisfying any of conditions 1, 2, or 3 above—that is, points where the derivative is 0 or undefined, and the endpoints of the interval—are called **critical points** of the function on the interval $[a, b]$. These are the only points at which the function can attain its maximum or minimum.

Let's see an easy example of how we can use critical points to find the minimum and maximum of a function on a closed interval.

> **Problem 4.9:** Let $f(x) = x^2 - 2x + 4$. We wish to find the minimum and maximum values of $f(x)$ on the interval $[0, 3]$.
>
> (a) First, solve this problem without using calculus—just use basic algebra (no derivatives).
>
> (b) Then, describe how calculus lets us solve the problem.

*Solution for Problem 4.9:*

(a) To better understand quadratic functions, we can complete the square:

$$f(x) = x^2 - 2x + 4 = (x^2 - 2x + 1) + 3 = (x - 1)^2 + 3.$$

Now it is clear that $f(x)$ is minimal when $x - 1 = 0$, since the $(x-1)^2$ term is always nonnegative. So $f$ attains its minimum when $x = 1$, and the minimum value is $f(1) = 3$.

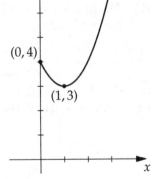

The $(x - 1)^2$ term will be maximal when $|x - 1|$ is as large as possible; that is, when $x$ is as far away from 1 as possible. On $[0, 3]$, the number that is farthest away from 1 is 3. So, $f$ attains its maximum at $x = 3$, and the maximum value is $f(3) = 7$.

(b) Maxima and minima can only occur at critical points of the interval. The two endpoints ($x = 0$ and $x = 3$) are critical points, and to find any others, we compute the derivative: $f'(x) = 2x - 2$. This is always defined, and is 0 only at $x = 1$. So the critical points are 0, 1, and 3. We now just need to check the values of $f$ at these points:

$$f(0) = 4, \ f(1) = 3, \ f(3) = 7.$$

So the minimum value of 3 is at $x = 1$, and the maximum value of 7 is at $x = 3$. Since the function is continuous, the Intermediate Value Theorem tells us that $f([0, 3]) = [3, 7]$.

$\square$

> **Concept:** Just because we have calculus, we don't have to use it. If there are simpler algebraic techniques that you can use—such as completing the square—go ahead and use them!

Now we have a basic procedure for finding the maximum and minimum values of a continuous function on a closed interval:

> **Concept:** Suppose $f$ is continuous on $[a, b]$. The extreme values (that is, maximum and minimum value) of $f$ on $[a, b]$ must occur at a **critical point**, which is one of
>
> - A point $c \in (a, b)$ where $f'(c) = 0$,
>
> - A point $c \in (a, b)$ where $f'(c)$ is undefined, or
>
> - A **boundary point** of $[a, b]$, namely $c = a$ or $c = b$.
>
> To find the maximum or minimum of $f$ on $[a, b]$, we find the critical points of $f$ and compute the value of the function at each critical point. The largest such value will be the maximum, and the smallest will be the minimum.

Let's try another basic example, one that would be hard to approach without calculus.

**Problem 4.10:** Find the maximum and minimum of the function $f(x) = x^3 - 5x$ on the interval $[0, 3]$.

*Solution for Problem 4.10:* First, we find the critical points. The endpoints $x = 0$ and $x = 3$ of the interval are automatically critical points. The others are the roots of

$$f'(x) = 3x^2 - 5.$$

The roots of this are $x = \pm\sqrt{\frac{5}{3}}$, but only $x = \sqrt{\frac{5}{3}}$ lies in the interval $[0, 3]$.

Now that we have the critical points, we can compute the values of the function at them:

$$f(0) = 0^3 - 5(0) = 0,$$
$$f\left(\sqrt{\frac{5}{3}}\right) = \left(\frac{5}{3}\right)^{\frac{3}{2}} - 5\left(\frac{5}{3}\right)^{\frac{1}{2}} = -\left(\frac{10}{3}\right)\sqrt{\frac{5}{3}},$$
$$f(3) = 3^3 - 5(3) = 12.$$

We now clearly see that $f(3) = 12$ is the maximum and $f\left(\sqrt{\frac{5}{3}}\right) = -\left(\frac{10}{3}\right)\sqrt{\frac{5}{3}}$ is the minimum on the interval $[0, 3]$. $\square$

Our previous examples of finding extreme values considered functions defined on a closed interval. Let's widen our view a bit and look at the entire function. The maximum or minimum that the function obtains over its entire domain is called the **global maximum** or **global minimum**, as follows:

> **Definition:** Let $f$ be a function.
>
> - We say that $f$ has a **global maximum** (or just a **maximum**) at $c$ if $f(c) \geq f(x)$ for all $x \in \text{Dom}(f)$.
>
> - We say that $f$ has a **global minimum** (or just a **minimum**) at $c$ if $f(c) \leq f(x)$ for all $x \in \text{Dom}(f)$.

Of course, with many functions (such as $f(x) = x$ for example), there is no guarantee that there will be any global extreme values at all.

Instead of finding a global maximum or minimum, we are sometimes interested in finding what we call a **local maximum** or **local minimum**. A function $f$ has a local maximum at $c$ if $f(c)$ is the largest possible value of $f(x)$ for $x$ "near" $c$. Of course, we'll have to be a bit more rigorous about what we mean by "near":

---

**Definition:** Let $f$ be a function.

- We say that $f$ has a **local maximum** (or **relative maximum**) at $c$ if there exists an open interval $I$ containing $c$ such that $f(c) \geq f(x)$ for any $x \in (I \cap \mathrm{Dom}(f))$.

- We say that $f$ has a **local minimum** (or **relative minimum**) at $c$ if there exists an open interval $I$ containing $c$ such that $f(c) \leq f(x)$ for any $x \in (I \cap \mathrm{Dom}(f))$.

---

The somewhat weird condition $x \in (I \cap \mathrm{Dom}(f))$ allows us to have local maxima or minima at the "endpoints" of the domain of $f$. For example, the function $f(x) = \sqrt{x}$ has domain $[0, +\infty)$, and it has a local minimum at $x = 0$, since for any open interval $I$ containing 0, we have $0 = f(0) \leq f(c)$ for any $c \in (I \cap [0, +\infty))$.

It is not always easy to find a global maximum or minimum. However, we can use our calculus tools to find local maxima and minima of a continuous function.

**Problem 4.11:** Suppose that $f$ is a continuous function with a local maximum or minimum at $c$ which is not an endpoint of the domain of $f$. Show that $f'(c) = 0$ or $f'(c)$ is undefined.

*Solution for Problem 4.11:* By definition, there is an interval $(a, b)$ such that $f(c)$ is an extreme value of $f$ on $(a, b)$. But this means that $c$ must be a critical point of $f$ on $[a, b]$, and since $c$ is not one of the endpoints, we must have either $f'(c) = 0$ or $f$ is not differentiable at $c$. $\square$

Thus, if $f$ is differentiable, we know that $f'(c) = 0$ at any point $c$ (other than an endpoint of the domain of $f$) that gives a local maximum or minimum. However, we can actually say something a bit stronger that this. Let's again look at our sketch of a local maximum, as shown at right. We see that $f$ is increasing to the left of $c$ and decreasing to the right of $c$. This makes perfect sense: a function increases up to a local maximum, and then decreases. So, from this sketch, we expect $f'(x) \geq 0$ for sufficiently close $x < c$, and $f'(x) \leq 0$ for sufficiently close $x > c$.

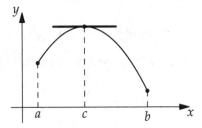

Sadly, this is not always true. We will leave it as a (hard) exercise to explore an example of a continuous differentiable function with a local maximum that does not have the above property.

---

**WARNING!!** Sketching a quick example is great to get an intuitive insight of a problem or concept, but a sketch is never a proof.

---

However, the converse of the above discussion *is* true. Let's write it formally and prove it, using our basic knowledge of the derivative:

**Problem 4.12:** Suppose $c$ is a point such that $f'(c) = 0$ and there exists some $\epsilon > 0$ such that:

1. $f'(x) \geq 0$ for all $x \in (c - \epsilon, c)$, and

2. $f'(x) \leq 0$ for all $x \in (c, c + \epsilon)$.

Prove that $f(c)$ is a local maximum.

*Solution for Problem 4.12:* Since $f' \geq 0$ on some interval $(c - \epsilon, c)$ to the left of $c$, we know that $f$ is increasing on this interval. Specifically, we know that $f(x) \leq f(c)$ for $x \in (c - \epsilon, c)$. Similarly, since $f' \leq 0$ on some interval $(c, c + \epsilon)$ to the right of $c$, we know that $f$ is decreasing to the right of $c$. Specifically, $f(c) \geq f(x)$ for $x \in (c, c + \epsilon)$. But this means that $f(c) \geq f(x)$ for all $x \in (c - \epsilon, c + \epsilon)$. This is precisely the definition of a local maximum. $\square$

---

We can reverse all of the inequalities in the solution to Problem 4.12 to get a comparable result for local minima. Putting this all together, removing the $\epsilon$ notation, and giving it a memorable name, we have:

> **Important:** The **First Derivative Test**: Let $f$ be a continuous differentiable function, and let $c \in \text{Dom}(f)$ be such that $f'(c) = 0$. Then:
>
> - If $f' \geq 0$ on an open interval to the left of $c$ and $f' \leq 0$ on an open interval to the right of $c$, then $f(c)$ is a local maximum.
>
> - If $f' \leq 0$ on an open interval to the left of $c$ and $f' \geq 0$ on an open interval to the right of $c$, then $f(c)$ is a local minimum.

Again, don't memorize the test as it's written above. Think about what it means. If a function increases (so that $f' > 0$), then "stops" (so that $f' = 0$), then decreases (so that $f' < 0$), then the point at which it "stops" must be a local maximum. Reversing all this (so that $f$ is decreasing, then "stopping," then increasing) gives a local minimum.

There's another way that we can tell how $f'$ is behaving, and that is by looking at $f''$.

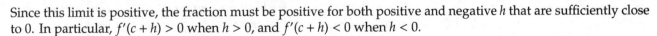

**Problem 4.13:** Let $f$ be a continuous differentiable function with $f'$ differentiable, and suppose $c$ is such that $f'(c) = 0$ and $f''(c) > 0$. Show that $f(c)$ is a local minimum.

*Solution for Problem 4.13:* As usual, we can first see this visually—we sketch a picture at right. Since $f''(c) > 0$, the function $f$ is concave up at $c$, and if a function is concave up, then any critical point must be a local minimum, as shown in the picture.

But, as usual, a sketch is not a proof—we want to prove it rigorously. So, we look at the definition of the second derivative:

$$f''(c) = \lim_{h \to 0} \frac{f'(c+h) - f'(c)}{h}.$$

We know that $f'(c) = 0$ and $f''(c) > 0$, so we have

$$0 < f''(c) = \lim_{h \to 0} \frac{f'(c+h) - f'(c)}{h} = \lim_{h \to 0} \frac{f'(c+h)}{h}.$$

Since this limit is positive, the fraction must be positive for both positive and negative $h$ that are sufficiently close to 0. In particular, $f'(c+h) > 0$ when $h > 0$, and $f'(c+h) < 0$ when $h < 0$.

But this means that $f' < 0$ to the left of $c$ and $f' > 0$ to the right of $c$. This is exactly the condition of the First Derivative Test! Thus, we see that $c$ is a local minimum. (Again, think of this informally: $f$ is decreasing as it approaches $c$, then "levels out," then increases as it moves past $c$.) $\square$

Combining this result with the similar result where $f''(c) < 0$ gives:

> **Important:** The **Second Derivative Test**: suppose $f$ is a continuous differentiable function and $c$ is such that $f'(c) = 0$.
>
> - If $f''(c) > 0$, then $f(c)$ is a local minimum.
>
> - If $f''(c) < 0$, then $f(c)$ is a local maximum.

You may wonder what happens in the Second Derivative Test if $f''(c) = 0$. Unfortunately, in this situation, we can't conclude anything. For example, $f(x) = x^3$ has $f'(0) = f''(0) = 0$, but $(0,0)$ is neither a minimum nor a maximum. On the other hand, $f(x) = x^4$ also has $f'(0) = f''(0) = 0$, but $(0,0)$ is a local minimum point. (In fact it's a global minimum.) Similarly $f(x) = -x^4$ has $f'(0) = f''(0) = 0$, but has a maximum at $(0,0)$. Thus, looking at these examples, we see that $c$ such that $f'(c) = f''(c) = 0$ might be a local maximum, a local minimum, or neither, and hence $f'(c) = f''(c) = 0$ gives us no information.

We use our knowledge of critical points, along with the First and Second Derivative Tests, to help us solve **optimization** problems. In an optimization problem, we are trying to maximize or minimize a certain quantity, often subject to additional constraints.

However, often our domain or our function will be unbounded, so we will find the following lemma useful:

**Problem 4.14:** Let $f$ be a differentiable function with $[a,b] \subseteq \text{Dom}(f)$ such that $f'(x) \le 0$ for all $x \le a$ and $f'(x) \ge 0$ for all $x \ge b$. Show that $f$ has a global minimum $f(c)$ with $c \in [a,b]$.

*Solution for Problem 4.14:* Since $f$ is continuous, we know that $f$ has a minimum on $[a,b]$—that is, there exists some $c \in [a,b]$ such that $f(c) \le f(x)$ for all $x \in [a,b]$. In particular, $f(c) \le f(a)$ and $f(c) \le f(b)$.

Further, for any $x \le a$, we know that $f$ is decreasing on $[x,a]$ (since $f' \le 0$ on this interval), so $f(x) \ge f(a) \ge f(c)$. Similarly, for any $b \le x$, we know that $f$ is increasing on $[b,x]$ (since $f' \ge 0$ on this interval), so $f(x) \ge f(b) \ge f(c)$.

Combining all this, we have $f(x) \ge f(c)$ for all $x$, and thus $f(c)$ is a global minimum. $\square$

Intuitively, the result of Problem 4.14 should make sense. It says that if we have a function that decreases until $x = a$ and then increases after $x = b$, then whatever minimum occurs on $[a,b]$ is actually the minimum for the entire function. Reversing our assumptions gives the opposite result: that is, if we have a function that increases until $x = a$ and then decreases after $x = b$, then whatever maximum occurs on $[a,b]$ is the maximum for the entire function.

This result is quite useful for optimization problems in which the domain is something other than a closed interval, as in the following example.

**Problem 4.15:** We wish to build a box with a square lid and a volume of 224 cubic inches. The material to build the lid of the box costs \$5 per square inch, and the material to build the sides and bottom costs \$2 per square inch. What is the cheapest box (including lid) that we can build?

*Solution for Problem 4.15:* Our goal is to minimize the cost of the box subject to the constraint that the volume is equal to 224 cubic inches. We begin by assigning variables for the relevant quantities. Let $x$ be the length (in inches) of a side of the lid (and thus also the length of a side of the bottom), and let $h$ be the height (in inches) of the box. Note that the bottom and the lid will each have area $x^2$ (in square inches) and each of the four sides will have area $xh$. We can now write an expression for the cost of the box:

$$\text{Cost} = 2(x^2 + 4xh) + 5x^2 = 7x^2 + 8xh.$$

Unfortunately, this expression has two variables in it. But we can use the volume constraint to eliminate one of the variables. In particular, the volume constraint means that $224 = x^2 h$, so $h = 224/x^2$. We substitute this into the expression for cost, and we have the cost as a function of the side length:

$$c(x) = 7x^2 + \frac{1792}{x}.$$

The domain of this function is $(0, +\infty)$. We compute the derivative:

$$c'(x) = 14x - \frac{1792}{x^2}.$$

This is always defined on the domain of $c$. We have $c'(x) = 0$ when $\frac{1792}{x^2} = 14x$, so $x^3 = \frac{1792}{14} = 128$, and $x = \sqrt[3]{128} = 4\sqrt[3]{2}$. Further, we see that $c'(x) < 0$ for $x < 4\sqrt[3]{2}$, and $c'(x) > 0$ for $x > 4\sqrt[3]{2}$.

Thus, we know, by applying the result from Problem 4.14 and the First Derivative Test, that $x = 4\sqrt[3]{2}$ gives the global minimum of the function. We can also use the Second Derivative Test:

$$c''(x) = 14 + \frac{3584}{x^3}.$$

Note $c'' > 0$ for all $x$ in the domain, so the function is concave up everywhere. Thus, any critical point must be a local minimum.

Our conclusion is that the cheapest box has side length $x = 4\sqrt[3]{2}$ and height $h = \frac{224}{16\sqrt[3]{4}} = 7\sqrt[3]{2}$. This box costs

$$\$7\left(16\sqrt[3]{4}\right) + \$8\left(4\sqrt[3]{2}\right)\left(7\sqrt[3]{2}\right) = \$336\sqrt[3]{4} \approx \$533.37.$$

(I guess that the box must be made of a *really* rare material!) □

---

**Problem 4.16:** A spring starts moving at time $t = 0$, and oscillates away from its equilibrium position; its position, as a function of time $t$ (in seconds), is given by $y = e^{-t}\cos t$. Find the maximum and minimum values of its position.

---

*Solution for Problem 4.16:* We're asked to find a global maximum and minimum. First, we note that since the values of $t$ that we are considering all are nonnegative, the domain of the position function is $[0, +\infty)$. So we'll need to check the critical point $t = 0$ (which is the endpoint of the domain interval), find all the local maxima and minima, and we'll have to take into account what happens as $t$ grows large.

At $t = 0$, we have $f(t) = e^0\cos(0) = 1$. Also, since $|\cos t| \leq 1$, we have $|f(t)| \leq e^{-t} \leq 1$, and thus for all $t > 0$, we have $f(t) < 1 = f(0)$. Hence, $f(0) = 1$ is the global maximum.

To find the other critical points, we can start by computing the derivative:

$$f'(t) = e^{-t}(-\sin t) + (-e^{-t})(\cos t) = -e^{-t}(\sin t + \cos t).$$

This derivative is always defined, so we don't need to worry about critical points that occur because of an undefined derivative. We just need to find where $f'(t) = 0$. Since $e^{-t}$ is always nonzero, we have that $f'(t) = 0$ if and only if

$$\sin t + \cos t = 0.$$

This simplifies to $\tan t = -1$. So $t \in \left\{\frac{3\pi}{4}, \frac{7\pi}{4}, \frac{11\pi}{4}, \ldots\right\}$ are the critical points.

To tell which are local maxima and which are local minima, we could try the Second Derivative Test. We compute:

$$f''(t) = -e^{-t}(\cos t - \sin t) + e^{-t}(\sin t + \cos t) = 2e^{-t}\sin t.$$

This is positive at $\frac{3\pi}{4}, \frac{11\pi}{4}, \ldots$, and negative at $\frac{7\pi}{4}, \frac{15\pi}{4}, \ldots$. So the critical points alternate being local minima and local maxima.

We can see that at each local minimum, we have $\cos(t) = -\frac{\sqrt{2}}{2}$, so we have $f(t) = -e^{-t}\frac{\sqrt{2}}{2}$. Thus, clearly $t = \frac{3\pi}{4}$ gives the smallest of the local minima, and we have that

$$f\left(\frac{3\pi}{4}\right) = -e^{-\frac{3\pi}{4}}\frac{\sqrt{2}}{2} \approx -0.067$$

is the global minimum.

---

Also, we see that at each local maximum, $\cos(t) = \frac{\sqrt{2}}{2}$, so $f(t) = e^{-t}\frac{\sqrt{2}}{2}$ at a local maximum. The largest of these is when $t = \frac{7\pi}{4}$, giving

$$f\left(\frac{7\pi}{4}\right) = e^{-\frac{7\pi}{4}}\frac{\sqrt{2}}{2} \approx 0.003.$$

Thus, again we see that $f(0) = 1$ is the global maximum. $\square$

We can draw a picture of the spring's movement (note the different scales for the $x$- and $y$-axes):

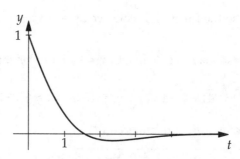

We see the minimum is indeed at $t = \dfrac{3\pi}{4} \approx 2.356$. The $\cos t$ term of the function provides the oscillation of the function between positive and negative values, whereas the $e^{-t}$ term contributes a "damping" effect, pushing the function close to 0 very quickly. This function is an example of **damped oscillation**, which is very common in physics; we will also see more of this in Chapter 9.

The next problem is a classic optimization problem:

**Problem 4.17:** Two hallways, of widths $a$ and $b$ meters, respectively, meet at a right angle. What is the longest ladder (of negligible width) that can be carried around the corner horizontally?

*Solution for Problem 4.17:* The word "longest" in the problem statement is our cue that this is an optimization problem. We need to model this problem as a function that we can optimize.

The length of a ladder that touches the corner can be expressed as a function of the angle of incidence with the corner, as in the picture to the right. In order to write this function, we'll need to label a few more lengths in the picture, which we have done in the diagram. Suppose the ladder makes angle $\theta$ with the corner, and that the corner divides the ladder into two pieces of lengths $m$ and $n$, as shown in the diagram. We now see that

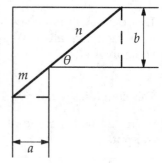

$$\sin\theta = \frac{b}{n},$$
$$\cos\theta = \frac{a}{m}.$$

So the length of the longest ladder that can touch the corner at an angle of $\theta$ is given by the function

$$f(\theta) = m + n = a\sec\theta + b\csc\theta.$$

Now we need to be careful and make sure that we know exactly what we want to do. Our ladder has to be able to rotate all the way around the corner, so its length can be no more than $f(\theta)$ for all $\theta \in \left(0, \frac{\pi}{2}\right)$. That is, we need a ladder that is at most as long as $f(\theta)$ for all relevant values of $\theta$. Thus, minimizing $f(\theta)$ will give us the longest possible ladder that works for all relevant values of $\theta$; that is, it will give us the longest ladder that can rotate around the corner.

Note that the effective domain of $f(\theta)$ is $\theta \in (0, \pi/2)$, which makes sense: setting $\theta = 0$ or $\theta = \pi/2$ would allow an "infinite" ladder parallel to one of the corridors. Thus, we need to find the minimum of $f(\theta)$ for $\theta \in (0, \pi/2)$.

Our next step is to compute the derivative, so that we can find the critical points:

$$f'(\theta) = a \sec \theta \tan \theta - b \csc \theta \cot \theta.$$

This derivative is defined on all of $(0, \pi/2)$, so we just find where it is equal to 0:

$$0 = a \sec \theta \tan \theta - b \csc \theta \cot \theta.$$

Thus $a \sec \theta \tan \theta = b \csc \theta \cot \theta$. This expression is easier to work with in terms of sin and cos:

$$a \frac{\sin \theta}{\cos^2 \theta} = b \frac{\cos \theta}{\sin^2 \theta}.$$

Thus

$$\frac{b}{a} = \frac{\sin^3 \theta}{\cos^3 \theta} = \tan^3 \theta,$$

and hence $\theta = \tan^{-1}\left(\sqrt[3]{\frac{b}{a}}\right)$.

Plugging this angle into $f$ will give the maximum allowed length, which (for the record) is

$$a \sec\left(\tan^{-1}\left(\sqrt[3]{\frac{b}{a}}\right)\right) + b \csc\left(\tan^{-1}\left(\sqrt[3]{\frac{b}{a}}\right)\right).$$

We can remove the trig functions from this answer by using the facts that for $x \in (0, \pi/2)$ we have

$$\sec(\tan^{-1} x) = \sqrt{x^2 + 1} \qquad \text{and} \qquad \csc(\tan^{-1} x) = \frac{\sqrt{x^2 + 1}}{x}.$$

Thus we can rewrite our length as

$$a \sqrt{(b/a)^{(2/3)} + 1} + b \frac{\sqrt{(b/a)^{(2/3)} + 1}}{(b/a)^{(1/3)}}.$$

Careful algebra can show that this equals $(a^{\frac{2}{3}} + b^{\frac{2}{3}})^{\frac{3}{2}}$. $\square$

---

## EXERCISES

**4.2.1** Find the maxima and minima of the following functions on the specified domains:

(a)   $2x^2 - x + 3$ on $[0, 2]$

(b)   $x^2/(x-1)$ on $(1, 3]$

(c)   $4x^3 - 8x^2 + 1$ on $[-1, 1]$

(d)   $\sin x + x$ on $[0, 2\pi]$

**4.2.2** Find the value of $k$ such that $f(x) = x - \dfrac{k}{x}$ has a local maximum at $x = -2$.

**4.2.3** A group of people wish to charter a boat for an around-the-world voyage. The fee is $1000 per person for the first 100 people, but decreases by $5 (for everyone) for each person beyond 100. The charter company will have costs of $40000 + 200n$, where $n$ is the number of people on the trip. The boat's capacity is 250. What number of people maximizes the company's profit?

**4.2.4**  Find a differentiable function (with domain $\mathbb{R}$) that has 3 critical points, one of which is a local maximum, one of which is a local minimum, and one of which is neither. **Hints:** 143, 69

**4.2.5**  We wish to make a soup can in the shape of a right circular cylinder (closed on both ends, of course) that will hold 200 cm$^3$ of soup. The aluminum to make the can costs 0.2 cents per square centimeter. What is the cheapest can that we can make?

**4.2.6**  Cody has a pet goat named Baroness Regina von Pufflestein, and he wants to create a grazing area for her along the back of his farmhouse. He has 40 meters of fencing, and will form a rectangular grazing area where the fencing makes up 3 sides of the rectangle and the side of the house makes up the fourth side of the rectangle. What is the maximum area that he can construct?

**4.2.7★**  You want to look at a 10-foot-tall statue that is on the top of a 50-foot-tall building (so that the top of the statue is 60 feet above the ground). Assume that you are 5 feet tall. How far away from the building should you stand in order to get the best view, which in this case means so that the statue takes up the largest possible angle in your field of vision? **Hints:** 10, 168

## 4.3  VELOCITY

In our previous discussions, we've alluded to our primary interpretation of the derivative: as a rate of change. In particular, if $f(t)$ is a function where the variable $t$ represents time, then $f'(t)$ represents the instantaneous rate of change of $f(t)$. As a special case, if $f(t)$ represents a position of an object at time $t$, then $f'(t)$ represents the object's **velocity**. Further, $f''(t)$ represents the rate of change of velocity, which we call **acceleration**.

Here's an example:

**Problem 4.18:**  A particle's position on the coordinate line is given by $s(t) = 2t^3 - 21t^2 + 60t + 3$, where $t$ is the time in seconds. Describe the position, velocity, and acceleration of the particle.

*Solution for Problem 4.18:* The rate of change—that is, the derivative—of position is velocity, and the rate of change of velocity is acceleration. We can compute these functions. (For obvious reasons, we typically denote velocity at time $t$ by $v(t)$ and acceleration at time $t$ by $a(t)$.)

$$s(t) = 2t^3 - 21t^2 + 60t + 3,$$
$$v(t) = s'(t) = 6t^2 - 42t + 60,$$
$$a(t) = v'(t) = s''(t) = 12t - 42.$$

We can make a few observations. For instance, the particle starts at $t = 0$ at position $s(0) = 3$ with initial velocity $v(0) = 60$ and initial acceleration $a(0) = -42$. In words, the particle is moving to the right at 60 units/second, but is decelerating at a rate of 42 units/sec/sec.

We also note the inflection point where $a(t) = 0$ at $t = 7/2$. This is the time at which the particle switches from accelerating to the left and starts accelerating to the right.

We can also analyze the velocity. Specifically, we can factor $v(t) = 6(t - 2)(t - 5)$. So the velocity is negative for $2 < t < 5$ and positive otherwise. This means that the particle is moving to the left between $t = 2$ and $t = 5$, and moving to the right otherwise.

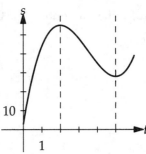

Using this information, we can now sketch a graph of the particle's movement, shown at right. Note that motion upwards on this graph is motion where $s$ is increasing, so the particle is moving to the right; conversely downward motion on the graph corresponds to the particle moving to the left. Between the dashed lines, where $2 < t < 5$, the particle is moving to the left (that is, its position is decreasing). We also note that the "peak" position of the particle during the interval $0 \le t \le 5$ comes at $t = 2$. This is where the particle stops moving to the right and starts moving back to the left. Note that $v(2) = s'(2) = 0$ at this time. $\square$

One very common application is acceleration due to gravity. On Earth, the acceleration due to the force of the planet's gravity is a constant 32 ft/sec². (This neglects things like air resistance and the fact that at very high altitudes the Earth's gravity is marginally smaller, but we will for now ignore such details.) A free-falling body's height (in feet) is given by the equation

$$y(t) = -16t^2 + v_0 t + y_0,$$

where $t$ is in seconds, $v_0$ is the initial velocity in feet/second, and $y_0$ is the initial height in feet. (In the next chapter, we will see how to derive this formula.) Note that $y(0) = y_0$. Also, we can differentiate $y(t)$ to get functions for velocity and acceleration:

$$v(t) = y'(t) = -32t + v_0,$$
$$a(t) = v'(t) = y''(t) = -32.$$

Notice how these functions make sense: in particular, the velocity starts at $v_0$ and decreases by 32 every second, and the acceleration is our constant $-32$.

In metric, the acceleration due to gravity is $-9.8$ m/sec². The formula for the body's height in meters is thus:

$$y(t) = -4.9t^2 + v_0 t + y_0,$$

giving

$$v(t) = y'(t) = -9.8t + v_0,$$
$$a(t) = v'(t) = y''(t) = -9.8.$$

Here is a typical problem involving gravity:

**Problem 4.19:** A cannon shoots a cannonball off of the top of a 1000-foot high cliff with an initial upwards velocity of 200 feet per second.

(a) What is the maximum height (above the ground) that the cannonball attains?

(b) How fast is the cannonball traveling downwards when it hits the ground (1000 feet below the top of the cliff)?

*Solution for Problem 4.19:* We have $y(0) = 1000$ and $v_0 = 200$, so the height of the cannonball is given by

$$y(t) = -16t^2 + 200t + 1000.$$

(a) We know that the maximum height is reached at the time when $v(t) = y'(t) = 0$. This should (by now) make intuitive sense to you. Moreover, this is the only critical point of the function other than its endpoints (at $t = 0$ and at the time at which the cannonball hits the ground), and the heights of the cannonball at the endpoints are lower than the height at the critical point.

We know that the velocity is $v(t) = -32t + 200$, so the velocity is 0 at $t = 200/32$ seconds after the launch. Thus, the maximum height is

$$y(200/32) = -16(200/32)^2 + 200(200/32) + 1000 = 1625 \text{ feet.}$$

(b) The cannonball hits the ground when $y(t) = 0$, so we solve

$$0 = -16t^2 + 200t + 1000.$$

Using the quadratic formula, we find

$$t = \frac{-200 \pm \sqrt{40000 + 4(16)(1000)}}{-32} = \frac{25 \pm 5\sqrt{65}}{4}.$$

Since we only want to consider $t \geq 0$, the cannonball hits the ground $(25 + 5\sqrt{65})/4 \approx 16.328$ seconds after launch. At this time, it is traveling downwards at a velocity of

$$v\left(\frac{25 + 5\sqrt{65}}{4}\right) = -\frac{32(25 + 5\sqrt{65})}{4} + 200 = -40\sqrt{65} \approx -322.49$$

feet per second. (This is about 220 miles per hour).

$\square$

---

## EXERCISES

**4.3.1** A rock is thrown straight down from the top of a 480-foot high building, with an initial downward velocity of 16 feet/second. When does it hit the ground, and at what speed is it traveling when it hits the ground?

**4.3.2** A cannonball is shot at a 30 degree angle from the ground with an initial velocity of 30 meters/second. How far from the cannon is the cannonball when it hits the ground?

**4.3.3** A certain road has speed limit $L(x)$ (in miles per hour), where $x$ is the distance from the start of the road in miles. Cars $A$ and $B$ start at mile 0 and are at position $a(t)$ and $b(t)$ at time $t$ (in hours); in particular note that $a(0) = b(0) = 0$.

(a) Write an inequality that states the fact that car $A$ is always going as fast or faster than car $B$.

(b) Write an equation that states the fact that car $B$ is always going exactly at the speed limit.

(c) Say (in words) what the equation $a(t + 1) = b(t)$ means (for all $t \geq 0$).

(d) Say (in words) what the equation $a'(t) = L(a(t - 1))$ means (for all $t \geq 1$).

---

## 4.4 TANGENT LINE APPROXIMATION

Another application of the derivative comes directly from its definition as the slope of the tangent line to a point on a graph. Suppose $f$ is a function that is continuous and differentiable at $x = a$. We can approximate $f$ near $a$ by its tangent line at $(a, f(a))$. The advantage of this is that the tangent line is a *line*, and lines are really easy to work with.

Let's see a simple example.

**Problem 4.20:** Let $f(x) = \sqrt[3]{x}$. Using $f$ and $f'$, approximate $\sqrt[3]{8.1}$ by constructing the tangent line to $f$ at $(8, 2)$ and finding the point on this line with $x = 8.1$.

*Solution for Problem 4.20:* We start by sketching $f(x) = \sqrt[3]{x}$ and drawing the tangent line at the point $(8, 2)$:

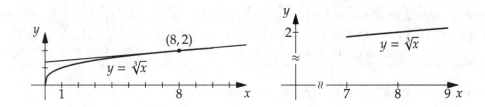

On the right above, we have zoomed in the graph near the point $(8, 2)$. We see that the graph looks really similar to its tangent line near the point $(8, 2)$. We can use this information to estimate $f(8.1)$. The tangent line to $f$ at $(8, 2)$ has slope $f'(8)$, so we need to compute $f'$:

$$f'(x) = \frac{d}{dx}(\sqrt[3]{x}) = \frac{d}{dx}x^{\frac{1}{3}} = \frac{1}{3}x^{-\frac{2}{3}}.$$

So $f'(8) = \frac{1}{3} \cdot 8^{-\frac{2}{3}} = \frac{1}{3} \cdot \frac{1}{4} = \frac{1}{12}$. Thus the tangent line we want passes through $(8, 2)$ and has slope $\frac{1}{12}$. The equation of this line is

$$y - 2 = \frac{x - 8}{12},$$

so $y = \frac{x - 8}{12} + 2$. Plugging in $x = 8.1$ gives us $y = \frac{0.1}{12} + 2 = \frac{241}{120}$. $\square$

Using a calculator, we see that $\frac{241}{120} \approx 2.00833$ and $\sqrt[3]{8.1} \approx 2.00830$, so our approximation is good to 4 decimal places (in this example). In Chapter 7, we'll see how to estimate the error more generally.

Let's try to generalize our example from Problem 4.20.

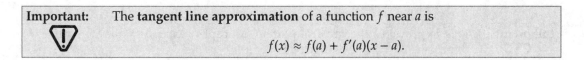

**Problem 4.21:** Let $f$ be a function that is differentiable at a point $a$. Find the equation of the tangent line to $f$ at $(a, f(a))$.

*Solution for Problem 4.21:* The tangent line through the point $(a, f(a))$ has slope $f'(a)$. This gives us the point-slope form

$$y - f(a) = f'(a)(x - a),$$

or $y = f(a) + f'(a)(x - a)$. $\square$

We can use the equation from Problem 4.21 as a method for approximating functions near the point $(a, f(a))$.

> **Important:** The **tangent line approximation** of a function $f$ near $a$ is
>
> $$f(x) \approx f(a) + f'(a)(x - a).$$

We can see what's going on by looking at the diagram to the right. We see that the point on the tangent line has $y$-coordinate $f(a) + f'(a)(x - a)$, and this is a close approximation to the actual value $f(x)$.

The general idea is that we can use a tangent line approximation in situations where $f(a)$ and $f'(a)$ are easy to compute but $f(x)$ may be difficult to compute.

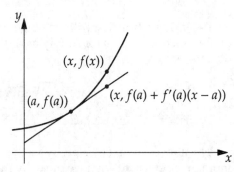

> **Concept:**  We can use tangent line approximation to compute the approximate value of a function at a value that is hard to compute (such as $\sqrt[3]{8.1}$ in Problem 4.20), but that is near a value that is easy to compute (such as $\sqrt[3]{8}$ in Problem 4.20).

Intuitively, the closer $x$ is to $a$, the more accurate the approximation

$$f(x) \approx f(a) + f'(a)(x - a)$$

will be. We will discuss this more precisely in Chapter 7.

We often write the above formula using differential notation, as follows. We are trying to approximate $f$ near the point $(a, f(a))$. If we look at the tangent line at $(a, f(a))$, we see that the ratio of the change in $y$ (denoted $\Delta y$) to the change in $x$ (denoted $\Delta x$) is approximately the slope of the tangent line, which is $f'(a)$. This gives us $\Delta y/\Delta x \approx f'(a)$, or $\Delta y \approx f'(a)\Delta x$.

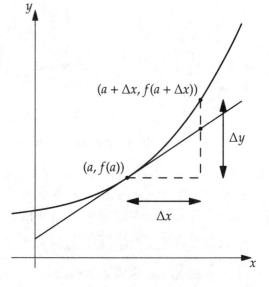

We can also do this computation algebraically. We start with our tangent line approximation

$$f(x) \approx f(a) + f'(a)(x - a).$$

Subtracting $f(a)$ from both sides gives

$$f(x) - f(a) \approx f'(a)(x - a).$$

Note that $f(x) - f(a)$ is the change in the $y$-coordinate on the graph of the function as we move from $(a, f(a))$ to $(x, f(x))$, so we have $\Delta y = f(x) - f(a)$. Similarly, $\Delta x = x - a$. Thus:

> **Important:** $\quad$ Near the point $(a, f(a))$, we have $\Delta y \approx f'(a)\Delta x$.

Thus, once again, the derivative represents the rate of change of $y$ with respect to $x$.

> **Important:** $\quad$ This is probably the most important concept of calculus: the derivative $f'$ represents the rate of change of $f$.

Replacing a function with its tangent line approximation at a point $x = a$ is also called the **local linearization** of the function at $x = a$ (or simply at $a$).

> **Concept:**  Near $x = a$, a differentiable function and its local linearization at $a$ are almost the same.

The above statement is pretty vague, with the mathematically imprecise words "near" and "almost." We can more precisely state what we mean by the local linearization being "almost" the same as $f(x)$ "near" $x = a$:

**Problem 4.22:** Let $f$ be a differentiable function with $f'$ continuous. Define $E(x)$ to be the error in the approximation of $f(x)$ using $f(a)$; that is

$$E(x) = f(x) - (f(a) + f'(a)(x - a)).$$

Prove that $\lim\limits_{x \to a} \dfrac{E(x)}{x - a} = 0$. What (in words) does this mean?

*Solution for Problem 4.22:* We simply compute:

$$\lim_{x \to a} \frac{E(x)}{x - a} = \lim_{x \to a} \frac{f(x) - (f(a) + f'(a)(x - a))}{x - a}$$
$$= \lim_{x \to a} \frac{f(x) - f(a)}{x - a} - f'(a)$$
$$= f'(a) - f'(a) = 0.$$

In words, this means that $E(x)$ approaches 0 faster than $x - a$ does when $x \to a$. So as $x$ gets near $a$, the error in the linear approximation approaches 0 faster than $x$ approaches $a$. This is the formal explanation of what we mean when we say that the linear approximation is "close" to $f(x)$ "near" $x = a$. $\square$

You can explore this idea further in Challenge Problem 4.51.

**Problem 4.23:** Find the local linearization of $f(x) = e^{2x}$ at $x = 0$, and use it to approximate $e^{.002}$.

*Solution for Problem 4.23:* We first compute $f'(x) = 2e^{2x}$. So $f'(0) = 2e^0 = 2$, and thus the tangent line at $x = 0$ has slope 2. Since $f(0) = 1$, the tangent line passes through $(0, 1)$. Therefore the tangent line is $y = 2x + 1$, and this is the local linearization of $e^{2x}$ at $x = 0$.

To approximate $e^{.002} = f(.001)$, we plug in $x = .001$ to the local linearization:

$$f(.001) \approx 2(.001) + 1 = 1.002.$$

The actual value of $e^{.002}$ to 6 decimal places is 1.002002, so this is a very close approximation. $\square$

One nice advantage of the $\Delta y \approx f'(x)\Delta x$ perspective is that sometimes we're only interested in the value of the change away from a point. Specifically, one application of tangent line approximation—also called **linear approximation**—is to estimate the error of an observable quantity when we know that there is an error in our measurement. Let's look at a couple of examples.

**Problem 4.24:** Paul is trying to measure the height of a building using a sextant. He stands 100 meters away and determines that the angle from the ground where he is standing to the top of the building is $30°$, so he computes that the height of the building is $\dfrac{100\sqrt{3}}{3}$ meters. But, if his sextant is only accurate to within 1 degree, then (approximately) by how much might his measurement of the height of the building be off?

*Solution for Problem 4.24:* We start by determining the function that converts Paul's sextant measurement to a height measurement. But be careful! Don't do this:

**Bogus Solution:** The height of the building is given by $f(x) = 100\tan(x)$.

This won't work, because the angle given by the sextant is in degrees! In calculus, we always need to have our angles in radians, or else we won't get the correct derivatives. So we must convert the angle to radians first, and we get the height function

$$f(x) = 100 \tan\left(\frac{x\pi}{180}\right),$$

where $x$ is the angle in degrees.

To compute how much our height might be off, we use our $\Delta y \approx f'(x)\Delta x$ formula. We are told that $|\Delta x| \leq 1$. We now need to compute the derivative of $f$:

$$f'(x) = \frac{100\pi}{180} \sec^2\left(\frac{x\pi}{180}\right) = \frac{5\pi}{9} \sec^2\left(\frac{x\pi}{180}\right).$$

Therefore, since we have $x = 30$, we get

$$f'(30) = \frac{5\pi}{9} \sec^2 \frac{\pi}{6} = \frac{5\pi}{9} \cdot \frac{4}{3} = \frac{20\pi}{27}.$$

Thus, using $|\Delta x| \leq 1$ we have

$$|\Delta y| \approx |f'(30)\Delta x| \leq f'(30) = \frac{20\pi}{27}.$$

So we estimate that Paul's measurement may be off by approximately $\frac{20\pi}{27}$ meters, which is about 2.327 meters. $\square$

---

**Problem 4.25:** A distant planet (assumed to be a perfect sphere) is measured, using a telescope, to have a diameter of 2000 kilometers. However, it is known that the telescope will introduce a measurement error of within ±1%. What is the estimated percentage error in the computed volume of the planet?

---

*Solution for Problem 4.25:* We can write the volume as a function of the diameter:

$$V = \frac{4}{3}\pi \left(\frac{d}{2}\right)^3 = \frac{\pi}{6}d^3.$$

Note that we use $V$ for volume and $d$ for diameter, for the obvious reason that's it's easier to remember what the variables stand for.

> **Concept:** Don't be too attached to $x$ and $y$. Use variable names that relate to the quantities that they represent.

The error in the computation of the volume can be approximated by

$$\Delta V \approx V'\Delta d.$$

Note that $V' = 3\frac{\pi}{6}d^2 = \frac{\pi}{2}d^2$, so when $d = 2000$ we have $V' = \frac{\pi}{2}(2000)^2 = 2000000\pi$. We are also given that $|\Delta d| \leq 0.01d = 20$, so

$$|\Delta V| \approx |V'\Delta d| \leq (2000000\pi)(20) = (4 \cdot 10^7)\pi.$$

Also we know that $V = \frac{\pi}{6}d^3 = \frac{\pi}{6}(2000)^3 = \frac{4}{3} \cdot 10^9\pi$. So

$$\frac{|\Delta V|}{V} \approx \frac{(4 \cdot 10^7)\pi}{(4/3) \cdot 10^9\pi} = \frac{3}{100} = 3\%.$$

So the error in the volume measurement is approximately ±3%.

In fact, we didn't need to plug in $d$. We could have left the expressions in terms of $d$ and simplified algebraically, as follows:

$$\frac{|\Delta V|}{V} \approx \frac{|V'\Delta d|}{V} = \frac{\frac{\pi}{2}d^2|\Delta d|}{\frac{\pi}{6}d^3} = 3\frac{|\Delta d|}{d}.$$

Thus, whatever the relative error in the measurement of $d$, we see that the relative error in the measurement of $V$ is approximately 3 times as great. Specifically, in our problem, since we are given that $\frac{|\Delta d|}{d} = 1\%$, we conclude that $\frac{|\Delta V|}{V} \approx 3(1\%) = 3\%$. $\square$

Once again, we will explore how to compute the error in a tangent line approximation in Chapter 7, but there's one thing that we can usually easily determine: is the approximation given by the tangent line too small or too large? To do this, we can look at the second derivative.

> **Problem 4.26:** If $f''(x) > 0$ near $x = a$, then explain why the tangent line approximation of $f(a + \epsilon)$ is less than the actual value of $f(a + \epsilon)$ for small values of $\epsilon$.

*Solution for Problem 4.26:* If $f''(x) > 0$ near $x = a$, then the curve is concave up, meaning that the tangent line lies below the curve, as shown in the picture to the right. So the $y$-coordinate of a point on the tangent line (with $x$-coordinate near $a$) is going be less than the $y$-coordinate of the corresponding point on the graph of $f$. Therefore, the tangent line approximation is going to be too low. $\square$

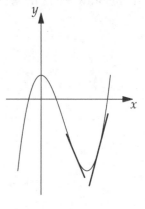

Conversely, if $f''(x) < 0$ near $x = a$, then the curve is concave down, meaning that the tangent line lies above the curve. So in this case, a tangent line approximation is going to be too high.

---

## EXERCISES

**4.4.1** Use tangent line approximation to approximate the following quantities:

(a) $\sqrt[4]{80}$     (b) $\cos 62°$     (c) $\log_2 17$

**4.4.2** A cube is measured to have side 30 cm, but the measuring equipment (a cheap ruler) has a measurement error of 2 mm. What is the approximate error in the measured volume of the cube?

**4.4.3** I want to paint a sphere (with diameter 1 meter) with a 2 mm-thick coating of paint. Approximately what volume of paint do I need?

**4.4.4** We have a right circular cylinder whose radius equals its height. I want to measure the height in such a way that the measured volume is estimated to be within 2% of the actual volume. How much error (as a percentage) can I tolerate in the measurement of the height?

**4.4.5★** Let $f(x) = x^n$ where $n$ is a positive integer. Use the Binomial Theorem to explain why $f(x+\epsilon) \approx f(x)+\epsilon f'(x)$ for small values of $\epsilon$.

---

## 4.5 NEWTON'S METHOD

One profound application of tangent line approximation is called **Newton's Method** for approximating a root of a function. This is a *numerical* method, meaning that its use gives us a numerical approximation of the root.

---

One nice thing (as we'll see) about Newton's Method is that using it repeatedly usually lets us get as close an approximation to a root as we want.

Here's the setup: we have a differentiable function $f$, and we want to find a root $r$ (so that $f(r) = 0$). We start by making an initial guess $r_0$. The idea is to guess a value that's easy to calculate. Unless we are psychic, this initial guess will probably be wrong. Then we think about how can we use tangent line approximation to refine our guess.

> **Problem 4.27:** Let $f$ be a differentiable function with $r_0 \in \text{Dom}(f)$ such that $f'(r_0) \neq 0$. Find, in terms of $r_0$, $f(r_0)$, and $f'(r_0)$, the $x$-intercept of the tangent line to $f$ at $r_0$.

*Solution for Problem 4.27:* Using the tangent line approximation at $r_0$, we get

$$f(x) \approx f(r_0) + f'(r_0)(x - r_0).$$

Let's draw a picture with our initial guess $r_0$ and the tangent line at $(r_0, f(r_0))$ displayed:

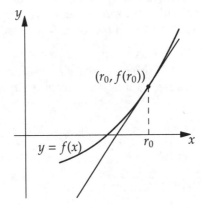

We solve for the $x$-intercept of the tangent line:

$$0 = f(r_0) + f'(r_0)(x - r_0).$$

This simplifies to

$$x - r_0 = -\frac{f(r_0)}{f'(r_0)},$$

so we have $x = r_0 - \dfrac{f(r_0)}{f'(r_0)}$. $\square$

Of course, unless we were really lucky, this value of $x$ is not actually a root of $f$; it is only a root of the tangent line approximation. But we hope that this $x$ is a better approximation of a root of $f$ than our initial blind guess $r_0$, because we believe that the tangent line is a good approximation to $f$. So let's set

$$r_1 = r_0 - \frac{f(r_0)}{f'(r_0)},$$

with the idea that $r_1$ is a better guess for a root of $f$ than $r_0$ was.

Now, we repeat the process from Problem 4.27 again, starting at $r_1$.

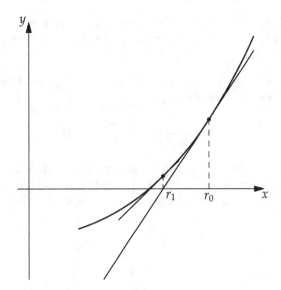

Referring to the picture above (which we've blown up a bit for clarity), we take the root of the first tangent line approximation, call that $r_1$, and use that as our next "guess" of the root of the function. We repeat the process—we take the tangent line approximation to the function at $r_1$ and find the root of this new tangent line. This root, we hope, should be a lot closer to the actual root of $f$.

Specifically, we let

$$r_2 = r_1 - \frac{f(r_1)}{f'(r_1)},$$

and now $r_2$ should be an even better guess at the root than $r_1$ (and a lot better than our initial blind guess $r_0$).

More generally, we can repeat this for as long as we want. At each step, we take our guess $r_{n-1}$ from the previous step, and set

$$r_n = r_{n-1} - \frac{f(r_{n-1})}{f'(r_{n-1})}$$

for all positive integers $n$. As we perform more and more steps, we should get closer and closer to an actual root.

Let's see a basic example.

**Problem 4.28:** Approximate $\sqrt[5]{23}$ to five decimal places using Newton's Method.

*Solution for Problem 4.28:* We might first think of simply using a tangent line approximation. However, trying to use a tangent line approximation using the function $x^{\frac{1}{5}}$ is not going to work very well, because 23 is pretty far from any known values of $x^{\frac{1}{5}}$ that we can use as the point at which we construct our tangent line.

For example, we could try a tangent line approximation using $f(x) = x^{\frac{1}{5}}$ at the point $(32, 2)$. We have $\Delta x = 23 - 32 = -9$ and $f'(x) = \frac{1}{5}x^{-4/5}$. So $f'(32) = \frac{1}{5} \cdot 32^{(-4/5)} = \frac{1}{5} \cdot \frac{1}{16} = \frac{1}{80}$. Thus our approximation is

$$f(23) \approx 2 - 9\left(\frac{1}{80}\right) = \frac{151}{80} = 1.8875.$$

This is not horrible, but because $\Delta x$ was so large, it doesn't match the actual value of $\sqrt[5]{23}$ very closely. (We do know that our estimate is too high, since $f''(x) = -\left(\frac{4}{25}\right)x^{-\frac{9}{5}} < 0$, so $f$ is concave down.)

Let's see how Newton's Method gives a better answer. Instead of working with $f(x) = x^{\frac{1}{5}}$, we note that $\sqrt[5]{23}$ is a root of $g(x) = x^5 - 23$. So we try to estimate the numerical value of the root of $g$ using Newton's Method. First, note that $g'(x) = 5x^4$.

We start with an initial guess of $r_0 = 2$, because the fifth root of 23 is reasonably close to the fifth root of 32, which is 2. Then the first step of Newton's Method gives

$$r_1 = 2 - \frac{g(2)}{g'(2)} = 2 - \frac{9}{80} = 1.8875.$$

Note that this is the same answer as the tangent line approximation gave us. This is not a coincidence: the first step of Newton's Method is just using a tangent line approximation to guess at the root. The advantage of Newton's Method, though, is that we can refine our initial estimate by applying tangent line approximation again and again.

In general, we have

$$r_n = r_{n-1} - \frac{f(r_{n-1})}{f'(r_{n-1})} = r_{n-1} - \frac{r_{n-1}^5 - 23}{5r_{n-1}^4}.$$

So we can continue:

$$r_2 = 1.8875 - \frac{g(1.8875)}{g'(1.8875)}$$
$$\approx 1.8875 - \frac{0.95713}{63.46260}$$
$$\approx 1.8875 - 0.01508$$
$$\approx 1.87242.$$

Now our estimate is 1.87242.

We could do as many more iterations as we like; let's do one more:

$$r_3 = 1.87242 - \frac{g(1.87242)}{g'(1.87242)}$$
$$\approx 1.87242 - \frac{0.01528}{61.45866}$$
$$\approx 1.87242 - 0.00025$$
$$\approx 1.87217.$$

Now our estimate is 1.87217.

You can put $23^{.2}$ into your calculator, and you'll see that this is now accurate to 5 decimal places. □

A more typical example of Newton's Method might be to approximate a solution to an equation:

**Problem 4.29:** Using Newton's Method, estimate the positive value of $x$ such that $\cos x = x$. Perform enough iterations of Newton's Method so that your estimate gives $\cos x$ within 0.001 of $x$.

*Solution for Problem 4.29:* What we're really doing is trying to find a root of $f(x) = x - \cos x$. This function has derivative $f'(x) = 1 + \sin x$.

Part of the skill in applying Newton's Method is making a decent initial guess. In this problem, $r_0 = 0$ seems like a simple place to start. We then compute:

$$r_1 = -\frac{f(0)}{f'(0)} = \frac{\cos 0}{1 + \sin 0} = 1.$$

The next step is then

$$r_2 = 1 - \frac{f(1)}{f'(1)} = 1 - \frac{1 - \cos 1}{1 + \sin 1}.$$

We can approximate these trig functions to 3 decimal places using a calculator:

$$r_2 \approx 1 - \frac{0.460}{1.841} \approx 0.750.$$

We continue:

$$r_3 = 0.750 - \frac{f(0.750)}{f'(0.750)} = 0.750 - \frac{0.750 - \cos 0.750}{1 + \sin 0.750}.$$

Again, we approximate this to 3 decimal places:

$$r_3 \approx 0.750 - \frac{0.018}{1.682} \approx 0.739.$$

Let's do it one more time:

$$r_4 = 0.739 - \frac{f(0.739)}{f'(0.739)} = 0.739 - \frac{0.739 - \cos 0.739}{1 + \sin 0.739}.$$

Computing again to 3 decimal places:

$$r_4 \approx 0.739 - \frac{0.000}{1.674} \approx 0.739.$$

The "0.000" in the numerator of the above fraction indicates that we are at a point in the process where our answer will not change in the first 3 decimal places, so we can stop now.

Indeed, we check using a calculator that $\cos 0.739 = 0.739142477\ldots$, and these quantities agree in the first three decimal places. $\square$

If we wanted more accuracy, we could continue to run Newton's Method, keeping track of more decimal places.

Newton's Method seems like a good method for finding a root. It is simple enough that you can write a very short computer program to execute it. But it's not foolproof, and it's worth thinking about situations where it might fail to accurately approximate a root. Obviously it will fail if there is no root to be found. For example, try Newton's Method on the function $f(x) = x^2 + 1$ and see what happens! It might also converge to the wrong root if you choose a bad starting point, since many functions have more than one root. Also, we get stuck if we end up at a point with $f' = 0$, because then the tangent line is horizontal, so the formula for Newton's Method would require us to divide by 0.

## EXERCISES

**4.5.1**  Use Newton's Method to estimate $\sqrt[4]{2}$. (Whatever starting point you pick, do two iterations, then check against a calculator to see how close you are.)

**4.5.2★**  A classic example in which Newton's Method fails is $f(x) = \sqrt[3]{x}$ where we start too far away from 0. Compute 3 steps of Newton's Method for this function using the initial guess $r_0 = 1$. Can you explain what is happening? **Hints:** 210

## 4.6  RELATED RATES

We have already mentioned several times that the most important interpretation of the derivative of a function is as the rate of change of that function. We can take this a step further. Suppose we have two (or more) functions that are somehow dependent on each other. We can use their derivatives to compare their rates of change.

The term **related rates** refers to two quantities that are dependent on each other and that are changing over time. We can use the dependent relationship between the quantities to determine a relationship between their rates of change.

Here is a basic example:

> **Problem 4.30:** A balloon in the shape of a sphere is being inflated at the rate of 2 cm$^3$/sec. At the time at which the radius of the balloon is 3 cm, how fast is its radius increasing?

*Solution for Problem 4.30:* Let $r$ denote the radius of the balloon (in cm) and $V$ be its volume (in cm$^3$). This already is a little bit deceptive, since both of the quantities are changing over time. So what we should really do is let $r(t)$ denote the radius and $V(t)$ denote the volume, where $r$ and $V$ are functions of $t$, and where $t$ denotes the time (in seconds). The relationship between the quantities is

$$V(t) = \frac{4}{3}\pi(r(t))^3.$$

What we want is an expression that relates the *rates of change* of these quantities. For that, we take the derivative of the entire equation with respect to $t$; that is, we take

$$\frac{d}{dt}V(t) = \frac{d}{dt}\left(\frac{4}{3}\pi(r(t))^3\right).$$

The left side of this equation is just $\frac{dV}{dt}$. On the right side, we must use the Chain Rule:

$$\frac{d}{dt}\left(\frac{4}{3}\pi(r(t))^3\right) = \frac{4}{3}\pi\frac{d}{dt}((r(t))^3) = 4\pi(r(t))^2\frac{dr}{dt}.$$

Thus $\frac{dV}{dt} = 4\pi(r(t))^2\frac{dr}{dt}$. Now we can plug in our given data. The rate of change of the volume is given as a constant 2 cm$^3$/sec, so $\frac{dV}{dt} = 2$. Also, at the time $t$ we are interested in, we are given $r(t) = 3$. So we plug these in:

$$2 = 4\pi(3)^2\frac{dr}{dt}.$$

Thus, we solve to get $\frac{dr}{dt} = \frac{1}{18\pi}$. So the radius is increasing by $\frac{1}{18\pi}$ cm/sec. $\square$

This is the basic premise behind all related rates problems. We have two quantities, both of which are a function of the same independent variable (usually time). If there is an equation relating the two quantities, then we can implicitly differentiate that equation with respect to the independent variable to get an equation relating the variables and their derivatives.

In related rates problems, it is customary not to write explicitly the ($t$) part of the notation. For example, in Problem 4.30, we would typically write the equation relating the quantities as simply $V = \frac{4}{3}\pi r^3$, omitting the mention of the variable $t$. Then, the derivative of this equation is $V' = 4\pi r^2 r'$. However, it's important to remember that in this expression, $V$ and $r$ (and $r'$) are quantities that depend on $t$.

> **Problem 4.31:** An observer is 1 kilometer away from a rocket launch pad. At time $t = 0$, the rocket lifts off straight upwards, and at time $t$ seconds has achieved an altitude of $10t^2$ meters. At 5 seconds after takeoff, how fast is the distance between the rocket and the observer increasing?

*Solution for Problem 4.31:* Even though there is only one moving object—the rocket—there are two quantities that we are interested in that are changing with respect to time: the altitude of the rocket (which we'll call $h$) and the distance from the rocket to the observer (which we'll call $x$).

The picture at right shows how these quantities are related. But don't make the following mistake:

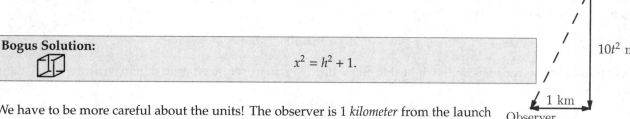

**Bogus Solution:**

$$x^2 = h^2 + 1.$$

We have to be more careful about the units! The observer is 1 *kilometer* from the launch pad, but the height of the rocket is given in *meters*. So, if we want to express everything in meters, we have the equation

$$x^2 = h^2 + (1000)^2.$$

Taking the derivative of both sides with respect to $t$, we get

$$2x\frac{dx}{dt} = 2h\frac{dh}{dt}.$$

We are given $t = 5$. But $t$ doesn't directly appear as a term in the above expression. So we need to figure out what the quantities in the above equation are in terms of $t$.

When $t = 5$, we have $h = 10t^2 = 250$. This means that $x^2 = (250)^2 + (1000)^2 = 17(250)^2$, so $x = 250\sqrt{17}$. Also, $\frac{dh}{dt} = 20t = 100$. Thus, we have

$$
\begin{aligned}
& 2x\frac{dx}{dt} && = 2h\frac{dh}{dt} \\
\Rightarrow \quad & x\frac{dx}{dt} && = h\frac{dh}{dt} \\
\Rightarrow \quad & (250\sqrt{17})\frac{dx}{dt} && = (250)(100) \\
\Rightarrow \quad & \frac{dx}{dt} && = \frac{100}{\sqrt{17}} = \frac{100\sqrt{17}}{17}.
\end{aligned}
$$

So the distance between the rocket and the observer is increasing at a rate of $\frac{100\sqrt{17}}{17}$ m/sec. $\square$

The next problem is a classic related rates problem:

**Problem 4.32:** A 10-foot-tall ladder rests against a wall, but the foot of the ladder is slipping away from the wall at a rate of 1 in/sec. When the ladder forms a 60° degree angle to the ground, how fast is the top of the ladder sliding down?

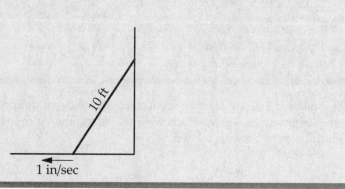

*Solution for Problem 4.32:* We should set this up to have as our two "variables" the functions whose rates we care about. Therefore, we should use $w$ (the distance from the wall) and $h$ (the height of the top of the ladder). We can then write an equation relating these quantities:

$$w^2 + h^2 = 100.$$

But this uses feet as the units on the right side. Since the rate is in in/sec, maybe we should write the whole thing in inches:

$$w^2 + h^2 = 14400.$$

Although it is always good practice to keep our units consistent, it doesn't really matter here, because the next step is to take the derivative with respect to time:

$$2ww' + 2hh' = 0.$$

Now we need to plug in the values of these quantities so that we can solve for $h'$. We know that $w' = 1(\text{in/sec})$. We need to figure out $w$ and $h$. But the other bit of information that we haven't used yet is the 60° angle. This gives us $w = 5$ (feet) and $h = 5\sqrt{3}$ (feet). But the rate of change is in inches per second! So we need to use $w = 60$ (inches) and $h = 60\sqrt{3}$ (inches). We then plug these values in to our related rates expression:

$$2(60)(1) + 2(60\sqrt{3})h' = 0.$$

Solving for $h'$ gives $h' = -\frac{1}{\sqrt{3}}$. So the top of the ladder is falling at a rate of $\frac{1}{\sqrt{3}}$ inches per second. □

By the way, in Problem 4.32, what does the function $h'(t)$ look like in general? We can solve for $h'$ in our related rates equation:

$$h' = -w'\frac{w}{h} = -\frac{w}{h}$$

since $w' = 1$. But we know what the quantity $w/h$ is: it's the cotangent of the angle that the ladder makes with the ground. So we have

$$h' = -\cot\theta,$$

where $\theta$ is the angle that the ladder makes with the ground.

This makes "real world" sense. At $\theta = \pi/2$, the ladder is vertical, and $\cot(\pi/2) = 0$, meaning that the top of the ladder is stationary. As $\theta$ decreases, $\cot\theta$ increases, so the top of the ladder moves faster and faster downwards.

Let's look at one more related rates problem that's a bit harder.

**Problem 4.33:** A cone-shaped filter has a hole at the top of radius 4 cm and a hole at the bottom of radius 1 cm, and is 6 cm in height. Water flows out of the bottom at a rate of 2 cm³/sec. If the filter begins completely filled at time $t = 0$, how fast is the water level decreasing after 30 seconds?

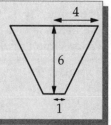

*Solution for Problem 4.33:* We start by identifying the relevant quantities that are changing with respect to time. These are the height of the water, which we'll call $h$, and the volume of water in the filter, which we'll call $V$. We need to determine how they are related.

We see that the filter is a **frustum**, which is a cone with a smaller cone chopped off. The volume of a frustum is most easily computed as the difference in volume between the two cones. To compute the volumes of the cones, we need their heights. So we will be much better off if our height is measured from the vertex of the imaginary cones, not from the bottom of the filter.

Next, the formula for the volume of a cone is $\frac{1}{3}\pi r^2 h$, where $r$ is the radius and $h$ is the height. So we need to determine how the height is related the radius. They are directly proportional, as we can see from our picture at right. In particular, decreasing the height by 6 causes a decrease of 3 in the radius, so we conclude that $h/r = 2$, and thus the radius at height $h$ is $h/2$. Note that the top of our frustum is at $h = 8$ (not $h = 6$), and at the top we have radius $8/2 = 4$, as expected. The bottom of the frustum is at $h = 2 \cdot 1 = 2$.

So the volume of the water at height $h$ is:

$$V = \frac{1}{3}\pi r^2 h - \frac{1}{3}\pi(1)^2(2) = \frac{1}{3}\pi\left(\frac{h}{2}\right)^2 h - \frac{1}{3}\pi(1)^2(2) = \frac{1}{12}\pi h^3 - \frac{2}{3}\pi.$$

We can differentiate this equation to get an equation relating the rates:

$$V' = \frac{1}{4}\pi h^2 h'.$$

We are told that $V' = -2$, as the rate of decrease of volume is constant. But we also need to find the value of $h$ in order to solve for $h'$. So we need to find the volume at $t = 30$ and compute its height.

We can start by finding the initial volume (at $t = 0$):

$$V(0) = \frac{1}{12}\pi(8)^3 - \frac{2}{3}\pi.$$

This simplifies to $42\pi$.

When $t = 30$, we will have lost $2 \cdot 30 = 60$ cm$^3$ of water, so the volume will be $V(30) = 42\pi - 60$. We can plug this in to our equation for volume to find $h$ at time $t = 30$:

$$42\pi - 60 = \frac{1}{12}\pi h^3 - \frac{2}{3}\pi.$$

This gives $h^3 = \dfrac{512\pi - 720}{\pi}$, and thus $h = \sqrt[3]{\dfrac{512\pi - 720}{\pi}} \approx 6.564$.

Finally, we can go back to our related rates equation:

$$-2 = \frac{1}{4}\pi h^2 h',$$

and plug in the found value of $h$. This gives:

$$-2 = \frac{1}{4}\pi\left(\frac{512\pi - 720}{\pi}\right)^{\frac{2}{3}} h'$$

We solve for $h'$ to get our answer:

$$h' = -\frac{8}{\sqrt[3]{\pi}(512\pi - 720)^{\frac{2}{3}}} = -\frac{2}{\sqrt[3]{\pi}(64\pi - 90)^{\frac{2}{3}}}.$$

This is approximately $-0.0591$, and thus at time $t = 30$ the water level is decreasing at a rate of $0.0591$ cm/sec. $\square$

## EXERCISES

**4.6.1**   A plane is flying overhead at an altitude of 10 km and a speed of 200 m/sec. The plane is 20 km away from a camera on the ground, and the plane is flying in a direction that will take it directly over the camera. The camera continuously rotates to keep the plane centered in its lens. When the plane is 15 km away from the camera, how fast is the camera rotating?

**4.6.2**   **Boyle's Law** states (assuming that the temperature is constant) that the pressure and volume of a gas are inversely proportional. Suppose Gas X starts at 1 atm (atmosphere) of pressure and takes up 200 cm$^3$. If the pressure is increased by 0.1 atm/min, then after 10 minutes, at what rate is the volume decreasing? **Hints:** 64

**4.6.3**   A spherical snowball is 10 cm in diameter, but is melting at the rate of 0.5 cm$^3$ per second. When the snowball is reduced to half its original volume, at what rate is its diameter decreasing?

**4.6.4**   A meteorite has entered the earth's atmosphere and is burning up at a rate that is proportional to the meteorite's surface area. What can you determine about the rate that the meteorite's radius is decreasing?

**4.6.5**   Two cars start at an intersection at time $t = 0$ with velocity 0. At $t = 0$, one car accelerates due north at 8 m/sec$^2$, and the other car accelerates due east at 5 m/sec$^2$. After 6 seconds, by what rate is the distance between the cars increasing?

**4.6.6★**   The clock on the wall at my office has an hour hand that's 6 cm long and a minute hand that's 10 cm long. At exactly 2:00, at what rate is the distance between the tips of the two hands changing? **Hints:** 148, 67

## REVIEW PROBLEMS

**4.34**   The following is the graph of the derivative $f'$ for some function $f$. Sketch possible graphs of $f$ and $f''$. Take into account where the function is increasing, decreasing, its concavity, and any inflection points.

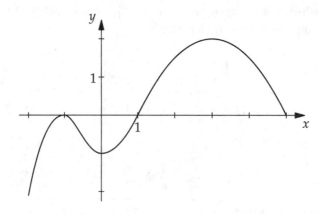

**4.35**   Suppose that $f$ is a function with domain $\mathbb{R}$ such that $f'(x) = x^2 - 3x + 3$ for all $x \in \mathbb{R}$. Prove that $f$ has an inverse.

**4.36**

(a)   Show that if $f$ is a quadratic polynomial, then the graph of $f$ has no inflection points.

(b)   Show that if $f$ is a cubic polynomial, then the graph of $f$ has exactly one inflection point.

(c)   Can you generalize?

**4.37** Describe the graph of $f(x) = x^3 + px + q$ where $p$ and $q$ are constants. Determine where the function is increasing or decreasing, where any local maxima or minima are located, and the concavity and inflection points of the graph.

**4.38** Let $m, n \geq 2$ be integers. Describe (in as much detail as possible) the graph of $f(x) = x^m(1-x)^n$ on the interval $[0, 1]$. **Hints:** 122

**4.39** A factory is making blivets. The factory costs \$2500 per day to run, and each blivet costs \$900 to make. Tina, the factory owner, knows that if she prices the blivets at \$$(2500 - x)$, then she will sell $x$ of them per day. What should she do to maximize her profit?

**4.40** We wish to construct a fenced garden with the shape of a circular sector, with area 300 m$^2$. What radius $r$ and angle $\theta$ should we choose to minimize the amount of fencing required (shown in dark black in the picture at right)? (Note that we could have $\theta < \pi$, contrary to the diagram; the only restriction is $0 < \theta < 2\pi$.)

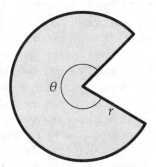

**4.41** Acceleration due to gravity is actually slightly lower at higher altitudes. In particular, $g = \frac{GM}{r^2}$, where $G$ is a constant (called the gravitational constant), $M$ is the mass of the Earth, and $r$ is the distance from the center of the Earth. If the radius of the Earth is 6400 km (approximately), estimate the percentage decrease in gravity on an airplane cruising at an altitude of 10 km above the surface of the Earth.

**4.42** The Ferris wheel at the County Fair is 60 meters in diameter and rotates at a rate of 4 revolutions per minute. If Natalie is sitting in one of the cars, at what rate is she gaining altitude when she is passing (on the way up) through a height of 40 meters?

**4.43** (Use a calculator for this one.) The temperature of a pie after it is removed from the oven is $70 + 230e^{-kt}$ degrees Fahrenheit, where $t$ is the time in minutes and $k$ is some constant. After 10 minutes, the pie has cooled to 200 degrees.

(a) When will the pie be 150 degrees?

(b) At the time in part (a), how fast is the pie cooling?

**4.44**

(a) Suppose that $f$ and $g$ are directly proportional (so that $f(t) = kg(t)$ for some constant $k$, for all $t$). What can you say about the relationship between the rates of change of $f$ and $g$?

(b) Suppose that $f$ and $g$ are inversely proportional (so that $f(t)g(t) = k$ for some constant $k$, for all $t$). What can you say about the relationship between the rates of change of $f$ and $g$?

## CHALLENGE PROBLEMS

**4.45** Explain and prove the **Racetrack Theorem**: if $f$ and $g$ are differentiable functions, with $f(a) = g(a)$ for some $a$ and $f'(x) > g'(x)$ for all $x > a$, then $f(x) > g(x)$ for all $x > a$.

**4.46** What is the relationship between the critical points of $f$ and the critical points of $f^2$?

**4.47** Determine the real number $a$ having the property that $f(a) = a$ is a relative minimum of

$$f(x) = x^4 - x^3 - x^2 + ax + 1.$$

*(Source: HMMT)* **Hints:** 247

**4.48**

(a) Sam wishes to cross a circular lake with diameter 1 km. He can row across the water at a rate of 4 km/hour, or he can walk along the shore (carrying the rowboat) at a rate of 6 km/hour. What is the minimum amount of time necessary to cross the lake? **Hints:** 71, 119, 218

(b) Now Sam wishes to cross a river of width 1 km, and reach a point on the opposite bank that is 1 km downstream. Again, he can row across the water at a rate of 4 km/hour (ignore the effect of the river's current), or he walk along the shore (carrying the rowboat) at a rate of 6 km/hour. What is the minimum amount of time necessary to reach his destination? **Hints:** 76, 54, 224

**4.49** The **Rule of 72** states that if an amount of money is invested at $r\%$ interest per year, then it will take approximately $72/r$ years for the money to double. Use linear approximation to explain why this rule is a good approximation for small values of $r$. **Hints:** 219

**4.50** **Snell's Law** describes how light passes through two mediums in which the speed of light is different. Suppose that light travels from the point A in the positive half-plane (where $y > 0$) to the point B in the negative half-plane (where $y < 0$). Further suppose that light has speed $c_1$ in the positive half-plane and speed $c_2$ in the negative half-plane. Find an equation that relates the angles that the light ray hits the $x$-axis with the speeds of light in the two half-planes, given that light will always travel such that its total travel time is minimized. **Hints:** 141, 47

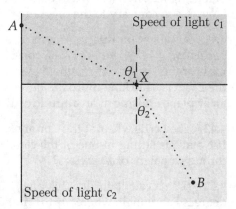

**4.51★** Suppose that a function $f$ is twice-differentiable. Recall from Problem 4.22 that we defined $E(x)$ to be the error in the approximation of $f(x)$ using $f(a)$; that is

$$E(x) = f(x) - (f(a) + f'(a)(x - a)).$$

Show that for any $z > a$, we have $|E(z)| \le M(z - a)^2$, where $M$ is the maximum value of $|f''(x)|$ on the interval $[a, z]$. (In fact, later in the book, we will show that $|E(z)| \le \frac{1}{2}M(z - a)^2$, but this is difficult with our current technology.) **Hints:** 279, 260

**4.52★** A snowplow can remove snow at a constant rate (in ft$^3$/min). One day, there was no snow on the ground at sunrise, but sometime in the morning it began snowing at a steady rate. At noon, the plow began to remove snow. It had cleared 2 miles of snow between noon and 1 PM, and 1 more mile of snow between 1 PM and 2 PM. At what time did it start snowing? **Hints:** 12, 189

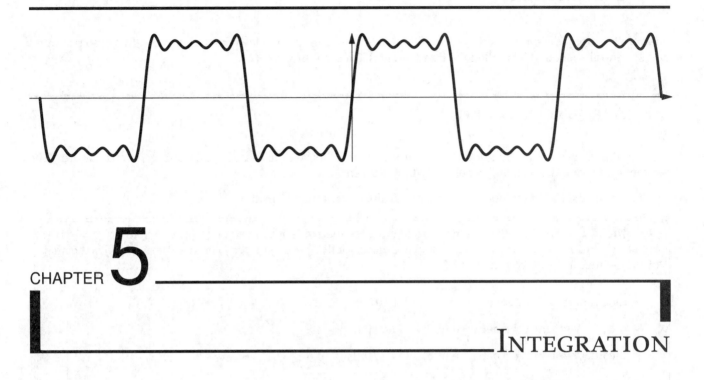

# CHAPTER 5

# INTEGRATION

Back in Chapter 3, we mentioned two fundamental geometric questions that motivate calculus:

**Question 1:** Given a real number $a$ in the domain of a function $f$, what is the slope of the line that is tangent to the graph $y = f(x)$ at the point $(a, f(a))$?

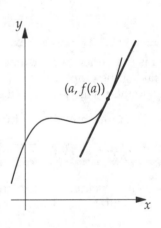

**Question 2:** Given real numbers $a \leq b$ such that the interval $[a, b]$ is a subset of the domain of a function $f$, what is the area of the region bounded by the graph $y = f(x)$, the lines $x = a$ and $x = b$, and the $x$-axis?

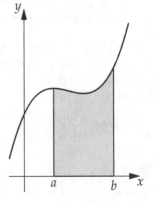

We developed the derivative to answer Question 1. In this chapter, we will develop the **definite integral** to answer Question 2. It turns out that the definite integral is intimately related to derivatives—this is so profound and so central a fact that it is called the **Fundamental Theorem of Calculus**.

## 5.1 AREA UNDER A CURVE

You already have a pretty good idea what we mean when we discuss the **area** of a geometric figure. The concept of "area under a curve" is not really that different.

For simplicity, we'll first look just at positive-valued continuous functions:

---

**Definition:** Let $[a, b]$ be a closed interval, and suppose that $f$ is continuous on $[a, b]$ such that $f(x) \geq 0$ for all $x \in [a, b]$. The **area under the curve** $y = f(x)$ (or, more briefly, the area under $f$) on the interval $[a, b]$ is the area of the geometric figure bounded by:

- the graph $y = f(x)$ between $(a, f(a))$ and $(b, f(b))$,

- the line segment $x = a$ between $(a, 0)$ and $(a, f(a))$,

- the line segment $x = b$ between $(b, 0)$ and $(b, f(b))$,

- and the $x$-axis between $(a, 0)$ and $(b, 0)$.

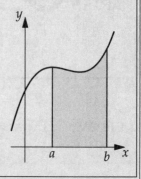

---

This is a rather cumbersome definition, but the picture to the right above makes clear what's going on. We're just taking the graph of $y = f(x)$ on the domain $a \leq x \leq b$, and extending vertical lines from the two endpoints down to the $x$-axis. We then take the area of the shaded region as shown in the picture.

If $f$ is sufficiently simple, then finding the area under $f$ is not much of a problem.

**Problem 5.1:** Let $f(x) = 3$. Find the area under $f$ on the interval $[-2, 5]$.

*Solution for Problem 5.1:* The graph of $y = 3$ is just a straight horizontal line. So the region in question is just a rectangle with height 3 and length $5 - (-2) = 7$. Thus the area is $3 \cdot 7 = 21$. □

**Problem 5.2:** Let $f(x) = 3x + 2$. Find the area under $f$ on the interval $[0, 4]$.

*Solution for Problem 5.2:* We draw $y = 3x + 2$ between $x = 0$ and $x = 4$, and the resulting region under the curve is a trapezoid with vertices $(0, 0)$, $(0, 2)$, $(4, 14)$, and $(4, 0)$. The bases have lengths $f(0) = 2$ and $f(4) = 14$, and the distance between the bases is 4. Thus the area is $4(2 + 14)/2 = 32$. □

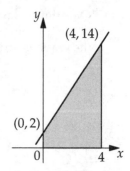

**Problem 5.3:** Let $f(x) = |x|$. Find the area under $f$ on the interval $[-3, 1]$.

*Solution for Problem 5.3:* When we draw the graph of $y = |x|$, we see that the region under the graph between $-3$ and $1$ consists of two triangles. The triangle to the left of the $y$-axis has base 3 and height 3, so it has area $\frac{9}{2}$. The triangle to the right of the $y$-axis has base 1 and height 1, so it has area $\frac{1}{2}$. Thus the total area is $\frac{9}{2} + \frac{1}{2} = 5$. $\square$

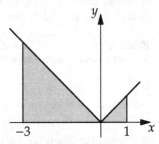

**Problem 5.4:** Let $f(x) = \sqrt{4 - x^2}$.

(a)  Find the area under $f$ on the interval $[-2, 2]$.

(b)  Find the area under $f$ on the interval $[0, 1]$.

*Solution for Problem 5.4:* At first, this looks like a difficult function to deal with. But if we write it as $y = \sqrt{4 - x^2}$ and square both sides, we get $y^2 = 4 - x^2$, so $x^2 + y^2 = 4$. In other words, the graph is the top half of a circle centered at the origin with radius 2.

(a)  The area under $f$ on the interval $[-2, 2]$ is just half of the area of a circle of radius 2. Thus the area is $(1/2)(4\pi) = 2\pi$.

(b)  The picture of the region whose area we wish to compute is shown at right. If we draw the segment from $(0, 0)$ to $(1, \sqrt{3})$, we see that this region is a right triangle with sides 1 and $\sqrt{3}$ together with $\frac{1}{12}$ of a circle of radius 2. Thus the area is $\frac{\sqrt{3}}{2} + \frac{\pi}{3}$.

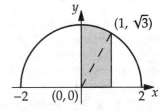

$\square$

We don't want to restrict ourselves just to positive-valued functions. We want to define area "under" the curve of functions that take on negative values as well. This is really area "over" such a curve, but we want this area to count "negatively," so we make the following definition:

**Definition:** Let $[a, b]$ be a closed interval, and suppose that $f$ is continuous on $[a, b]$ such that $f(x) \leq 0$ for all $x \in [a, b]$. The **area under the curve** $y = f(x)$ (or, more briefly, the area under $f$) on the interval $[a, b]$ is *minus* the area of the geometric figure bounded by:

- the graph $y = f(x)$ between $(a, f(a))$ and $(b, f(b))$,

- the line segment $x = a$ between $(a, 0)$ and $(a, f(a))$,

- the line segment $x = b$ between $(b, 0)$ and $(b, f(b))$,

- and the $x$-axis between $(a, 0)$ and $(b, 0)$.

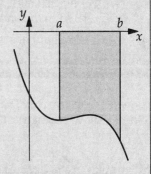

This is exactly the same definition except for the word "minus." So, for example, the area under the function $f(x) = -2$ on the interval $[1, 4]$ is $-(2 \cdot 3) = -6$. Even though this is really area "over" the curve, the convention is to call it area "under" the curve and to count any area below the $x$-axis as "negative" area.

This hopefully makes it clear what to do with an arbitrary continuous function that takes on some positive values and some negative values. We consider the part of the region that's above the $x$-axis as positive area, and we consider the part of the region that's below the $x$-axis as negative area. We'll define "area under a curve" more formally in a moment, but first let's just try to get a general understanding with a quick problem.

---

**Problem 5.5:** Let $f(x) = 2x - 5$. Compute the area under $f$ on the interval $[0, 6]$.

---

*Solution for Problem 5.5:* We draw $y = 2x - 5$ for $0 \leq x \leq 6$, and we see that it is negative for $x < \frac{5}{2}$ and positive for $x > \frac{5}{2}$. The portion on the interval $[0, \frac{5}{2}]$ contributes a negative area of $(\frac{1}{2})(\frac{5}{2})(-5) = -\frac{25}{4}$, and the portion on the interval $[\frac{5}{2}, 6]$ contributes a positive area of $(\frac{1}{2})(\frac{7}{2})(7) = \frac{49}{4}$. So the total area under the curve is $\frac{49}{4} - \frac{25}{4} = 6$. $\square$

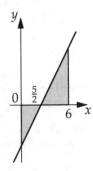

**Concept:** When computing area under a curve $y = f(x)$, the portion of the curve where $f(x) > 0$ contributes positive area, and the portion of the curve where $f(x) < 0$ contributes negative area.

All of the problems that we've solved so far were computing areas of regions that were triangles or trapezoids or circles or other simple geometric objects. But what about a region under an arbitrary curve? Also, what we've done so far in "defining" area under a curve is not very rigorous. For one thing, we never really defined what "area" means—rather, we relied on some geometric intuition about area (and most likely when you first learned about area in geometry you didn't really do it rigorously then either).

We need to begin somewhere, and one shape that we can hopefully all agree on is a rectangle: if a rectangle has length $l$ and width $w$, then it has area $lw$. We'll use rectangles to help us define areas for all other regions by approximating, in a systematic way, the area of a region under an arbitrary graph as a sum of areas of rectangles. We'll start with an example:

---

**Problem 5.6:** We wish to compute the area under the curve $f(x) = x^2$ on the interval $[1, 2]$.

(a) Draw a rectangle with opposite corners $(1, f(1))$ and $(2, 0)$. What is its area? How does its area compare to the area under $f$ on $[1, 2]$?

(b) Draw 2 rectangles: one with opposite corners $(1, f(1))$ and $(1.5, 0)$, and one with opposite corners $(1.5, f(1.5))$ and $(2, 0)$. What is the total area of the two rectangles? How is this total area related to the area under $f$ on $[1, 2]$? How does this area compare to the area from part (a)?

(c) For any positive integer $n$, draw $n$ rectangles: the $i^{\text{th}}$ rectangle (for $0 \leq i < n$) has opposite corners $\left(1 + \frac{i}{n}, f(1 + \frac{i}{n})\right)$ and $\left(1 + \frac{i+1}{n}, 0\right)$. What is the total area of the $n$ rectangles (in terms of $n$)? How is this total area related to the area under of curve?

(d) In (c), what happens as $n$ increases? What happens as $n$ grows large?

(e) Using (c) and (d), determine the area under $f$ on $[1, 2]$.

---

*Solution for Problem 5.6:* The region in question is shown in the diagram at right. Unfortunately, we don't know geometrically how to compute the area of a region bordered by a parabola.

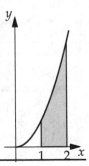

**Sidenote:** Actually, the ancient Greek mathematician Archimedes *did* know how to compute the area under a parabola! He used triangles instead of rectangles, but his method was not all that different from what we are about to do below.

However, we do know how to compute the area of simple shapes, and the simplest shape to compute the area of is a rectangle. We will use rectangles to approximate the area under the parabola. (Note: we will distort the horizontal scale of the pictures that follow, so that what we are doing is a bit more clear.)

(a) As a very crude estimate, we can draw a rectangle with opposite corners at $(1, 1)$ and $(2, 0)$. This rectangle has width 1 and height 1, so the rectangle has area 1. This is clearly a way-too-small subset of the area under $f$—in particular, the light-shaded area under the graph of $f$ but above the rectangle is not being counted—but it does give a lower bound of 1 for the area under $f$.

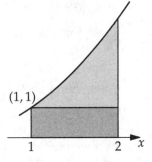

(b) To get a somewhat better estimate, we can draw two rectangles, each of width 0.5 and each with the upper-left corner touching the graph, as shown to the right. The first rectangle has opposite corners at $(1, 1)$ and $(1.5, 0)$, and has area 0.5. The second has opposite corners at $(1.5, 2.25)$ and $(2, 0)$, and has area 1.125. The total area of the rectangles—the dark region in the diagram at right—is thus $0.5 + 1.125 = 1.625$. That's a better estimate, but we can still clearly see from the picture that it's too small: the light-grey shaded area is still missing from our total.

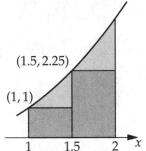

(c) We can do the same thing with an arbitrary number of rectangles. For example, to the right we show 7 rectangles. We can see from this picture that the sum of the areas of the rectangles—the entire region in dark grey to the right—is now a fairly close approximation to the entire area under the curve; only the light grey regions are missing.

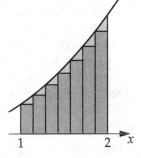

To be more precise, let $n$ be any positive integer, and we'll draw $n$ rectangles, each with width $\frac{1}{n}$. That is, each rectangle will have vertical sides at $x = 1 + \frac{i}{n}$ and $x = 1 + \frac{i+1}{n}$ for some integer $0 \le i < n$. The height of the $i^{\text{th}}$ rectangle is $f(1 + \frac{i}{n}) = (1 + \frac{i}{n})^2$. So the total area is

$$\sum_{i=0}^{n-1} \frac{1}{n} \cdot \left(1 + \frac{i}{n}\right)^2.$$

We can simplify this sum:

$$\sum_{i=0}^{n-1} \frac{1}{n} \cdot \left(1 + \frac{i}{n}\right)^2 = \frac{1}{n^3} \sum_{i=0}^{n-1} (n + i)^2 = \frac{1}{n^3} \sum_{i=0}^{n-1} (n^2 + 2ni + i^2).$$

Now, we can use the formulas $\sum_{i=0}^{n-1} i = \frac{n(n-1)}{2}$ and $\sum_{i=0}^{n-1} i^2 = \frac{n(n-1)(2n-1)}{6}$ to get a closed-form expression in terms of $n$:

$$\frac{1}{n^3} \sum_{i=0}^{n-1} (n^2 + 2ni + i^2) = \frac{1}{n^3} \left(n^3 + n^2(n-1) + \frac{n(n-1)(2n-1)}{6}\right) = \frac{\frac{7}{3}n^3 - \frac{3}{2}n^2 + \frac{1}{6}n}{n^3} = \frac{7}{3} - \frac{3}{2n} + \frac{1}{6n^2}.$$

(d) The expression that we got in part (c) for the area of $n$ rectangles,

$$\frac{7}{3} - \frac{3}{2n} + \frac{1}{6n^2},$$

is a lower bound for the area under $f$ on $[1, 2]$ for all $n$. As $n$ gets larger, this bound appears to get more and more accurate, since the rectangles more closely approximate the entire region under $f$.

(e)  As $n$ gets arbitrarily large, the $-\dfrac{3}{2n}$ and $\dfrac{1}{6n^2}$ terms in our rectangles-area expression approach 0. Thus, we guess that the area under $f(x) = x^2$ on $[1, 2]$ is $\dfrac{7}{3}$.

□

In fact, this "guess" is correct, as we will soon see.

We'll define area under a curve in much the same way as we did in our example in Problem 5.6, by subdividing the area into rectangles. However, in Problem 5.6, we took care to make sure that each rectangle had the same width: if we used $n$ rectangles, we constructed them so that each rectangle would have width $\frac{1}{n}$. In general, we don't need to be quite so picky. So let's first define a word for dividing up an interval $[a, b]$ into a bunch of smaller subintervals that we will use as the widths of our rectangles.

> **Definition:**  A **partition** $\mathcal{P}$ of a closed interval $[a, b]$ (into $n$ parts) is a sequence
>
> $$a = x_0 < x_1 < x_2 < \cdots < x_{n-1} < x_n = b.$$

In other words, we've divided up the interval $[a, b]$ into $n$ smaller intervals:

$$[a, b] = [x_0, x_1] \cup [x_1, x_2] \cup [x_2, x_3] \cup \cdots \cup [x_{n-1}, x_n].$$

Each of the intervals will serve as the base of one of our rectangles. But what should be the height?

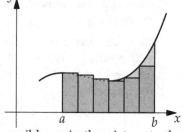

We could let the left side of each rectangle touch the curve, as we did for our parabola in Problem 5.6. But for a more general function, this may produce rectangles both above and below the curve, as in the figure to the right. This is slightly unpleasant, because then how do we know whether the sum of the areas of the rectangles is too big or too small an approximation for the area under the curve?

Instead, there are two more manageable choices for the height of each rectangle. We can take a rectangle whose height is the smallest possible, as in the picture to the left below. Or we can take a rectangle whose height is the largest possible, as in the picture to the right below. Clearly, the sum of the areas of the rectangles in the left picture is too small compared to the area under the curve, whereas the sum of the areas of the rectangles in the right picture is too large.

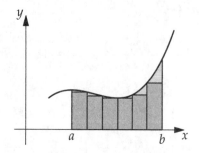
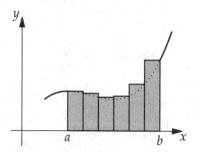

As the widths of the rectangles get narrower and narrower, the two areas should converge to equal the area under the curve. (Hopefully.)

Let's try to make this rigorous. For our partition $\mathcal{P}$, let $h_i$ be the minimum value of $f(x)$ on the $i^{\text{th}}$ piece of the partition; that is, for all $0 \leq i < n$,

$$h_i = \inf\{f(x) \mid x \in [x_i, x_{i+1}]\}.$$

Note that since $f$ is continuous, it must have a minimum value on any closed interval, so these values $h_i$ will exist. These will be the heights of our smaller rectangles.

Note that these heights don't have to be at one end or the other of the rectangle; they might be in the middle. For example, if we took a different partition of this function, we would get the rectangles on the right. In particular, note that the middle rectangle has a height "in the middle," not at either endpoint.

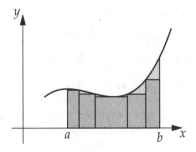

Similarly, we let $H_i$ be the maximum value of $f(x)$ on the $i^{\text{th}}$ piece of the partition; that is,

$$H_i = \sup\{f(x) \mid x \in [x_i, x_{i+1}]\}$$

for all $0 \leq i < n$. These will be the heights of our larger rectangles.

Using our smaller heights, we get the **lower area** for a partition $\mathcal{P}$ for the region under the curve $f$:

$$l(f, \mathcal{P}) = \sum_{i=0}^{n-1} h_i(x_{i+1} - x_i).$$

Our reasoning above tells us that this area should be less than (or perhaps equal to) the area under the curve. Of course, $l$ depends both on our function $f$ and our choice of partition $\mathcal{P}$ of $[a, b]$. This sum $l(f, \mathcal{P})$ is sometimes more technically referred to as a **lower Darboux sum**.

Similarly, using our larger heights for $\mathcal{P}$, we get an **upper area** for the region under the curve $f$:

$$u(f, \mathcal{P}) = \sum_{i=0}^{n-1} H_i(x_{i+1} - x_i).$$

This area should be greater than (or equal to) the area under the curve. $u(f, \mathcal{P})$ is sometimes called an **upper Darboux sum**.

Thus, for any choice of partition $\mathcal{P}$ we get a lower estimate $l(f, \mathcal{P})$ of the area and an upper estimate $u(f, \mathcal{P})$ of the area; that is, we expect that

$$l(f, \mathcal{P}) \leq \text{Area} \leq u(f, \mathcal{P})$$

for all partitions $\mathcal{P}$. By picking very *fine* partitions—that is, partitions that give us very narrow rectangles—both of these estimates should be very close to the actual area. In fact, we'll use a limit-like argument to *define* area this way.

> **Definition:** Let $f$ be a continuous function defined on a closed interval $[a, b]$. Let
>
> $$L_a^b(f) = \sup\{l(f, \mathcal{P}) \mid \mathcal{P} \text{ is a partition of } [a, b]\}$$
>
> and
>
> $$U_a^b(f) = \inf\{u(f, \mathcal{P}) \mid \mathcal{P} \text{ is a partition of } [a, b]\}.$$
>
> (This assumes that these quantities are defined.) $L_a^b(f)$ is called the **lower Darboux integral** of $f$ over $[a, b]$, and $U_a^b(f)$ is called the **upper Darboux integral** of $f$ over $[a, b]$. If $L_a^b(f) = U_a^b(f)$, then we define
>
> $$\int_a^b f = L_a^b(f) = U_a^b(f),$$
>
> and call this the **definite integral** of $f$ over $[a, b]$.

Let's step back and see the big picture of what we're doing here. We're dividing $[a, b]$ up into little pieces, and approximating the area under $f$ using rectangles with our little pieces as the widths of the rectangles. We're doing two different estimates: one with rectangles that are deliberately chosen to be too small, and the other with rectangles that are deliberately chosen to be too big. The former will give us a lower bound on the area under $f$, and the latter will give us an upper bound. As our partition of rectangles fits the curve more and more closely, the lower bound will rise and the upper bound will fall. If they meet, then the value at which they meet is the area under the curve.

The symbol $\int$ is called an **integral sign**, and is supposed to remind you of an elongated letter "S" (as in "sum"), because the definite integral is arrived at via a process involving sums of area of rectangles. We read $\int_a^b f$ as "the integral of $f$ from $a$ to $b$." The function $f$ is called the **integrand** of the integral, and the numbers $a$ and $b$ are called the **limits of integration**.

There's another peculiar feature of the notation, which is best illustrated by an example. If $f(x) = x^2$, then we could write

$$\int_1^2 f = \int_1^2 f(x)\, dx = \int_1^2 x^2\, dx$$

for the area under $f$ on $[1, 2]$. In particular, if we write the integral in terms of a dummy variable (like $x$) in the function expression, then we write $dx$ as a "term" of the integral. This looks a little silly right now, but as we will see soon there are very good reasons for doing so.

Even though our definition is fairly abstract, we can use it to deduce some basic properties and calculate some simple definite integrals. Here are some basic properties about Darboux sums and definite integrals:

---

**Important:**  Let $f$ be continuous on $[a, b]$.

- If $\mathcal{P}$ is any partition of $[a, b]$, then $l(f, \mathcal{P}) \leq u(f, \mathcal{P})$.

- If $\mathcal{P}$ and $\mathcal{Q}$ are any two partitions of $[a, b]$, then $l(f, \mathcal{P}) \leq u(f, \mathcal{Q})$.

- $L_a^b(f) \leq U_a^b(f)$.

- For any functions $f$ and $g$,

$$\int_a^b (f + g) = \int_a^b f + \int_a^b g,$$

provided the integrals on the right side are defined.

- For any functions $f$ and any $a < c < b$,

$$\int_a^b f = \int_a^c f + \int_c^b f,$$

provided the integrals on either side are defined.

---

Hopefully, you find all of these properties to make sense. We will leave the proof of the first property as an exercise. The proofs of the remainder of the above properties are not difficult but are *very* technical, so we will omit them in this book; you will likely revisit them if you study real analysis later in your mathematical career.

As a quick check that our definition is reasonable, let's check it on a simple region for which we already know the area:

**Problem 5.7:** Let $c$ be a constant and let $f(x) = c$. Compute $\int_a^b f$.

*Solution for Problem 5.7:* No matter what partition $\mathcal{P}$ we choose, we have that $h_i = H_i = c$ for all sections of the partition. Therefore, every Darboux sum is equal to $c(b - a)$, and thus $\int_a^b f = c(b - a)$. This is consistent with our intuitive notion of area: the region is just a rectangle with length $(b - a)$ and height $c$. $\square$

**Problem 5.8:** Compute $\int_0^1 x^3 \, dx$.

*Solution for Problem 5.8:* We'll use a method similar to that of Problem 5.6.

Let $\mathcal{P}_n$ be the partition consisting of the intervals $\left[0, \frac{1}{n}\right], \left[\frac{1}{n}, \frac{2}{n}\right], \ldots, \left[\frac{n-1}{n}, 1\right]$. Since $f(x) = x^3$ is a strictly increasing function, we have

$$h_i = f\left(\frac{i}{n}\right) = \frac{i^3}{n^3} \quad \text{and} \quad H_i = f\left(\frac{i+1}{n}\right) = \frac{(i+1)^3}{n^3}$$

for all $0 \le i < n$. This allows us to compute the Darboux sums for this function and these $\mathcal{P}_n$:

$$l(f, \mathcal{P}_n) = \sum_{i=0}^{n-1} \frac{i^3}{n^3}\left(\frac{1}{n}\right) = \frac{1}{n^4} \sum_{i=0}^{n-1} i^3,$$

$$u(f, \mathcal{P}_n) = \sum_{i=0}^{n-1} \frac{(i+1)^3}{n^3}\left(\frac{1}{n}\right) = \frac{1}{n^4} \sum_{i=0}^{n-1} (i+1)^3.$$

We now use the formula

$$\sum_{i=0}^{k} i^3 = \frac{k^2(k+1)^2}{4},$$

and thus we have

$$l(f, \mathcal{P}_n) = \frac{(n-1)^2 n^2}{4n^4} = \frac{1}{4} - \frac{1}{2n} + \frac{1}{4n^2} = \frac{1}{4} - \frac{1}{2n}\left(1 - \frac{1}{2n}\right),$$

$$u(f, \mathcal{P}_n) = \frac{n^2(n+1)^2}{4n^4} = \frac{1}{4} + \frac{1}{2n} + \frac{1}{4n^2} = \frac{1}{4} + \frac{1}{2n}\left(1 + \frac{1}{2n}\right).$$

We notice that $\frac{1}{4}$ is the lowest upper bound for all of these $l(f, \mathcal{P}_n)$ and that $\frac{1}{4}$ is the greatest lower bound for all of these $u(f, \mathcal{P}_n)$; in other words,

$$\frac{1}{4} = \sup\{l(f, \mathcal{P}_n) \mid n \ge 1\} = \inf\{u(f, \mathcal{P}_n) \mid n \ge 1\}.$$

We only examined a specific type of partition: those with $n$ intervals of equal width. However, we need to consider *all* partitions of $[0, 1]$ to compute the definite integral. Note that

$$L_0^1(f) = \sup\{l(f, \mathcal{P}) \mid \mathcal{P} \text{ is a partition of } [0, 1]\} \ge \sup\{l(f, \mathcal{P}_n) \mid n \ge 1\} = \frac{1}{4},$$

and

$$U_0^1(f) = \inf\{u(f, \mathcal{P}) \mid \mathcal{P} \text{ is a partition of } [0, 1]\} \le \inf\{u(f, \mathcal{P}_n) \mid n \ge 1\} = \frac{1}{4}.$$

Thus, we have

$$U_0^1(f) \le \frac{1}{4} \le L_0^1(f).$$

But we always have $L_0^1(f) \le U_0^1(f)$ (this is one of the facts in the box on page 132). Therefore, we must have $L_0^1(f) = U_0^1(f) = \frac{1}{4}$, and hence $\int_0^1 f = \frac{1}{4}$. $\square$

It turns out that we did not need to be so cautious in our definition of the definite integral:

> **Important:** For every continuous function $f$ defined on a closed interval $[a, b]$, the definite integral $\int_a^b f$ is defined.

This is a deep result and requires a substantial amount of technical $\delta$-$\epsilon$-style computations to prove. We will omit the proof in this book, but many advanced calculus or real analysis books (such as [**Sp**]) have the proof. However, it is well within our grasp to prove that the definite integral exists for a monotonic continuous function—we will leave this proof to you as a Challenge Problem.

Also, we can use the same definition to write the definite integral of many noncontinuous functions, although in this case there is no guarantee that the definite integral will exist. There is an example of a definite integral of a noncontinuous function in the exercises.

Although Darboux sums are very useful for defining integrals, there is a more general construction that is broadly applicable to a wide range of problems. Given a function $f$ continuous on $[a, b]$ and a partition $\mathcal{P}$ of $[a, b]$, we can construct a **Riemann sum** for $f$ over $\mathcal{P}$, by choosing *any* point in each piece of the partition to give us the height of the rectangle.

Specifically, let $\mathcal{P}$ be the partition $a = x_0 < x_1 < x_2 < \cdots < x_n = b$, and let $w_i \in [x_i, x_{i+1}]$ be a point in the $(i + 1)^{\text{st}}$ piece of the partition. Then the Riemann sum associated with this partition and choice of points is

$$r(f, \mathcal{P}, w_i) = \sum_{i=0}^{n-1} (x_{i+1} - x_i) f(w_i).$$

Again, this is just a sum of areas of rectangles: $(x_{i+1} - x_i)$ is the width and $f(w_i)$ is the height of each rectangle. Note that choosing $w_i$ such that $f(w_i)$ is minimal gives us our lower Darboux sum $l(f, \mathcal{P})$, and choosing $w_i$ such that $f(w_i)$ is maximal gives us our upper Darboux sum $u(f, \mathcal{P})$. Indeed, this shows that

$$l(f, \mathcal{P}) \le r(f, \mathcal{P}, w_i) \le u(f, \mathcal{P})$$

for any choice of $w_i$.

If we let $\Delta x$ denote the largest width in our partition, we have

$$\int_a^b f(x)\, dx = \lim_{\Delta x \to 0} \sum_{i=0}^{n-1} (x_{i+1} - x_i) f(w_i).$$

What this means is that as we let the widths of the rectangles of the Riemann sum get smaller and smaller, then the Riemann sum approaches the definite integral $\int_a^b f$. However, the above expression is a bit vague: what exactly does "the limit as $\Delta x \to 0$" mean? It takes a bit of work to make this concept rigorous, so for this reason, we prefer Darboux sums for our rigorous definition of $\int_a^b f$. However, the concept of Riemann sums is more general and turns out to be useful in applications, as we will soon see.

> **Concept:** Whenever we can express a quantity, such as area under a graph, as the "limit" of a Riemann sum as the widths of the pieces of the partition get smaller and smaller, then the quantity can be represented by a definite integral.

Some common choices for $w_i \in [x_i, x_{i+1}]$ are:

- $w_i = x_i$, giving a **left Riemann sum**,

- $w_i = x_{i+1}$, giving a **right Riemann sum**,

- $w_i = (x_i + x_{i+1})/2$, giving a **midpoint Riemann sum**.

There is one more definition that is very convenient to have:

**Definition:** If $a < b$, then $\int_b^a f = -\int_a^b f$, provided this definite integral is defined.

We think of $\int_b^a f$ as "the integral of $f$ from $b$ to $a$," which gives the area under the graph of $f$ on $[a, b]$ in the opposite direction, and thus gives $-1$ times the usual area.

## EXERCISES

**5.1.1** Compute the following:

(a) $\int_{-1}^3 4\,dx$      (b) $\int_2^6 (3x - 1)\,dx$      (c) $\int_1^2 (x^2 + 1)\,dx$

(d) $\int_{-2}^2 x^3\,dx$      (e) $\int_{-3}^4 (2x - 1)\,dx$      (f) $\int_0^3 \lfloor x \rfloor\,dx$

**5.1.2** If $f$ is a continuous function and $a \in \text{Dom}(f)$, then what is $\int_a^a f$?

**5.1.3** Prove, for any function $f$ and partition $\mathcal{P}$ of $[a, b]$, that $l(f, \mathcal{P}) \leq u(f, \mathcal{P})$.

## 5.2 THE FUNDAMENTAL THEOREM OF CALCULUS

It would be quite a hassle if every time we wished to compute a definite integral we had to set up Darboux sums or Riemann sums and compute areas of rectangles. Fortunately, there is a relatively easy way to compute definite integrals. There is a fundamental theorem of calculus—in fact, we call it the **Fundamental Theorem of Calculus**—that relates definite integrals to derivatives in an amazing way. The way we approach this is via the Mean Value Theorem.

Let $f$ be a continuous function on $[a, b]$, and let $F$ be a function whose derivative is $f$, so that $F' = f$. Such a function is called an **antiderivative** of $f$. We're interested in computing $\int_a^b f$, so we let $\mathcal{P}$ be a partition of $[a, b]$, given by

$$a = x_0 < x_1 < x_2 < \cdots < x_n = b.$$

For each interval $[x_i, x_{i+1}]$ in the partition, the Mean Value Theorem, applied to the function $F$, tells us that there is some value $z_i \in [x_i, x_{i+1}]$ such that

$$f(z_i) = F'(z_i) = \frac{F(x_{i+1}) - F(x_i)}{x_{i+1} - x_i}.$$

When we multiply both sides by the denominator, we get

$$f(z_i)(x_{i+1} - x_i) = F(x_{i+1}) - F(x_i).$$

When we sum this over all the intervals, we get

$$\sum_{i=0}^{n-1} f(z_i)(x_{i+1} - x_i) = \sum_{i=0}^{n-1} (F(x_{i+1}) - F(x_i)). \tag{$*$}$$

Let's look at the two sides of equation ($*$) separately.

On the left side of ($*$), we have a Riemann sum. In particular, going back to the notation in the previous section, we note that $h_i \le f(z_i) \le H_i$ for all $0 \le i < n$, and thus the left side of ($*$) lies between $l(f, \mathcal{P})$ and $u(f, \mathcal{P})$:

$$l(f, \mathcal{P}) = \sum_{i=0}^{n-1} (h_i)(x_{i+1} - x_i) \le \sum_{i=0}^{n-1} f(z_i)(x_{i+1} - x_i) \le \sum_{i=0}^{n-1} (H_i)(x_{i+1} - x_i) = u(f, \mathcal{P}). \tag{$**$}$$

On the right side of ($*$), we have a **telescoping sum**, which means that most of the terms cancel out:

$$\sum_{i=0}^{n-1} (F(x_{i+1}) - F(x_i)) = (F(x_1) - F(x_0)) + (F(x_2) - F(x_1)) + (F(x_3) - F(x_2)) + \cdots + (F(x_n) - F(x_{n-1}))$$
$$= -F(x_0) + F(x_n)$$
$$= F(b) - F(a).$$

Thus, the right side of ($*$) is just $F(b) - F(a)$. Substituting this expression into the middle of ($**$) gives

$$l(f, \mathcal{P}) \le F(b) - F(a) \le u(f, \mathcal{P})$$

for all partitions $\mathcal{P}$ of $[a, b]$. Thus, $F(b) - F(a)$ is an upper bound for the set of all $l(f, \mathcal{P})$ and is a lower bound for the set of all $u(f, \mathcal{P})$, and hence

$$L_a^b(f) \le F(b) - F(a) \le U_a^b(f).$$

But if the definite integral $\int_a^b f$ is defined, then $L_a^b(f) = \int_a^b f = U_a^b(f)$. Thus, there is exactly one value that can be placed in the middle of the above inequality for all $\mathcal{P}$, and that value—by definition—is $\int_a^b f$. Therefore, we conclude that

$$\int_a^b f(x)\, dx = F(b) - F(a),$$

provided that the definite integral is defined. As we mentioned in the last section, if $f$ is continuous on $[a, b]$, then the definite integral $\int_a^b f$ is defined, so we have:

> **Important:** ⚠ The **Fundamental Theorem of Calculus**, Part I: If $f$ is a continuous function on $[a, b]$ with antiderivative $F$, then
>
> $$\int_a^b f(x)\, dx = F(b) - F(a).$$

Note that we have assumed that $f$ has an antiderivative $F$. It turns out that every continuous function has an antiderivative: this is Part II of the Fundamental Theorem of Calculus, which we will see in a little bit.

Let's go back to our example from Problem 5.8, and we'll see how much the Fundamental Theorem of Calculus make our lives easier:

**Problem 5.9:** Compute $\int_0^1 x^3\, dx$.

*Solution for Problem 5.9:* In order to apply the Fundamental Theorem of Calculus, we need to determine an antiderivative of $f(x) = x^3$. Happily, that's easy: we let $F(x) = \frac{1}{4}x^4$, so that $F'(x) = x^3 = f(x)$. The Fundamental Theorem then tells us immediately that

$$\int_0^1 x^3\,dx = F(1) - F(0) = \frac{1}{4}(1)^4 - \frac{1}{4}(0)^4 = \frac{1}{4} - 0 = \frac{1}{4}.$$

$\square$

More commonly, the computation from Problem 5.9 is written like this:

$$\int_0^1 x^3\,dx = \left.\frac{x^4}{4}\right|_0^1 = \frac{1}{4} - 0 = \frac{1}{4}.$$

The vertical bar means to take the function $\left(\frac{x^4}{4}\right)$ evaluated at the top number ($x = 1$) minus the function evaluated at the bottom number ($x = 0$). If there is any question about what variable we are using to evaluate the function, we can list the variable explicitly, such as

$$\int_0^1 x^3\,dx = \left.\frac{x^4}{4}\right|_{x=0}^1.$$

However, we will usually omit the variable if there is no ambiguity.

Let's look at another basic example of computing a definite integral.

**Problem 5.10:** Compute the area under a positive half-period of the sine function; that is, compute

$$\int_0^\pi \sin x\,dx.$$

*Solution for Problem 5.10:* An antiderivative of $\sin x$ is $-\cos x$, because $\frac{d}{dx}(-\cos x) = -(-\sin x) = \sin x$. Thus, via the Fundamental Theorem, we have:

$$\int_0^\pi \sin x\,dx = \left.(-\cos x)\right|_0^\pi.$$

Therefore, the integral is equal to $(-\cos \pi) - (-\cos 0) = -(-1) - (-1) = 2$. $\square$

There is another version of the Fundamental Theorem of Calculus that is also very useful. Let's see how this works with an example.

**Problem 5.11:** Define a function $g$ by

$$g(x) = \int_0^x \cos t\,dt$$

for all $x \in \mathbb{R}$. Prove that $g(x) = \sin x$.

We notice that there are two variables in our equation. In particular, the variable $x$ is one of our limits of integration, so we need a different variable (in this example, $t$) to represent the variable in the function that we are integrating.

*Solution for Problem 5.11:* We proceed as usual: since sin is an antiderivative of cos, we can simply evaluate the integral as

$$g(x) = \int_0^x \cos t\,dt = \left.\sin t\right|_{t=0}^x = \sin x - \sin 0 = \sin x.$$

Evaluation of the integral eliminated the dummy variable $t$, and what remains is a function of $x$. □

More generally, we start with a continuous function $f$ and use the definite integral to define a new function, by selecting a point $x_0$ in the domain of $f$ and defining

$$g(x) = \int_{x_0}^{x} f(t)\, dt.$$

Note that we use a new dummy variable $t$ in our integral. If $F$ is an antiderivative of $f$, then the Fundamental Theorem gives us:

$$g(x) = \int_{x_0}^{x} f(t)\, dt = F(x) - F(x_0).$$

We now differentiate this with respect to $x$. Note that since $F(x_0)$ is a constant, we have $\frac{d}{dx} F(x_0) = 0$, and thus we get

$$g'(x) = \frac{d}{dx} F(x) - \frac{d}{dx} F(x_0) = f(x).$$

Putting this all together gives us:

> **Important:**
> ⚠️
>
> The **Fundamental Theorem of Calculus**, Part II: Let $f$ be a continuous function and $x_0$ a number in the domain of $f$. Define a function $g$ by
>
> $$g(x) = \int_{x_0}^{x} f(t)\, dt$$
>
> for all $x$ such that $[x_0, x]$ (for $x \geq x_0$) or $[x, x_0]$ (for $x \leq x_0$) is a subset of the domain of $f$. Then $g'(x) = f(x)$ for all $x$ where both functions are defined.

This is sometimes also written as

$$\frac{d}{dx} \int_{x_0}^{x} f(t)\, dt = f(x).$$

Unfortunately, our argument above presupposes the existence of an antiderivative $F$ of $f$. We want the Fundamental Theorem of Calculus to be stronger: we want it to imply the existence of an antiderivative.

> **Problem 5.12:** Let $f$ be a continuous function and $x_0 \in \mathrm{Dom}(f)$. We wish to prove Part II of the Fundamental Theorem of Calculus without presupposing the existence of an antiderivative of $f$. Define
>
> $$g(x) = \int_{x_0}^{x} f(t)\, dt$$
>
> wherever the right side is defined. We will prove that $g'(x) = f(x)$, as follows:
>
> (a) Show that $g(x + h) - g(x) = \int_{x}^{x+h} f(t)\, dt$ for any $h$.
>
> (b) Show that
>
> $$g'(x) = \lim_{h \to 0} \frac{g(x + h) - g(x)}{h} = f(x).$$

*Solution for Problem 5.12:*

> **WARNING!!**
> ☢☢
>
> The proof can be confusing, because of the different variables that are used. We are using the variable $x$ as the independent variable of the function $g$, and the variable $t$ as the dummy variable in the definite integrals.

(a) We know that

$$\int_{x_0}^{x+h} f(t)\,dt = \int_{x_0}^{x} f(t)\,dt + \int_{x}^{x+h} f(t)\,dt,$$

so rearranging gives

$$\int_{x}^{x+h} f(t)\,dt = \int_{x_0}^{x+h} f(t)\,dt - \int_{x_0}^{x} f(t)\,dt = g(x+h) - g(x).$$

(b) We only show the proof of the limit for $h > 0$; the proof for $h < 0$ is nearly the same. By the definition of limit, we must show that for any $\epsilon > 0$, there exists $\delta > 0$ such that

$$0 < h < \delta \quad \Rightarrow \quad \left| \frac{g(x+h) - g(x)}{h} - f(x) \right| < \epsilon.$$

Since $f$ is continuous, we may choose $\delta$ such that

$$|t - x| < \delta \quad \Rightarrow \quad |f(t) - f(x)| < \epsilon \quad \Rightarrow \quad f(x) - \epsilon < f(t) < f(x) + \epsilon.$$

Thus, if $h < \delta$, we have

$$\int_{x}^{x+h} (f(x) - \epsilon)\,dt < \int_{x}^{x+h} f(t)\,dt < \int_{x}^{x+h} (f(x) + \epsilon)\,dt.$$

But the outer integrals in the above expression are definite integrals of constant functions (that is, they don't depend on $t$), so they can be explicitly evaluated, and we get

$$h(f(x) - \epsilon) < \int_{x}^{x+h} f(t)\,dt < h(f(x) + \epsilon).$$

We now apply part (a) and divide by $h$, giving

$$f(x) - \epsilon < \frac{g(x+h) - g(x)}{h} < f(x) + \epsilon.$$

This means that

$$0 < h < \delta \quad \Rightarrow \quad \left| \frac{g(x+h) - g(x)}{h} - f(x) \right| < \epsilon,$$

hence, by definition,

$$g'(x) = \lim_{h \to 0^+} \frac{g(x+h) - g(x)}{h} = f(x),$$

as desired. The proof of the limit as $h \to 0^-$ is essentially the same.

$\square$

A nice feature of Part II of the Fundamental Theorem is that we no longer have to presuppose that a continuous function $f$ has an antiderivative $F$. The Fundamental Theorem not only tells us that $F$ must exist, it even tells us how to construct it:

$$F(x) = \int_{x_0}^{x} f(t)\,dt.$$

 **Concept:** A continuous function $f$ has an antiderivative. In fact, it has infinitely many antiderivatives, since if $F$ is an antiderivative, then so is $F + c$ where $c \in \mathbb{R}$ is any constant.

Another use of this version of the Fundamental Theorem of Calculus is to rigorously define functions that would otherwise be hard to describe. For example, back in Chapter 1, we gave a vague definition of the exponential and natural logarithm functions. This definition forced us to assume many of the nice properties that these functions satisfy. However, using a definite integral, we can rigorously *define* the natural logarithm to be the function whose derivative is $\frac{1}{x}$ by defining, for all $x > 0$,

$$\log x = \int_1^x \frac{1}{t} \, dt.$$

Using this definition, we can now prove all of the features of the natural logarithm function and its inverse, the exponential function. We present the details in Section 5.A.

Also, we often use definite integrals to define functions that couldn't really be defined any other way. For example, the following function is quite important in statistics:

$$\operatorname{erf}(x) = \frac{2}{\sqrt{\pi}} \int_0^x e^{-t^2} \, dt.$$

This is called the **error function**. Note that, by definition, we have

$$\frac{d}{dx} \operatorname{erf}(x) = \frac{2}{\sqrt{\pi}} e^{-x^2}.$$

The constant $\frac{2}{\sqrt{\pi}}$ is there to make certain calculations in statistics come out nicely.

## EXERCISES

**5.2.1** Compute the following definite integrals:

(a) $\displaystyle\int_{-1}^{2} x^4 \, dx$  (b) $\displaystyle\int_{0}^{1} e^x \, dx$  (c) $\displaystyle\int_{\pi/6}^{\pi/4} \sec^2 \theta \, d\theta$  (d) $\displaystyle\int_{-4}^{-2} 2x \, dx$

**5.2.2** Suppose $f$ is continuous (with antiderivative $F$) and $a < c < b$. Explain why

$$\int_a^b f = \int_a^c f + \int_c^b f.$$

**5.2.3** Recall that a function $f$ is called **odd** if $f(-x) = -f(x)$ for all $x$. Show that, if $f$ is continuous and odd, and $[-a, a]$ is in the domain of $f$, then $\int_{-a}^{a} f(x) \, dx = 0$. **Hints:** 215

**5.2.4** Suppose $f$ is differentiable and $g$ is continuous. Show that

$$\frac{d}{dx} \int_0^{f(x)} g(t) \, dt = g(f(x)) f'(x).$$

**Hints:** 281

## 5.3 INTEGRATION METHODS

In order to apply the Fundamental Theorem of Calculus to compute definite integrals of the form $\int_a^b f \, dx$, we need to be able to find an antiderivative of $f$; that is, we need a function $F$ such that $F' = f$. This process is called **antidifferentiation** (for obvious reasons), and while finding derivatives is pretty easy, finding antiderivatives can be much more difficult, as we will explore in this section.

## 5.3.1 Definition and basic examples

Recall the definition:

**Definition:** Let $f$ be a function. A function $g$ is called an **antiderivative** of $f$ if $g$ is differentiable and $g' = f$.

As we saw when discussing the Fundamental Theorem of Calculus, the usual convention is that if a function is denoted by a lowercase letter, then its antiderivative is denoted by the same letter, but in uppercase. For example, $F$ is an antiderivative of $f$, meaning that $F' = f$.

Notice that we said *an* antiderivative rather than *the* antiderivative. Did we need to be so careful? In other words, does a function have a unique antiderivative?

**Problem 5.13:** Suppose that $F_1$ and $F_2$ are antiderivatives of $f$. How are $F_1$ and $F_2$ related? Must they be equal?

*Solution for Problem 5.13:* It's not so hard to come up with an example of two different functions that have the same derivative. For example, if $f = 0$ and $g = 1$ (the constant functions 0 and 1, respectively), then $f' = g' = 0$. Furthermore, all constant functions have derivative 0, so any constant function is an antiderivative of the function $f = 0$. Perhaps this generalizes somehow.

Suppose $F_1$ and $F_2$ are both antiderivatives of $f$; that is, $F_1' = F_2' = f$. Then

$$(F_1 - F_2)' = F_1' - F_2' = f - f = 0.$$

So $F_1 - F_2$ is a function whose derivative is 0 everywhere, and we know that the only such functions are constant functions. Thus $F_1 - F_2 = c$ for some constant $c$. $\square$

**Important:** If $F_1$ and $F_2$ are antiderivatives of the same function $f$, then $F_1 - F_2 = c$ for some constant $c \in \mathbb{R}$.

So there is no "unique" antiderivative of a function, but the antiderivative is determined up to a constant term.

Antiderivatives are also called **indefinite integrals**, and have a familiar notation: if $F$ is an antiderivative of $f$, then we write

$$F = \int f = \int f(x)\,dx.$$

Note that this is the same notation as we use for definite integrals, except that an indefinite integral does not have limits of integration. As with definite integrals, if we write a dummy variable (like $x$) in the function expression of the indefinite integral, then we write $dx$ as a "term" of the integral.

The use of an equal sign in the above "equation" is a little strange, as we know that $\int f$ is determined only up to a constant term. Instead, we write

$$\int f = F + C,$$

where $C$ denotes the arbitrary constant term. (Traditionally, it's almost always written with a capital "$C$.")

This notation also gives us a convenient shorthand that relates our two types of integrals via the Fundamental Theorem of Calculus:

$$\int_a^b f(x)\,dx = \left( \int f(x)\,dx \right)\Bigg|_a^b$$

Pay close attention to the difference between the two types of integrals. The integral on the left, $\int_a^b f(x)\,dx$, is a **definite** integral, and is equal to a *number*, specifically the area under the curve $y = f(x)$ on the interval $[a, b]$. The integral on the right, $\int f(x)\,dx$, is an **indefinite** integral, and is equal to a *function*, specifically the antiderivative of $f$. (Actually, since it's only determined up to a constant, it's a whole set of functions.) When we then take the difference of this antiderivative evaluated at $x = b$ and $x = a$, we get the definite integral on the left side of the above equation.

Since differentiation is linear—that is, $(f + g)' = f' + g'$ and $(cf)' = cf'$—we expect that antidifferentiation is too.

> **Problem 5.14:**
> (a)  Show that if $F$ and $G$ are antiderivatives of $f$ and $g$, respectively, then $F + G$ is an antiderivative of $f + g$.
>
> (b)  Show that if $F$ is an antiderivative of $f$ and $c \in \mathbb{R}$ is a constant, then $cF$ is an antiderivative of $cf$.

*Solution for Problem 5.14:*   For both parts, we simply use the corresponding linearity properties of the derivative, namely $(F + G)' = F' + G' = f + g$ and $(cF)' = c(F') = cf$. $\square$

We can express the linearity of antidifferentiation in integral notation:

> **Important:**    If $f$ and $g$ are continuous functions and $c \in \mathbb{R}$, then
> $$\int (f + g) = \int f + \int g \quad \text{and} \quad \int cf = c \int f.$$

> **WARNING!!**   Statements "equating" indefinite integrals are only true up to a constant.

By the Fundamental Theorem, these linearity properties extend to definite integrals too:

> **Important:**    If $f$ and $g$ are continuous functions with $[a, b] \subseteq (\mathrm{Dom}(f) \cap \mathrm{Dom}(g))$, and $c \in \mathbb{R}$, then
> $$\int_a^b (f + g) = \int_a^b f + \int_a^b g \quad \text{and} \quad \int_a^b cf = c \int_a^b f.$$

## 5.3.2   Antiderivatives of common functions

We have a nice catalog of functions—polynomials, trig functions, exponentials, etc.—that we know how to differentiate. We'll try to develop a similar catalog of functions that we can antidifferentiate.

We'll start with the class of functions that we typically find easiest to deal with: polynomials.

> **Problem 5.15:**
> (a)  If $n$ is any positive integer, find $\int x^n\,dx$.
>
> (b)  Does your formula from part (a) work for $n = 0$? Why or why not?
>
> (c)  Does your formula from part (a) work for negative integers? Why or why not?

*Solution for Problem 5.15:*

(a)  We know that when we take the derivative of a monomial, the exponent decreases by 1:

$$\frac{d}{dx}x^m = mx^{m-1}.$$

Therefore, when we take the antiderivative, which is the opposite of taking the derivative, we expect the exponent to increase by 1. We start with

$$\frac{d}{dx}x^{n+1} = (n+1)x^n.$$

But we want something whose derivative is $x^n$, not $(n+1)x^n$, so we divide by $n+1$:

$$\frac{d}{dx}\frac{x^{n+1}}{n+1} = x^n.$$

Therefore,

$$\int x^n\,dx = \frac{x^{n+1}}{n+1} + C.$$

Don't forget the "$+C$"! Remember that antiderivatives are only determined up to a constant term.

(b)  Our derivative formula $(x^m)' = mx^{m-1}$ works for any integer $m$, whether positive, zero, or negative. Thus, everything that we did is valid for $n = 0$ too. Hence,

$$\int x^0\,dx = \int 1\,dx = x + C.$$

(c)  Why can't we do the same thing?

> **Bogus Solution:** Everything that we did in part (a) is valid for any integer, not just positive integers. Therefore,
>
> $$\int x^n\,dx = \frac{x^{n+1}}{n+1} + C$$
>
> for any integer $n$.

It's correct that the statement

$$\frac{d}{dx}x^{n+1} = (n+1)x^n$$

is true for any integer $n$. However, it's the last little step from our argument in part (a) that might break: dividing by $n+1$ is only valid if $n \neq -1$, since we can't divide by 0.

> **Concept:** Inadvertently dividing by 0 is one of the most common mistakes in algebra and calculus. Always be on the lookout for it.

Thus, the formula holds for every integer except $-1$.

□

> **Important:** If $n$ is any integer and $n \neq -1$, then
>
> $$\int x^n\,dx = \frac{x^{n+1}}{n+1} + C.$$

> **WARNING!!** It's easy for calculus beginners to make computational mistakes while taking the derivatives and antiderivatives of polynomials.
>
> To take the derivative of $x^n$, we *decrease* the exponent by 1, then *multiply* by the *original* exponent:
>
> $$\frac{d}{dx}x^n = nx^{n-1}.$$
>
> To take the antiderivative of $x^n$, we *increase* the exponent by 1, then *divide* by the *new* exponent:
>
> $$\int x^n\,dx = \frac{x^{n+1}}{n+1} + C.$$
>
> Make sure that you see how these two operations are the reverse of each other. Eventually, these operations will be as automatic as addition and subtraction.

This naturally leads us to wonder: what is the antiderivative of $f(x) = x^{-1} = \frac{1}{x}$? Fortunately, we know a function whose derivative is $\frac{1}{x}$. We saw this in Chapter 3:

$$\frac{d}{dx}(\log x) = \frac{1}{x}.$$

But be careful!

> **Bogus Solution:**  Therefore we conclude that
>
> $$\int \frac{1}{x}\,dx = \log x + C.$$

The problem is that $\frac{1}{x}$ is defined for all nonzero $x$, whereas $\log x$ is defined only for positive $x$. But we can fix this! Notice that

$$\frac{d}{dx}(\log(-x)) = -\frac{1}{-x} = \frac{1}{x}.$$

So for $x < 0$, the function $\log(-x)$ is an antiderivative of $\frac{1}{x}$. We can combine the $x > 0$ and $x < 0$ cases by using absolute value:

$$\int \frac{1}{x}\,dx = \log|x| + C.$$

This now makes sense for all nonzero $x$. Note that we sometimes "put the $dx$ in the numerator" and write this as $\int \frac{dx}{x} = \log|x| + C.$

> **WARNING!!** Don't forget the absolute value when taking the antiderivative of $\frac{1}{x}$.

Combining our antiderivatives of monomials with our linearity rules from Problem 5.14, we can find the antiderivative of any polynomial.

**Problem 5.16:** Find the following antiderivatives:

(a) $\int (3x^2 - 7x + 2)\, dx$

(b) $\int \left( \dfrac{4}{x^{11}} - \dfrac{2}{x^5} \right) dx$

(c) $\int (5x + 2)^3\, dx$

*Solution for Problem 5.16:*

(a) We use our formula from Problem 5.15, and the fact that antiderivatives are linear:

$$\int (3x^2 - 7x + 2)\, dx = 3 \int x^2\, dx - 7 \int x\, dx + 2 \int 1\, dx$$

$$= 3\left( \frac{x^3}{3} \right) - 7\left( \frac{x^2}{2} \right) + 2x + C$$

$$= x^3 - \frac{7}{2}x^2 + 2x + C.$$

Once you've gotten the hang of this, there's no need to write all the intermediate steps. Just do the whole thing in one step:

$$\int (3x^2 - 7x + 2)\, dx = x^3 - \frac{7}{2}x^2 + 2x + C.$$

One thing that might worry you is the constant "+C" at the end. Specifically, since we broke up our integral into 3 smaller integrals, why don't we have 3 constants? In other words, shouldn't the answer be the following:

$$\int (3x^2 - 7x + 2)\, dx = 3 \int x^2\, dx - 7 \int x\, dx + 2 \int 1\, dx$$

$$= \left[ 3\left( \frac{x^3}{3} \right) + C_1 \right] - \left[ 7\left( \frac{x^2}{2} \right) + C_2 \right] + [2x + C_3]$$

$$= x^3 - \frac{7}{2}x^2 + 2x + (C_1 + C_2 + C_3)?$$

One way to answer this is that we just say $C = C_1 + C_2 + C_3$, so we don't have to worry about it. A more thoughtful answer is that any antiderivative of $3x^2 - 7x + 2$ is going to differ from $x^3 - \frac{7}{2}x^2 + 2x$ by a constant, and we label that single constant $C$. All of this is a result of the rather sloppy notation of writing that $\int f(x)\, dx = F(x) + C$, when actually $\int f(x)\, dx$ signifies *any* function that is an antiderivative of $f(x)$, not one particular function. But the "sloppy" notation is nearly universal, so we'll stick with it.

(b) We can do the same sort of calculation with negative exponents, but extra caution is required as it is a lot easier to make computational mistakes when dealing with negative exponents:

$$\int \left( \frac{4}{x^{11}} - \frac{2}{x^5} \right) dx = 4 \int \frac{dx}{x^{11}} - 2 \int \frac{dx}{x^5}$$

$$= -4\left( \frac{1}{10x^{10}} \right) + 2\left( \frac{1}{4x^4} \right) + C$$

$$= -\frac{2}{5x^{10}} + \frac{1}{2x^4} + C.$$

Again, while you're still getting accustomed to these calculations, be extra careful with the signs and the constants. You might find it easier to rewrite the original integral in terms of negative exponents before

145

proceeding with computing the antiderivatives:

$$\int \left( \frac{4}{x^{11}} - \frac{2}{x^5} \right) dx = \int (4x^{-11} - 2x^{-5}) \, dx.$$

Once you've become more comfortable with antidifferentiation, you'll be able to do the whole thing in one line without writing the intermediate steps:

$$\int \left( \frac{4}{x^{11}} - \frac{2}{x^5} \right) dx = -\frac{4}{10x^{10}} + \frac{2}{4x^4} + C = -\frac{2}{5x^{10}} + \frac{1}{2x^4} + C.$$

(c) Just as with the corresponding derivative calculation, it's tempting to take the following "shortcut":

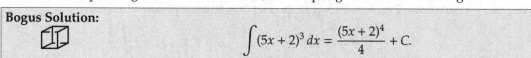

**Bogus Solution:**

$$\int (5x + 2)^3 \, dx = \frac{(5x + 2)^4}{4} + C.$$

We can see the error of our ways by reversing the process—that is, by taking the derivative. Of course, doing so requires using the Chain Rule.

$$\frac{d}{dx} \frac{(5x + 2)^4}{4} = 4 \left( \frac{(5x + 2)^3}{4} \right) \left( \frac{d}{dx}(5x + 2) \right) = 5(5x + 2)^3.$$

So we're off by a factor of 5. Indeed, what we've just shown is that

$$\int 5(5x + 2)^3 \, dx = \frac{(5x + 2)^4}{4} + C,$$

and therefore, dividing by 5 gives our answer:

$$\int (5x + 2)^3 \, dx = \frac{(5x + 2)^4}{20} + C.$$

As you might suspect, this leads us to a Chain Rule for antiderivatives; we'll see this in the next subsection.

$\square$

Let's continue building our catalog of antiderivatives of common functions. By now, we should be very comfortable using trigonometric and exponential functions, and we know their derivatives, so we should be able to find their antiderivatives too.

**Problem 5.17:**
(a) Find $\int \sin x \, dx$ and $\int \cos x \, dx$.

(b) Find $\int e^x \, dx$.

*Solution for Problem 5.17:*

(a) Since we know that

$$\frac{d}{dx} \sin x = \cos x \qquad \text{and} \qquad \frac{d}{dx} \cos x = -\sin x,$$

we immediately see that

$$\int \cos x \, dx = \sin x + C \qquad \text{and} \qquad \int \sin x \, dx = -\cos x + C.$$

**WARNING!!** Be very careful about the signs in the above formulas!

(b)  Since $e^x$ is the derivative of $e^x$, it is also an antiderivative of $e^x$. In other words,

$$\int e^x \, dx = e^x + C.$$

$\square$

### 5.3.3  The Chain Rule

With differentiation, we've got it pretty easy. Using our catalog of basic functions, such as polynomials, trig functions, and exponentials, together with some basic rules such as the Product and Quotient Rules, the Chain Rule, and the Inverse Function Rule, we can take the derivative of pretty much any "nice" function that we're likely to encounter.

With antidifferentiation, however, we're going to have to work up a little bit of a sweat. Antidifferentiation is straightforward for really simple functions like polynomials, basic trig functions, and exponentials, but once we start getting away from the basics, we quickly find that antidifferentiation is a *lot* harder than differentiation. There are some general techniques that we can use, but as you'll discover as you work through the progressively-harder examples in this section, antidifferentiation is a bit of an art form, and requires lots of practice.

> **Sidenote:** Every January, the Massachusetts Institute of Technology holds its annual **Integration Bee**, where MIT students compete against the clock and each other to quickly and accurately evaluate integrals. The winner is crowned **Grand Integrator**.

Recall that, in Chapter 3, we learned the Chain Rule for taking derivatives. We can use the Chain Rule in reverse to compute many antiderivatives, such as the following:

**Problem 5.18:** Compute $\int (12x)(2x^2 + 1)^2 \, dx$.

*Solution for Problem 5.18:* We have

$$\frac{d}{dx}(2x^2 + 1)^3 = 3(2x^2 + 1)^2 \cdot \frac{d}{dx}(2x^2 + 1) = 3(2x^2 + 1)^2(4x) = (12x)(2x^2 + 1)^2.$$

Thus $\int (12x)(2x^2 + 1)^2 \, dx = (2x^2 + 1)^3 + C.$ $\square$

Our goal is to develop a systematic way to apply the Chain Rule in reverse. That is, if we start with a function like $(12x)(2x^2 + 1)^2$, how do we "undo" the Chain Rule in order to compute $\int (12x)(2x^2 + 1)^2 \, dx$?

To see how we do this for antiderivatives, we go back and think about what the Chain Rule really means. One way that we wrote the Chain Rule was:

$$\frac{df}{dx} = \frac{df}{du} \cdot \frac{du}{dx}.$$

For example, if $f(x) = (2x^2 + 1)^3$ as in Problem 5.18, then we can set $u = 2x^2 + 1$. We then write $f(u) = u^3$, so that $\frac{df}{du} = 3u^2$. Also we have $\frac{du}{dx} = \frac{d}{dx}(2x^2 + 1) = 4x$. When we put all this together, we get

$$\frac{df}{dx} = \frac{df}{du} \cdot \frac{du}{dx} = 3u^2 \cdot 4x = 3(2x^2 + 1)^2 \cdot 4x = (12x)(2x^2 + 1)^2.$$

Of course, by now you've probably internalized this procedure so that you don't explicitly write the "$u$" step—you just go straight to the result $\frac{df}{dx}$, as we did above when we first presented this example. However, when we try to apply the Chain Rule "in reverse" to compute an antiderivative, as we're about to see, we'll usually be explicit about denoting what $u$ is in our Chain Rule calculation.

Let's now look at our example from Problem 5.18:

$$\int (12x)(2x^2 + 1)^2 \, dx$$

We will make a clever substitution so that we can use the Chain Rule in reverse. We substitute $u = 2x^2 + 1$. If we just did this alone, and nothing else, we'd have

$$\int (12x)u^2 \, dx.$$

That's not too good—this integral is an ugly mix of $x$ and $u$. So not only do we need to substitute $u$, we also need to substitute for the derivative of $u$. Specifically, we have

$$\frac{du}{dx} = \frac{d}{dx}(2x^2 + 1) = 4x,$$

so our integral becomes

$$\int (12x)u^2 \, dx = \int 3u^2 \left( \frac{du}{dx} \right) dx.$$

We now have the terms from the Chain Rule explicitly shown in our integral, since

$$\frac{d}{dx}(u^3) = 3u^2 \left( \frac{du}{dx} \right),$$

so our integral is

$$\int (12x)u^2 \, dx = \int 3u^2 \left( \frac{du}{dx} \right) dx = \int \frac{d}{dx}(u^3) \, dx = u^3 + C,$$

where the final step is simply applying the Fundamental Theorem of Calculus.

We have a notational shortcut that is often used for this sort of Chain Rule calculation. Starting with $\frac{du}{dx} = 4x$, we "multiply by $dx$" and get $du = 4x \, dx$. When we make this substitution in our integral, we're left with

$$\int 3u^2 \, du.$$

Note that $du$ is notational shorthand for $\frac{du}{dx} \, dx$. Now it is clear that the antiderivative is just $u^3 + C$.

But we don't want our final answer in terms of $u$—we want it in terms of $x$, our original variable. When we undo the substitution, we have our final answer of $(2x^2 + 1)^3 + C$.

More generally, we can use the Chain Rule for antiderivatives whenever we have an integral of the form

$$\int g(f(x))f'(x) \, dx.$$

We then make the substitutions $u = f(x)$ and $du = f'(x) \, dx$ to get a simpler integral of the form

$$\int g(u) \, du.$$

We take the antiderivative of this integral to get a function $G(u) + C$, and finally we rewrite it in terms of $x$ to get our final answer $G(f(x)) + C$. Note that reversing all of these steps gives us our usual Chain Rule for derivatives.

> **Concept:**  The Chain Rule for antiderivatives—although a bit more cumbersome to use than the Chain Rule for derivatives—is really nothing new! It's just the Chain Rule for derivatives in reverse.

The tricky part is recognizing when our function is of the form $g(f(x))f'(x)$. This can be hard in practice and is part of the reason why computing antiderivatives is so much more difficult than computing derivatives.

Let's see the Chain Rule at work in a few problems.

> **Problem 5.19:** Compute $\int x \sqrt{3x^2 - 1}\, dx$.

*Solution for Problem 5.19:* Usually when trying to apply the Chain Rule to an antiderivative, we look for the "ugly" expression in the integral. In this case, the ugly expression is $\sqrt{3x^2 - 1}$. So our guess is to try $u = 3x^2 - 1$. Note that we don't set $u$ to be the *entire* ugly expression; rather, we set $u$ to be something that's *inside* our ugly expression.

Now we have to get lucky. We need to have $du$ appear somewhere in the integral. In this problem, $du = 6x\, dx$, and sure enough, there's an $x$ term sitting in there, so we multiply and divide by 6 to get

$$\int \frac{1}{6}(6x) \sqrt{3x^2 - 1}\, dx.$$

Then, after making the substitutions $u = 3x^2 - 1$ and $du = 6x\, dx$, our integral becomes

$$\int \frac{1}{6} \sqrt{u}\, du.$$

Don't overlook the factor of $\frac{1}{6}$ that we had to throw in there. We have $du = 6x\, dx$, but we only had $x\, dx$ in the integral, so $x\, dx = \frac{1}{6} du$.

An alternative method of making the substitution is to start with our original integral

$$\int x \sqrt{3x^2 - 1}\, dx$$

and then make the substitution $u = 3x^2 - 1$, but then take our $du = 6x\, dx$ expression and "solve for $dx$" to get $dx = \dfrac{du}{6x}$. We then substitute into the integral to get

$$\int x \sqrt{u}\, \frac{du}{6x},$$

from which the $x$'s cancel and leave

$$\int \frac{1}{6} \sqrt{u}\, du.$$

This method looks a bit uglier, because of the intermediate step of $\int x \sqrt{u}\, \frac{du}{6x}$, which is a nasty mix of $x$'s and $u$'s. But happily the $x$'s cancel, which we *must* have happen in order for this method to work.

Using either method, we are left with an indefinite integral in terms of $u$ that we can evaluate:

$$\int \frac{1}{6} \sqrt{u}\, du = \frac{1}{6} \int u^{\frac{1}{2}}\, du = \frac{1}{6}\left(\frac{u^{\frac{3}{2}}}{\frac{3}{2}}\right) + C = \frac{1}{9} u^{\frac{3}{2}} + C.$$

To finish, we put everything back in terms of $x$:

$$\frac{1}{9} u^{\frac{3}{2}} + C = \frac{1}{9}(3x^2 - 1)^{\frac{3}{2}} + C.$$

As a check, you can take the derivative of this last expression and verify that it is equal to the integrand of the integral that we started with. □

> **Concept:**  The general strategy for using the Chain Rule is to look for an expression inside the integral to set equal to $u$. However, we must also be able to find the expression for $du$ in the integral as well. After substituting for $u$, and replacing the corresponding $dx$ expression with $du$, we must have an integral that is entirely in terms of $u$ with no $x$ terms remaining.

> **WARNING!!** The most common mistake is not correctly converting from $dx$ to $du$. We cannot just replace $dx$ with $du$—we must solve for $du$ in terms of $dx$, or vice versa, and substitute accordingly.

**Problem 5.20:** Compute $\displaystyle\int \frac{x-3}{2x^2 - 12x}\, dx$.

*Solution for Problem 5.20:* The denominator is the more complicated expression. So we'll try $u = 2x^2 - 12x$. This gives $du = (4x - 12)\, dx$, so the numerator $(x - 3)\, dx$ is $du/4$. Therefore, the integral is:

$$\int \frac{x-3}{2x^2 - 12x}\, dx = \int \frac{1}{4u}\, du.$$

This antiderivative is

$$\frac{1}{4} \log |u| + C = \frac{1}{4} \log |2x^2 - 12x| + C.$$

□

**Problem 5.21:**

(a) Compute $\displaystyle\int e^{3x}\, dx$.

(b) Compute $\displaystyle\int xe^{x^2}\, dx$.

(c) Compute $\displaystyle\int (e^x + 1)^3\, dx$.

*Solution for Problem 5.21:*

(a) Usually with exponentials, we'll try setting $u$ to be the quantity in the exponent, because we know how to integrate $e^u$. So for part (a), we let $u = 3x$ and $du = 3\, dx$. Then the integral becomes

$$\int e^{3x}\, dx = \int \frac{1}{3} e^u\, du.$$

The antiderivative is just $\frac{1}{3} e^u + C = \frac{1}{3} e^{3x} + C$. We can immediately see that this is correct, since $\dfrac{d}{dx} \dfrac{1}{3} e^{3x} = e^{3x}$.

> **Concept:** Setting $u = cx$ for some constant $c$ is a simple application of the Chain Rule. This will produce $du = c\, dx$, so the effect of substituting $u$ for $cx$ is to divide the integral by $c$. This application of the Chain Rule is so common that you will probably end up internalizing it and not need to write $du$ out explicitly.

(b)  The $x^2$ in the exponent is hard to deal with, so we let $u = x^2$. This makes $du = 2x\,dx$, and we're in good shape since we have an $x$ term out front. We get

$$\int xe^{x^2}\,dx = \int \frac{1}{2}e^u\,du = \frac{1}{2}e^u + C = \frac{1}{2}e^{x^2} + C.$$

(c)  This is more tricky. We might try $u = e^x + 1$, but then $du = e^x\,dx$, and we don't have an "extra" $e^x$ term to combine with $dx$ and create $du$. So we can't just apply the Chain Rule naively. However, our problems go away simply by expanding the cubic:

$$\int (e^x + 1)^3\,dx = \int (e^{3x} + 3e^{2x} + 3e^x + 1)\,dx = \frac{1}{3}e^{3x} + \frac{3}{2}e^{2x} + 3e^x + x + C.$$

> **Concept:**  Don't be afraid to do some algebra to make antiderivatives easier to evaluate.

□

We have to be especially careful when we evaluate a definite integral using a substitution:

> **Problem 5.22:**  Compute $\displaystyle\int_1^2 xe^{x^2}\,dx$.

*Solution for Problem 5.22:* To get the antiderivative, we use the substitution $u = x^2$, so $du = 2x\,dx$. But this is where we have to be careful:

> **Bogus Solution:**
> $$\int_1^2 xe^{x^2}\,dx = \int_1^2 \frac{1}{2}e^u\,du.$$

This is not correct, because the new limits of integration need to be in terms of $u$, not $x$, since our integral is now in terms of $u$. We have two methods by which to proceed.

*Method 1: Find the antiderivative in terms of x.* We compute the antiderivative of $xe^{x^2}$ in terms of $x$ in the usual way:

$$\int xe^{x^2}\,dx = \frac{1}{2}\int e^u\,du = \frac{1}{2}e^u + C = \frac{1}{2}e^{x^2} + C.$$

We then use this antiderivative to compute the definite integral:

$$\int_1^2 xe^{x^2}\,dx = \frac{1}{2}e^{x^2}\Big|_1^2 = \frac{1}{2}(e^4 - e).$$

*Method 2: Change the limits of the definite integral to be in terms of u.* We can change the interval on which we are computing the definite integral, from an interval on $x$ to an interval on $u$. We see that when $x = 1$, we have $u = x^2 = 1$, and when $x = 2$, we have $u = x^2 = 4$. Thus,

$$\int_1^2 xe^{x^2}\,dx = \int_1^4 \frac{1}{2}e^u\,du.$$

We now finish the computation doing everything in terms of $u$. This gives

$$\int_1^4 \frac{1}{2}e^u\,du = \frac{1}{2}e^u\Big|_1^4 = \frac{1}{2}(e^4 - e).$$

□

The second method in the above solution is usually easier, since we can then skip the step of converting the antiderivative back in terms of the original variable.

> **Important:** When we do a substitution of variables in a definite integral, we also need to be careful that the limits of integration are in terms of the correct variable.

The Chain Rule is also useful with trigonometric antiderivatives:

---

**Problem 5.23:**

(a) Compute $\int \cos 3\theta \, d\theta$.

(b) Compute $\int \sin^3 \theta \cos \theta \, d\theta$.

(c) Compute $\int \sin^2 \theta \cos^2 \theta \, d\theta$.

---

*Solution for Problem 5.23:*

(a) Once again, the simple substitution $u = c\theta$ is the key. In this case, we substitute $u = 3\theta$ and $du = 3 \, d\theta$, and we get:

$$\int \cos 3\theta \, d\theta = \int \frac{1}{3} \cos u \, du = \frac{1}{3} \sin u + C = \frac{1}{3} \sin 3\theta + C.$$

We can quickly check that $\frac{d}{d\theta} \frac{1}{3} \sin 3\theta = \cos 3\theta$, as required.

(b) We don't know how to integrate $\sin^3$. But we do know how to integrate $u^3$. So let's try $u = \sin \theta$. Then $du = \cos \theta \, d\theta$, and we have:

$$\int \sin^3 \theta \cos \theta \, d\theta = \int u^3 \, du = \frac{1}{4}u^4 + C = \frac{1}{4} \sin^4 \theta + C.$$

(c) Why doesn't this work:

> **Bogus Solution:** Let $u = \sin \theta$. Then $du = \cos \theta \, d\theta$ and we have $\int u^2 \, du = \frac{1}{3}u^3 + C = \frac{1}{3} \sin^3 \theta + C$.

The problem is that we have $\cos^2 \theta$ in our original integral, but $du$ only has a single factor of $\cos \theta$.

So instead we'll try some algebraic manipulation. We can write

$$\sin^2 \theta \cos^2 \theta = (\sin \theta \cos \theta)^2$$
$$= \left(\frac{1}{2} \sin(2\theta)\right)^2$$
$$= \frac{1}{4} \sin^2(2\theta).$$

Then, we have

$$\int \sin^2 \theta \cos^2 \theta \, d\theta = \frac{1}{4} \int \sin^2 2\theta \, d\theta.$$

That's still not good enough, because we don't know how to integrate $\sin^2$. We have to do more trig manipulation to reduce the number of powers of trig functions, by noting that $\cos 2x = 1 - 2\sin^2 x$. So

$\sin^2 x = \frac{1}{2}(1 - \cos 2x)$, and thus we have

$$\frac{1}{4} \int \sin^2 2\theta \, d\theta = \frac{1}{8} \int (1 - \cos 4\theta) \, d\theta.$$

Now we can integrate:

$$\frac{1}{8} \int (1 - \cos 4\theta) \, d\theta = \frac{1}{8} \left( \theta - \frac{1}{4} \sin 4\theta \right) + C = \frac{1}{8} \theta - \frac{1}{32} \sin 4\theta + C.$$

□

### 5.3.4 Integration by parts

We recall the Product Rule for derivatives:

$$(fg)' = fg' + f'g.$$

This may lead us to wonder if there is a similar product rule for antiderivatives. The answer is "sort of," as we can see in the following example:

**Problem 5.24:** Compute $\int xe^x \, dx$.

*Solution for Problem 5.24:* We can't do much with this using the techniques that we already have. Letting $u = x$ or $u = e^x$ doesn't help at all. But noticing that we have a product gives us an idea.

We know that

$$(xe^x)' = x(e^x)' + (x)'e^x = xe^x + e^x.$$

Rearranging, we have

$$xe^x = (xe^x)' - e^x.$$

Now we can take the antiderivative of both sides:

$$\int xe^x \, dx = \int ((xe^x)' - e^x) \, dx = \int (xe^x)' \, dx - \int e^x \, dx = xe^x - e^x + C.$$

In the last step, notice that we used the "trivial" antidifferentiation rule $\int f' = f + C$. □

"Undoing the Product Rule" as in Problem 5.24 is the general idea of the technique called **integration by parts**. Suppose that we want to find the antiderivative of something of the form $uv'$, where $u$ and $v$ are functions. We can write out the product rule for the derivative of $uv$:

$$(uv)' = uv' + u'v.$$

Solving for $uv'$ gives

$$uv' = (uv)' - u'v.$$

So the antiderivative of $uv'$ is just the antiderivative of $(uv)' - u'v$. That is,

$$\int uv' \, dx = \int ((uv)' - u'v) \, dx = uv - \int u'v \, dx.$$

Typically, we write the above equation using our usual notational shortcuts $du = u' \, dx$ and $dv = v' \, dx$, giving:

> **Important:** **Integration By Parts**
>
> $$\int u\,dv = uv - \int v\,du$$

Let's revisit Problem 5.24 using this new notation. We set $u = x$ and $dv = e^x\,dx$. Then $du = dx$ (the derivative of $u$) and $v = e^x$ (the antiderivative of $dv$). Thus, our integration by parts formula is

$$\int xe^x\,dx = xe^x - \int e^x\,dx.$$

The advantage of this is that we know how to compute the antiderivative on the far right: it's just $e^x + C$. Therefore, $\int xe^x\,dx = xe^x - e^x + C = (x-1)e^x + C$.

This is the general strategy for applying integration by parts: if we have an integral that is difficult to evaluate, but which has a *part* (denoted by $dv$) that is easier to integrate, then we can try applying integration by parts. This is especially useful if the other part of the integral—the $u$ part—has a simple derivative. Keep this general strategy in the back of your mind as we work through the following examples.

> **Problem 5.25:**
>
> (a) Compute $\int x \sin x\,dx$.
>
> (b) Compute $\int x^2 e^x\,dx$.

*Solution for Problem 5.25:*

(a) Often, a tricky step in using integration by parts is deciding which part should be $u$ and which part should be $dv$. If we make the wrong choice, we can make things worse:

> **Bogus Solution:** Let $u = \sin x$ and $dv = x\,dx$. Then $du = \cos x\,dx$ and $v = \frac{1}{2}x^2$, and integration by parts gives us:
>
> $$\int x \sin x\,dx = \frac{1}{2}x^2 \sin x - \int \frac{1}{2}x^2 \cos x\,dx.$$

Although our calculation above is correct, we see that we've made our integral more complicated, because now we have to integrate a quadratic term times a trigonometric function. That's because we picked the parts incorrectly.

> **Concept:** Try to pick $u$ and $dv$ so that $du$ and $v$ are simpler, if possible. This usually means we don't want to pick polynomial terms to be in $dv$, since their antiderivatives are more complicated.

In our problem, we should set $u = x$ and $dv = \sin x\,dx$. Then $du = dx$ and $v = -\cos x$, and our integration by parts formula gives us:

$$\int x \sin x\,dx = -x\cos x - \int(-\cos x)\,dx = -x\cos x + \sin x + C.$$

(b) We set $u = x^2$ (so that $du = 2x\,dx$) and $dv = e^x\,dx$ (so that $v = e^x$). Then integration by parts gives us:

$$\int x^2 e^x\,dx = x^2 e^x - \int 2xe^x\,dx.$$

We know how to do the latter integral: it's integration by parts again! We let $u = 2x$ and $dv = e^x \, dx$, so that $du = 2 \, dx$ and $v = e^x$. Thus, the entire computation is

$$\int x^2 e^x \, dx = x^2 e^x - \int 2x e^x \, dx$$

$$= x^2 e^x - \left( 2x e^x - \int 2 e^x \, dx \right)$$

$$= x^2 e^x - 2x e^x + 2 e^x + C$$

$$= (x^2 - 2x + 2) e^x + C.$$

□

Let's again revisit Problem 5.24, but this time let's make it a definite integral and see how that works:

**Problem 5.26:**  Compute $\int_0^2 x e^x \, dx$.

*Solution for Problem 5.26:*  As before, we apply integration by parts by letting $u = x$ (so that $du = dx$) and $dv = e^x \, dx$ (so that $v = e^x$). Then integration by parts gives

$$\int_0^2 x e^x \, dx = x e^x \Big|_0^2 - \int_0^2 e^x \, dx.$$

Notice that the $uv$ term must now be evaluated at the limits of integration. We continue:

$$\int_0^2 x e^x \, dx = x e^x \Big|_0^2 - \int_0^2 e^x \, dx$$

$$= (2e^2 - 0e^0) - e^x \Big|_0^2$$

$$= 2e^2 - (e^2 - e^0)$$

$$= e^2 + 1.$$

□

**Problem 5.27:**  Compute $\int e^x \sin x \, dx$.

*Solution for Problem 5.27:*  It's not clear which part we should set equal to $u$ and which part to $dv$: they both have "easy" derivatives and antiderivatives. So let's just try one and see what happens.

If we set $u = e^x$ (so that $du = e^x \, dx$) and $dv = \sin x \, dx$ (so that $v = -\cos x$), then we have

$$\int e^x \sin x \, dx = -e^x \cos x + \int e^x \cos x \, dx.$$

This doesn't seem all that helpful, since we still have an integral that we don't know how to compute. But it's very similar to the integral that we started with. So let's try integration by parts again. Let $u = e^x$ and $dv = \cos x \, dx$; then $du = e^x \, dx$ and $v = \sin x$, so we have

$$\int e^x \sin x \, dx = -e^x \cos x + \int e^x \cos x \, dx = -e^x \cos x + \left( e^x \sin x - \int e^x \sin x \, dx \right) = e^x(\sin x - \cos x) - \int e^x \sin x \, dx.$$

We seem to be back where we started, with $\int e^x \sin x \, dx$ on the right side. Are we stuck?

No! If we move the integral on the right side over to the left side, we have

$$2 \int e^x \sin x \, dx = e^x(\sin x - \cos x),$$

and hence, dividing by 2, we have our answer:

$$\int e^x \sin x \, dx = \frac{e^x(\sin x - \cos x)}{2} + C.$$

(Note the $C$ that we add at the end.) □

Integration by parts also lets us compute the antiderivative of a "simple" function:

**Problem 5.28:** Compute $\int \log x \, dx$.

*Solution for Problem 5.28:* This integral seems a little hard to grasp. What are the "parts"? There seems to just be one term: $\log x$. So what can we set to be $u$ and $dv$? We don't seem to have much choice for $u$: since we don't know how to integrate $\log x$, we have little choice but to set $u = \log x$, so that $du = \frac{1}{x} \, dx$. What does that leave for $dv$? All that's left in the integral is $dx$, so we set $dv = dx$. This makes $v = x$, and our integration by parts calculation gives us:

$$\int \log x \, dx = x \log x - \int x \left( \frac{1}{x} \right) dx$$
$$= x \log x - \int 1 \, dx$$
$$= x \log x - x + C.$$

As a check, note that

$$\frac{d}{dx}(x \log x - x) = x \left( \frac{1}{x} \right) + 1(\log x) - 1 = 1 + \log x - 1 = \log x.$$

□

> **Concept:** Integration by parts is nothing more than a rearranged version of the Product Rule for derivatives. If you can remember
>
> $$(uv)' = uv' + u'v,$$
>
> you can just rearrange it to
> $$uv' = (uv)' - u'v$$
> and then integrate this formula to get
>
> $$\int u \, dv = uv - \int v \, du.$$

## 5.3.5 Substitution methods

The Chain Rule is one example of a **substitution method** for evaluating antiderivatives. There are other more sophisticated sorts of substitutions that we can make that let us evaluate more difficult integrals. All of the substitutions follow the same basic rule:

**Important:** If we substitute for $x$ in $\int f(x)\,dx$, then we have to substitute for $dx$ too.

The methods that we will discuss in this subsection are essentially "backwards" versions of the Chain Rule substitutions that we studied earlier. Before, we would take an integral of the form

$$\int g(f(x))f'(x)\,dx$$

and make the substitutions $u = f(x)$ and $du = f'(x)\,dx$ to get an integral of the form

$$\int g(u)\,du.$$

However, now we are going to consider substitutions in the other direction. Specifically, we'll start with an integral of the form

$$\int g(x)\,dx$$

and make a substitution of the form $x = f(u)$. This gives $dx = f'(u)\,du$, so after substitution, our integral becomes

$$\int g(f(u))f'(u)\,du.$$

This seems strange—it looks like we've made our integral a lot more complicated! But for the right type of function, this sort of substitution actually makes things work out nicely.

Let's see some examples. Our first example is a substitution that might seem quite surprising!

**Problem 5.29:** Compute $\displaystyle\int \frac{1}{\sqrt{1-x^2}}\,dx$.

*Solution for Problem 5.29:* We don't have any good way to deal with that ugly denominator. But the expression $\sqrt{1-x^2}$ may remind us of the unit circle, and the unit circle should remind us of trig functions. So we try the substitution $x = \sin\theta$. We note that this substitution makes sense, because the function that we're integrating is only defined for $-1 < x < 1$, and $\sin\theta$ contains the interval $(-1,1)$ in its range.

This means that $dx = \cos\theta\,d\theta$, so we have

$$\int \frac{1}{\sqrt{1-x^2}}\,dx = \int \frac{\cos\theta}{\sqrt{1-\sin^2\theta}}\,d\theta.$$

Note that the $\cos\theta$ term in the numerator comes from the conversion of $dx$ to $d\theta$.

Now the denominator simplifies nicely! We have

$$\sqrt{1-\sin^2\theta} = \sqrt{\cos^2\theta} = |\cos\theta|,$$

so our integral becomes

$$\int \frac{\cos\theta}{|\cos\theta|}\,d\theta.$$

This looks very nice except for that annoying absolute value sign. Perhaps we can make it go away....

We can! Notice that in the substitution $x = \sin\theta$, we can restrict to $\theta \in \left(-\frac{\pi}{2}, \frac{\pi}{2}\right)$ and we get $x \in (-1, 1)$. But on the interval $\left(-\frac{\pi}{2}, \frac{\pi}{2}\right)$, the cosine function is strictly positive. So we can replace $|\cos\theta|$ with just $\cos\theta$. Hence, our integral is simply

$$\int \frac{\cos\theta}{\cos\theta}\, d\theta = \int 1\, d\theta = \theta + C.$$

But we don't want the final answer in terms of $\theta$, so we make the reverse substitution $\theta = \arcsin x$, to get the final answer of

$$\int \frac{1}{\sqrt{1-x^2}}\, dx = \arcsin x + C.$$

Again, note that the domain of arcsin is $(-1, 1)$ and its range is $\left(-\frac{\pi}{2}, \frac{\pi}{2}\right)$, so all of our substitutions are consistent. □

But wait a minute. What if we had instead made the substitution $x = \cos\theta$ over the interval $\theta \in (0, \pi)$? Then we'd have $dx = -\sin\theta\, d\theta$, and the integral becomes:

$$\int \frac{1}{\sqrt{1-x^2}}\, dx = \int -\frac{\sin\theta}{\sqrt{1-\cos^2\theta}}\, d\theta$$

$$= \int -\frac{\sin\theta}{\sin\theta}\, d\theta$$

$$= \int (-1)\, d\theta$$

$$= -\theta + C = -\arccos x + C.$$

How can this be? Is the integral equal to *both* $\arcsin x$ and $-\arccos x$? It can't possibly be, since any two antiderivatives must differ by a constant, right?

There's no problem, because $\arcsin x$ and $-\arccos x$ *do* differ by a constant! Recall that $\sin(\frac{\pi}{2} - \theta) = \cos\theta$. This implies that $\arcsin x = \frac{\pi}{2} - \arccos x$ for any $-1 \le x \le 1$. (Note that there are also some issues with the ranges of arcsin and arccos, but these also amount to merely adding or subtracting a constant.)

In general, we can use substitutions—trigonometric or otherwise—to make "ugly" terms in integrals come out nicer. A common use is as in the last problem: when we have a term of the form $1 - x^2$, especially $\sqrt{1-x^2}$, we use $x = \sin\theta$ or $x = \cos\theta$ so that we can apply the trigonometric identity $\sin^2\theta + \cos^2\theta = 1$.

We'll reiterate a subtle point about this substitution: we can only make the substitution $x = \sin\theta$ if $x$ only takes on values between $-1$ and $1$, because those are the only values in the range of $\sin\theta$. But when we make a substitution for $x$ in $\sqrt{1-x^2}$, we must have $1 - x^2 \ge 0$ (in order to take the square root), so we must have $x^2 \le 1$, giving $-1 \le x \le 1$, which makes the trig substitution valid.

The next problem is similar and also quite important:

**Problem 5.30:** Compute $\displaystyle\int_0^1 \frac{1}{1+x^2}\, dx$.

*Solution for Problem 5.30:* This is very similar to Problem 5.29, except we have $1 + x^2$ in the denominator instead of $\sqrt{1-x^2}$. One thing to note is that the domain of $x$ is all of $\mathbb{R}$, so we know that we can't make the substitution $x = \sin\theta$ (since that only takes values between $-1$ and $1$). Fortunately, we do know a trig function that has a range of all the reals: tangent.

We let $x = \tan\theta$. Then $dx = \sec^2\theta\, d\theta$, and we have

$$\int \frac{1}{1+x^2}\, dx = \int \frac{\sec^2\theta}{1+\tan^2\theta}\, d\theta.$$

This may look ugly, but actually we're in great shape. We use the identity $1 + \tan^2 \theta = \sec^2 \theta$, so our integral becomes

$$\int \frac{\sec^2 \theta}{1 + \tan^2 \theta} \, d\theta = \int 1 \, d\theta = \theta + C.$$

As always, we want to put this back in terms of $x = \tan \theta$. This means that $\theta = \arctan x$, and we have

$$\int \frac{1}{1 + x^2} \, dx = \arctan x + C.$$

Finally, we compute the definite integral:

$$\int_0^1 \frac{1}{1 + x^2} \, dx = \left. \arctan x \right|_0^1 = \tan^{-1} 1 - \tan^{-1} 0 = \frac{\pi}{4}.$$

Note that we could have also written the entire calculation, including the substitution, in terms of a definite integral, as follows:

$$\int_0^1 \frac{1}{1 + x^2} \, dx = \int_0^{\pi/4} \frac{\sec^2 \theta}{1 + \tan^2 \theta} \, d\theta = \int_0^{\pi/4} d\theta = \frac{\pi}{4}.$$

□

The integrals in the previous two problems are fairly common; you should learn them.

> **Important:**
>
> $$\int \frac{1}{\sqrt{1 - x^2}} \, dx = \arcsin x + C,$$
>
> $$\int \frac{1}{1 + x^2} \, dx = \arctan x + C.$$

> **Concept:** More generally, whenever we see a term of the form $1 \pm x^2$, we can consider using a trigonometric substitution.

Here's a more complicated example of this:

**Problem 5.31:** Compute $\int x^3 \sqrt{1 - x^2} \, dx$.

*Solution for Problem 5.31:* We have a $\sqrt{1 - x^2}$ term, so we think to use the trig substitution $x = \sin \theta$. This gives $dx = \cos \theta \, d\theta$, so the integral becomes

$$\int x^3 \sqrt{1 - x^2} \, dx = \int \sin^3 \theta \sqrt{1 - \sin^2 \theta} \cos \theta \, d\theta = \int \sin^3 \theta \cos^2 \theta \, d\theta.$$

There are a number of ways to continue from here. One method is to use the identity $\sin^2 \theta = 1 - \cos^2 \theta$ on two of the sine factors, giving

$$\int \sin^3 \theta \cos^2 \theta \, d\theta = \int (\cos^2 \theta - \cos^4 \theta) \sin \theta \, d\theta.$$

Now we can make the substitution $u = \cos \theta$ and $du = -\sin \theta \, d\theta$, giving us

$$\int (\cos^2 \theta - \cos^4 \theta) \sin \theta \, d\theta = \int -(u^2 - u^4) \, du = \int (u^4 - u^2) \, du = \frac{1}{5} u^5 - \frac{1}{3} u^3 + C.$$

Finally, we use the fact that $u = \cos \theta = \sqrt{1 - \sin^2 \theta} = \sqrt{1 - x^2}$, giving the solution:

$$\int x^3 \sqrt{1 - x^2} \, dx = \frac{1}{5}(1 - x^2)^{\frac{5}{2}} - \frac{1}{3}(1 - x^2)^{\frac{3}{2}} + C.$$

Alternatively, noting that we had $u = \sqrt{1 - x^2}$ at the end of our calculation above, we could have made this substitution to begin with. Then $u^2 = 1 - x^2$, so $2u \, du = -2x \, dx$, hence $-u \, du = x \, dx$, and we have

$$\int x^3 \sqrt{1 - x^2} \, dx = \int (1 - u^2) u(-u) \, du = \int (u^4 - u^2) \, du = \frac{1}{5}u^5 - \frac{1}{3}u^3 + C = \frac{1}{5}(1 - x^2)^{\frac{5}{2}} - \frac{1}{3}(1 - x^2)^{\frac{3}{2}} + C.$$

$\square$

Although trig substitution is by far the most commonly used substitution method, some functions can be integrated with an unusual substitution, such as the following example:

**Problem 5.32:** Compute $\displaystyle\int \frac{e^{2x}}{\sqrt{1 + e^x}} \, dx$.

*Solution for Problem 5.32:* There's no obvious way to attack this integral. Substituting $u = e^x$ might work. This gives $du = e^x \, dx$, and we have

$$\int \frac{e^{2x}}{\sqrt{1 + e^x}} \, dx = \int \frac{u}{\sqrt{1 + u}} \, du.$$

Now we can evaluate this by parts. We let $u = u$ (convenient!) and $dv = (1 + u)^{-\frac{1}{2}} du$, so that $v = 2(1 + u)^{\frac{1}{2}}$. This gives us

$$\int \frac{u}{\sqrt{1 + u}} \, du = 2u \sqrt{1 + u} - 2 \int \sqrt{1 + u} \, du$$

$$= 2u \sqrt{1 + u} - \frac{4}{3}(1 + u)^{\frac{3}{2}} + C.$$

To finish, we replace $u = e^x$ to get

$$\int \frac{e^{2x}}{\sqrt{1 + e^x}} \, dx = 2e^x(1 + e^x)^{\frac{1}{2}} - \frac{4}{3}(1 + e^x)^{\frac{3}{2}} + C.$$

Alternatively, we could use a more creative substitution on the original integral. Let's get rid of the whole messy denominator at once, by making the substitution $u = \sqrt{1 + e^x}$. Now we need to convert $e^{2x} \, dx$ into something in terms of $u$. To isolate $e^{2x}$, we "solve" our substitution:

$$u = \sqrt{1 + e^x} \quad \Rightarrow \quad e^x = u^2 - 1.$$

Thus, the numerator of our integral will become $(u^2 - 1)^2$.

We also need to convert $dx$ into something involving $du$. We continue solving for $x$, so that we can compute $dx$:

$$e^x = u^2 - 1 \quad \Rightarrow \quad x = \log(u^2 - 1) \quad \Rightarrow \quad dx = \frac{2u}{u^2 - 1} \, du.$$

Now we can write our integral in terms of $u$:

$$\int \frac{e^{2x}}{\sqrt{1 + e^x}} \, dx = \int \frac{(u^2 - 1)^2}{u} \frac{2u}{u^2 - 1} \, du.$$

How nice! A lot of things cancel, and we're left with just

$$\int 2(u^2 - 1)\, du = \frac{2}{3} u^3 - 2u + C,$$

and converting this back into $x$ gives us our answer:

$$\int \frac{e^{2x}}{\sqrt{1 + e^x}}\, dx = \frac{2}{3}(1 + e^x)^{\frac{3}{2}} - 2(1 + e^x)^{\frac{1}{2}} + C.$$

The answers that we got from our two different methods may look different, but if you check them carefully (and rearrange some terms), you will see that they are the same. $\square$

### 5.3.6 Partial fractions

The technique of **partial fractions** is designed for integrals such as the following:

**Problem 5.33:** Compute $\int \frac{1}{x^2 - 1}\, dx$.

*Solution for Problem 5.33:* We can see that a trig substitution won't help. In particular, since $x$ can be any real number except for $\pm 1$, the only possibilities are $x = \tan \theta$ or $x = \cot \theta$, but the quantities $\tan^2 \theta - 1$ and $\cot^2 \theta - 1$ are not particularly nice.

However, we notice that we can factor $x^2 - 1 = (x - 1)(x + 1)$. Surely that must help. Indeed, that factorization lets us rewrite the function in terms of simpler fractions:

$$\frac{1}{x^2 - 1} = \frac{1}{2}\left( \frac{1}{x - 1} - \frac{1}{x + 1} \right).$$

This is very helpful, because those simpler fractions have easy antiderivatives. This lets us easily finish the problem:

$$\int \frac{1}{x^2 - 1}\, dx = \frac{1}{2}\left( \int \frac{1}{x - 1}\, dx - \int \frac{1}{x + 1}\, dx \right)$$

$$= \frac{1}{2}(\log |x - 1| - \log |x + 1|) + C$$

$$= \frac{1}{2} \log \left| \frac{x - 1}{x + 1} \right| + C.$$

$\square$

Problem 5.33 is a basic example of the technique of partial fractions. The general idea is that we break up a complicated fraction into simpler pieces that are easy to integrate. Here is a slightly more complicated example:

**Problem 5.34:** Compute $\int \frac{x + 2}{x^2 - 2x - 3}\, dx$

*Solution for Problem 5.34:* If we were lucky, we could try the Chain Rule substitution $u = x^2 - 2x - 3$. But then $du = (2x - 2)\, dx$ doesn't match the term in the numerator, so we're stuck.

However, we notice that $x^2 - 2x - 3$ factors as $(x - 3)(x + 1)$, so we can try partial fractions. We hope to write

$$\frac{x + 2}{x^2 - 2x - 3} = \frac{A}{x - 3} + \frac{B}{x + 1},$$

where $A$ and $B$ are suitable constants.

It is an easy algebra exercise to solve for $A$ and $B$. One method is to place the right side of the above expression over a common denominator:

$$\frac{x+2}{x^2-2x-3} = \frac{A}{x-3} + \frac{B}{x+1} = \frac{A(x+1) + B(x-3)}{x^2-2x-3},$$

so that we must have

$$x + 2 = A(x+1) + B(x-3).$$

We can then match coefficients to get the system of equations $A + B = 1$ and $A - 3B = 2$, which gives $A = \frac{5}{4}$ and $B = -\frac{1}{4}$. Alternatively, we can plug in $x = -1$ to the above equation to get $1 = B(-4)$, hence $B = -\frac{1}{4}$, and we can plug in $x = 3$ to get $5 = A(4)$, so $A = \frac{5}{4}$.

Thus, our integral becomes

$$\int \frac{x+2}{x^2-2x-3}\, dx = \frac{5}{4}\int \frac{1}{x-3}\, dx - \frac{1}{4}\int \frac{1}{x+1}\, dx.$$

Both of the integrals on the right side of the above equation give us logarithm terms in our final answer:

$$\int \frac{x+2}{x^2-2x-3}\, dx = \frac{5}{4}\log|x-3| - \frac{1}{4}\log|x+1| + C.$$

Some people might prefer to combine the logarithm terms into one expression to get a more compact final answer:

$$\int \frac{x+2}{x^2-2x-3}\, dx = \frac{1}{4}\log\left|\frac{(x-3)^5}{x+1}\right| + C.$$

$\square$

## 5.3.7 A monster example

We'll finish this long section on antiderivative methods with an example that combines a few different techniques.

**Problem 5.35:** Compute $\displaystyle\int \frac{3}{x^3-1}\, dx.$

*Solution for Problem 5.35:* There appears to be no clever substitution that seems to help us. But we have a factorization of the denominator as $(x^3 - 1) = (x-1)(x^2+x+1)$, so we can try for a partial fraction decomposition:

$$\frac{3}{x^3-1} = \frac{?}{x-1} + \frac{?}{x^2+x+1}.$$

We can try for constant terms in the numerators, but that runs into problems:

**Bogus Solution:** We wish to have

$$\frac{3}{x^3 - 1} = \frac{A}{x - 1} + \frac{B}{x^2 + x + 1}.$$

Clearing the denominators gives

$$3 = (x^2 + x + 1)A + (x - 1)B = Ax^2 + (A + B)x + (A - B).$$

Comparing quadratic terms gives $A = 0$, so we have

$$3 = Bx - B.$$

Comparing linear terms gives $B = 0$, so $3 = 0$. Uh-oh.

Instead, we will need a linear term in the numerator over $x^2 + x + 1$, otherwise we have no hope of canceling the quadratic factor that will result when we place the right side over a common denominator. Specifically, we will have

$$\frac{3}{x^3 - 1} = \frac{A}{x - 1} + \frac{Bx + C}{x^2 + x + 1},$$

where $A, B, C$ are constants that we need to find. Placing the right side over a common denominator gives

$$\frac{3}{x^3 - 1} = \frac{A(x^2 + x + 1) + (Bx + C)(x - 1)}{x^3 - 1} = \frac{(A + B)x^2 + (A - B + C)x + (A - C)}{x^3 - 1}.$$

Matching the corresponding coefficients of the numerators gives us the system of linear equations

$$A + B = 0,$$
$$A - B + C = 0,$$
$$A - C = 3.$$

Solving this yields $A = 1$, $B = -1$, and $C = -2$.

Thus, our partial fraction decomposition is

$$\int \frac{3}{x^3 - 1} = \int \left( \frac{1}{x - 1} - \frac{x + 2}{x^2 + x + 1} \right) dx.$$

The first term of the integral on the right side above is straightforward:

$$\int \frac{1}{x - 1} \, dx = \log |x - 1| + C.$$

But how do we compute $\int \frac{x + 2}{x^2 + x + 1} \, dx$? The denominator doesn't factor any further, and trying the Chain Rule with $u = x^2 + x + 1$ gives $du = (2x + 1) \, dx$, which doesn't match the numerator.

But we can force this substitution to match at least partially, by writing

$$\frac{x + 2}{x^2 + x + 1} = \frac{1}{2} \cdot \frac{2x + 1}{x^2 + x + 1} + \frac{3}{2} \cdot \frac{1}{x^2 + x + 1}.$$

Now the Chain Rule does work on the first summand:

$$\int \frac{1}{2} \frac{2x + 1}{x^2 + x + 1} \, dx = \int \frac{1}{2} \frac{du}{u} = \frac{1}{2} \log |u| + C = \frac{1}{2} \log |x^2 + x + 1| + C.$$

The term that remains is

$$\frac{3}{2} \int \frac{1}{x^2 + x + 1} \, dx.$$

This looks a little bit like an arctangent, but there's that annoying linear term in there. We can make it look more like the derivative of an arctangent if we complete the square of the denominator:

$$\frac{1}{x^2 + x + 1} = \frac{1}{\left(x + \frac{1}{2}\right)^2 + \frac{3}{4}}.$$

We evaluate the antiderivative of this via a trig substitution. We want the denominator of the above fraction to look like a constant times $\tan^2 \theta + 1$, so we let $x = \frac{\sqrt{3}}{2} \tan \theta - \frac{1}{2}$. Noting that $dx = \frac{\sqrt{3}}{2} \sec^2 \theta \, d\theta$, we get

$$\int \frac{1}{x^2 + x + 1} \, dx = \int \frac{1}{\left(x + \frac{1}{2}\right)^2 + \frac{3}{4}} \, dx = \int \frac{\frac{\sqrt{3}}{2} \sec^2 \theta}{\frac{3}{4}(\tan^2 \theta + 1)} \, d\theta.$$

But $\tan^2 \theta + 1 = \sec^2 \theta$, so this is just

$$\int \frac{2}{\sqrt{3}} \, d\theta = \frac{2}{\sqrt{3}} \theta + C.$$

Undoing the substitution, we see that $\theta = \tan^{-1}\left(\frac{2}{\sqrt{3}}\left(x + \frac{1}{2}\right)\right)$, so we get

$$\int \frac{1}{x^2 + x + 1} \, dx = \frac{2}{\sqrt{3}} \tan^{-1}\left(\frac{2}{\sqrt{3}}\left(x + \frac{1}{2}\right)\right) + C.$$

Putting all of these steps together, we get our answer:

$$\int \frac{3}{x^3 - 1} \, dx = \int \frac{1}{x - 1} \, dx - \int \frac{x + 2}{x^2 + x + 1} \, dx$$

$$= \log|x - 1| - \frac{1}{2} \int \frac{2x + 1}{x^2 + x + 1} \, dx - \frac{3}{2} \int \frac{1}{x^2 + x + 1} \, dx$$

$$= \log|x - 1| - \frac{1}{2} \log|x^2 + x + 1| - \frac{3}{2} \int \frac{1}{\left(x + \frac{1}{2}\right)^2 + \frac{3}{4}} \, dx$$

$$= \log|x - 1| - \frac{1}{2} \log|x^2 + x + 1| - \sqrt{3} \tan^{-1}\left(\frac{2}{\sqrt{3}}\left(x + \frac{1}{2}\right)\right) + C.$$

□

This last problem combined several nontrivial integration techniques. Also worth noting is that we started with the relatively simple function $\frac{3}{x^3-1}$ and ended up with a really ugly-looking antiderivative. This is quite common: relatively "nice" functions can have really horrible antiderivatives.

**Concept:** While it's good to slog through an integral like the one in Problem 5.35 at least once in your life, in practice it's much easier to just have your favorite calculator, computer, or website do it for you. It's just like in elementary school, where at first you learned how to multiply three-digit numbers by hand, but quickly started using a calculator instead. Learning to do the process by hand at first will help you learn the deeper meaning behind it, but there's no reason not to take advantage of the technology that is available.

> **WARNING!!** ☢ However, evaluating an integral using technology may not give you an answer in the form that you expect. For example, if you enter the integral from Problem 5.35,
>
> $$\int \frac{3}{x^3 - 1}\, dx$$
>
> into a TI-Nspire CAS (computer algebra system) calculator, it outputs
>
> $$\frac{-\left(\ln\left(\left|x^2 + x + 1\right|\right) - 2 \cdot \left(\ln\left(|x - 1|\right) - \sqrt{3} \cdot \tan^{-1}\left(\frac{\sqrt{3} \cdot (2 \cdot x + 1)}{3}\right)\right)\right)}{2}.$$
>
> Note that the TI (like most calculators) uses ln for the natural logarithm, and that the arbitrary constant is omitted, but otherwise this is a correct antiderivative. It is the same as our answer from Problem 5.35, but it is arranged somewhat differently.

## Exercises

**5.3.1** Compute the following integrals:

(a) $\int (x^3 - x + 2)\, dx$

(b) $\int \left(3x^5 - x - \frac{2}{x^4}\right) dx$

(c) $\int (2\sin x - 3\cos x)\, dx$

(d) $\int \frac{x^3 + x^2 + x + 1}{x}\, dx$

(e) $\int e^{-2x}\, dx$

(f) $\int x \sin x^2\, dx$

(g) $\int \sin^4 \theta \cos \theta\, d\theta$

(h) $\int \frac{1}{2x - 3}\, dx$

(i) $\int \frac{1}{(\cos^2 x)\sqrt{\tan x}}\, dx$

(j) $\int x e^{5x}\, dx$

(k) $\int 2x^2 e^{3x}\, dx$

(l) $\int x \log x\, dx$

(m) $\int \frac{1}{x^2 + 4}\, dx$

(n) $\int \frac{1}{x^2 + x + 1}\, dx$

(o) $\int \frac{1}{x^2 - 4x + 3}\, dx$

(p) $\int \frac{x + 3}{x^2 - 4x - 5}\, dx$

(q) $\int \frac{x^2 - 2}{x^3 - x}\, dx$

(r) $\int \frac{1}{1 + e^x}\, dx$

(s) $\int \frac{1}{1 + \sqrt{x}}\, dx$

(t) $\int \frac{1}{1 + \sqrt[3]{x}}\, dx$

(u) $\int \sqrt{2 + \sqrt{x}}\, dx$

**Hints:** (b) 7 (d) 49 (e) 181 (f) 223 (g) 180 (i) 107 (j) 104 (k) 182 (l) 136, 34 (m) 294 (n) 214, 145 (p) 160 (q) 126 (r) 231 (s) 9 (t) 25 (u) 296

**5.3.2** Let $f$ be a differentiable function. Compute $\int_a^b f'(x)f(x)\, dx$ in terms of $f(a)$ and $f(b)$.

**5.3.3**

(a) Describe a method for computing $\int \sin^n x\, dx$ and $\int \cos^n x\, dx$, where $n$ is a positive integer. **Hints:** 149, 134

(b) Describe a method for computing $\int \sin^m x \cos^n x\, dx$, where $m$ and $n$ are positive integers. **Hints:** 154, 192

**5.3.4** Compute $\int_2^3 \frac{1}{x(x-1)^2}\, dx$. **Hints:** 57

**5.3.5★** Compute $\int \sin^{-1} x \, dx$. **Hints:** 202

## 5.4 APPLICATIONS OF THE DEFINITE INTEGRAL

The definite integral has many different applications. Although we will present a number of different types of applications, we will not do very many examples of each application. Once you understand the concept, the "examples" are primarily just practice computing antiderivatives, at which you should by now be somewhat proficient.

### 5.4.1 Areas of regions in the plane

We defined the definite integral in order to compute the area of a very specific region of the plane: the integral $\int_a^b f$ equals the area of the region below the curve $y = f(x)$, above the $x$-axis, and between the lines $x = a$ and $x = b$. But the definite integral is a flexible instrument, and we can use it to compute areas of other regions of the plane. For example:

> **Problem 5.36:** Let $f$ and $g$ be continuous functions on $[a, b]$, with $f(x) \geq g(x) \geq 0$ for all $x \in [a, b]$. What is the area between the graphs of $f$ and $g$ and the lines $x = a$ and $x = b$?

*Solution for Problem 5.36:* We can see what's going on by looking at a picture such as the one to the right. The area under $f$ is $\int_a^b f$, and the area under $g$ is $\int_a^b g$. So the area between the two curves is their difference, given by

$$\int_a^b (f - g).$$

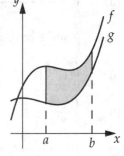

□

Often, we will have to do a little bit of work to determine the proper definite integral, as in the following problem:

> **Problem 5.37:** Find the area of the region in the first quadrant bounded by the graph of $y = \cos x$, the graph of $y = \sin x$, and the $y$-axis.

*Solution for Problem 5.37:* We can see from the picture that we want the area between $\cos x$ and $\sin x$. However, we still need to determine the limits of integration. It is clear from the picture that the lower limit of integration is $x = 0$. The upper limit is the smallest positive value of $x$ at which $\sin x = \cos x$. This means that $\tan x = 1$, so $x = \frac{\pi}{4}$.

Thus, the area is given by the definite integral

$$\int_0^{\frac{\pi}{4}} (\cos x - \sin x) \, dx = (\sin x + \cos x) \Big|_0^{\frac{\pi}{4}} = \sqrt{2} - 1.$$

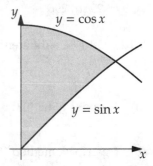

□

> **Problem 5.38:** Find the area of the region bounded by the curves $y = 1$, $y = -x + 6$, and $y = \sqrt{x}$.

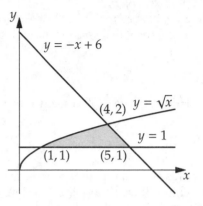

*Solution for Problem 5.38:* We can start by sketching a picture of the region, as shown to the right. In order to work with the region, it's necessary to determine the intersection points of the graphs. Some easy algebra will verify that the intersection points are as labeled in the picture. So our region ranges from $x = 1$ to $x = 5$. However, the shaded region is not the region between two graphs, as in our previous examples.

We can break up our desired region into two smaller regions. We note that for $x \in [1, 4]$, we have the region between $y = \sqrt{x}$ and $y = 1$. Similarly, for $x \in [4, 5]$, we have the region between $y = -x + 6$ and $y = 1$. The sum of these two subregions will give us our entire region.

Thus, the area that we want is

$$\int_1^4 (\sqrt{x} - 1)\, dx + \int_4^5 (-x + 6 - 1)\, dx.$$

The first integral gives us

$$\left. \left( \frac{2}{3} x^{3/2} - x \right) \right|_1^4 = \left( \frac{16}{3} - 4 \right) - \left( \frac{2}{3} - 1 \right) = \frac{5}{3}.$$

We could also evaluate the other integral using calculus, but we could instead just observe that it is an isosceles right triangle with legs 1, and thus has area $\frac{1}{2}$. Therefore, the total area is $\frac{5}{3} + \frac{1}{2} = \frac{13}{6}$.

A slightly more elegant solution is to reverse the roles of $x$ and $y$. That is, we think of the curves as graphs of functions of $x$ in terms of $y$, as labeled in the picture to the right. We now see that the region that we want is just the region between the graphs of $x = -y + 6$ and $x = y^2$ in the interval from $y = 1$ to $y = 2$. Thus, we have the definite integral

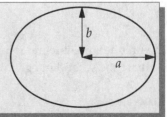

$$\int_1^2 (6 - y - y^2)\, dy = \left. \left( 6y - \frac{1}{2} y^2 - \frac{1}{3} y^3 \right) \right|_1^2 = \left( 12 - 2 - \frac{8}{3} \right) - \left( 6 - \frac{1}{2} - \frac{1}{3} \right) = \frac{22}{3} - \frac{31}{6} = \frac{13}{6},$$

as before. $\square$

This is an important technique to keep in mind. It is sometimes easier to think of $x$ as a function of $y$, rather than the usual $y$ as a function of $x$. Of course, we can only do this if the function is invertible, or if we can restrict the domain suitably to where the function is 1-to-1.

> **Concept:** When we are working with invertible functions, it may be easier to think of them as functions of $y$ instead of functions of $x$.

Here's a harder area-computation example where we use a definite integral:

> **Problem 5.39:** Determine (with proof) the area of an ellipse with semimajor axis $a$ and semiminor axis $b$. (**Semimajor axis** means half the distance in the longer direction, and **semiminor axis** means half the distance in the shorter direction, as in the picture to the right.)
>
>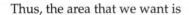

*Solution for Problem 5.39:* We can make this calculation simplest if we center the ellipse at the origin of the plane. Then, the ellipse passes through the points $(\pm a, 0)$ and $(0, \pm b)$, and is given implicitly by the equation

$$\frac{x^2}{a^2} + \frac{y^2}{b^2} = 1.$$

However, we can't directly integrate an implicit equation, so we solve for $y$ in terms of $x$:

$$y = \pm b \sqrt{1 - \frac{x^2}{a^2}}.$$

This is not a function (since it produces two values of $y$ for each value of $x \in (-a, a)$), but we get the top half of the ellipse if we choose the "+" sign (and the bottom half if we choose the "−" sign). Thus, the area of top half of the ellipse is the area under the curve

$$y = b \sqrt{1 - \frac{x^2}{a^2}}$$

on the interval $[-a, a]$, and thus the area of the whole ellipse is twice this area. Therefore, the area is equal to

$$2 \int_{-a}^{a} b \sqrt{1 - \frac{x^2}{a^2}} \, dx.$$

All we have left to do is to compute this integral. The form of this function strongly suggests a trig substitution. Indeed, we can use the substitution $x = a \sin \theta$, so that $dx = a \cos \theta \, d\theta$. But we also have to change the limits of integration! When $x = -a$, we have $\theta = -\pi/2$, and when $x = a$, we have $\theta = \pi/2$, so the interval $[-a, a]$ in terms of $x$ becomes the interval $\left[-\frac{\pi}{2}, \frac{\pi}{2}\right]$ in terms of $\theta$.

Therefore, the area of the ellipse is equal to

$$2 \int_{-\frac{\pi}{2}}^{\frac{\pi}{2}} b \sqrt{1 - \frac{a^2 \sin^2 \theta}{a^2}} (a \cos \theta) \, d\theta.$$

The expression under the square root is just $1 - \sin^2 \theta = \cos^2 \theta$, and for $\theta \in \left[-\frac{\pi}{2}, \frac{\pi}{2}\right]$, the cosine function is nonnegative, so the square root term is just $\cos \theta$, and we have

$$2ab \int_{-\frac{\pi}{2}}^{\frac{\pi}{2}} \cos^2 \theta \, d\theta.$$

(We have moved the constants $a$ and $b$ to the front of the integral.) At this point, there are a number of different ways that we could finish the problem. One method is to use the trig identity $\cos^2 \theta = \frac{1}{2}(1 + \cos 2\theta)$, making our integral

$$ab \int_{-\frac{\pi}{2}}^{\frac{\pi}{2}} (1 + \cos 2\theta) \, d\theta.$$

(Note the $\frac{1}{2}$ cancels with the 2 that used to be out front.) This can be broken up into a sum of definite integrals:

$$ab \int_{-\frac{\pi}{2}}^{\frac{\pi}{2}} 1 \, d\theta + ab \int_{-\frac{\pi}{2}}^{\frac{\pi}{2}} \cos 2\theta \, d\theta.$$

The first definite integral is just $\pi$ (since the length of the interval $\left[-\frac{\pi}{2}, \frac{\pi}{2}\right]$ is $\pi$), so the first term is $\pi ab$. We could evaluate the second integral using the Fundamental Theorem:

$$\int_{-\frac{\pi}{2}}^{\frac{\pi}{2}} \cos 2\theta \, d\theta = \frac{1}{2} \sin 2\theta \Big|_{-\frac{\pi}{2}}^{\frac{\pi}{2}} = \frac{1}{2}(\sin(\pi) - \sin(-\pi)) = \frac{1}{2}(0 - 0) = 0.$$

But we didn't need to compute it explicitly to see that it would be 0. Instead, we notice that the interval $\left[-\frac{\pi}{2}, \frac{\pi}{2}\right]$ is an entire period of the function $\cos 2\theta$ (which is periodic with period $\pi$). Looking at the graph of $y = \cos 2x$ for $x \in \left[-\frac{\pi}{2}, \frac{\pi}{2}\right]$, we see that the area under the graph of the part above the $x$-axis will exactly cancel with the area under the graph of the part below the $x$-axis, leaving a net area of 0.

Thus, the area of the ellipse is $\pi a b$. Note that if our ellipse satisfies $a = b = r$, then the ellipse is in fact a circle of radius $r$, and we get our usual area of $\pi r^2$. $\square$

## 5.4.2 Volumes

Although we defined the definite integral to compute areas, we can go up one dimension and use them to compute certain volumes as well. Recall that, for computing areas, we constructed a Darboux (or Riemann) sum by breaking up our region into a sum of rectangles, where we used a partition of an interval to determine widths and a function to determine heights. For volumes, we'll form a Riemann sum by breaking up a three-dimensional solid into a sum of slices, where we'll again use a partition of an interval to determine the widths of the slices, but where a function will determine the cross-sectional area of each slice.

Let's begin with an example for which you probably already know the answer.

**Problem 5.40:** Determine the volume of a pyramid of height 5 with a square base of side length 4.

*Solution for Problem 5.40:* We'll try a 3-dimensional version of the same strategy that we used to find area under a curve. Specifically, we'll approximate the volume of the pyramid by breaking it up into a sum of rectangular 3-dimensional solids (called **cuboids**), as shown to the right. We partition the height interval $[0, 5]$ into

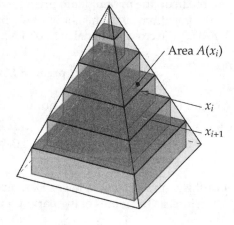

$$0 = x_0 < x_1 < x_2 < \cdots < x_n = 5.$$

At distance $x_i$ from the vertex, we will construct a cuboid whose base is a square of area $A(x_i)$ (where $A$ is a function that we haven't yet determined) and whose height is $x_{i+1} - x_i$, as shown in the picture to the right. This cuboid thus has volume $A(x_i)(x_{i+1} - x_i)$. If we sum the volumes of the cuboid over our entire partition, we have

$$\text{Volume} \approx \sum_{i=0}^{n-1} A(x_i)(x_{i+1} - x_i).$$

This is a lower Darboux sum of the function $A(x)$ on the interval $[0, 5]$, so if we take the limit as the sizes of the pieces of the partition become arbitrarily small, we get

$$\text{Volume} = \int_0^5 A(x)\, dx.$$

What remains is to determine the function $A(x)$ that gives the area of the cross-section that is $x$ units from the vertex. We know that the side length of the cross-section varies linearly, from 0 at $x = 0$ (this is the vertex of the pyramid) to 4 at $x = 5$ (this is the base of the pyramid). Thus, the side length of the cross-section at height $x$ is $\frac{4}{5}x$. Therefore, the area is $A(x) = \left(\frac{4}{5}x\right)^2 = \frac{16}{25}x^2$. Now that we know $A(x)$, we can evaluate the definite integral and compute the volume:

$$\text{Volume} = \int_0^5 A(x)\, dx = \int_0^5 \frac{16}{25}x^2\, dx = \frac{16}{75}x^3 \Big|_0^5 = \frac{16}{75}(5^3) = \frac{80}{3}. \qquad \square$$

The technique of Problem 5.40 can easily be generalized to an arbitrary pyramid.

**Problem 5.41:** Compute the volume of a pyramid (or cone) with a base of area $b$ and height $h$.

*Solution for Problem 5.41:* Note that we're not assuming anything about the shape of the base. Our only basic assumption is that the cross-sectional area is proportional to the square of the distance from the vertex. In particular, let $A(x)$ denote the area of the cross-sectional slice that is $x$ units from the vertex of the pyramid; we are given that $A(0) = 0$ and $A(h) = b$. We note that each cross section is similar to the base, which means that the cross-sectional area that is $x$ units from the base satisfies the proportionality equation

$$\left(\frac{x}{h}\right)^2 = \frac{A(x)}{A(h)} = \frac{A(x)}{b},$$

because the square of the ratio of lengths gives us the ratio of corresponding areas. Thus

$$A(x) = b\left(\frac{x}{h}\right)^2.$$

We will use these cross-sectional areas to estimate the volume of the pyramid. Just as we did in Problem 5.40, we'll start with a partition of the interval $[0, h]$:

$$0 = x_0 < x_1 < x_2 < \cdots < x_n = h.$$

We break up the pyramid into prisms, where each prism has a height given by the size of the corresponding piece of the partition, so the height of the $i^{\text{th}}$ prism (for $0 \le i < n$) is $x_{i+1} - x_i$. The area of the base of this prism is given by $A(x_i)$, the cross-sectional area of the pyramid at height $x_i$. Thus, the volume of the $i^{\text{th}}$ prism is

$$\text{Volume of } i^{\text{th}} \text{ prism} = (\text{Area of base}) \cdot (\text{Height}) = A(x_i)(x_{i+1} - x_i) = b\left(\frac{x_i}{h}\right)^2 (x_{i+1} - x_i).$$

Summing these volumes over our partition gives

$$\text{Sum of volumes} = \sum_{i=0}^{n-1} A(x_i)(x_{i+1} - x_i) = \sum_{i=0}^{n-1} b\left(\frac{x_i}{h}\right)^2 (x_{i+1} - x_i).$$

But this sum is exactly a lower Darboux sum for the definite integral of the function $A(x)$ on the interval $[0, h]$. Therefore, as the pieces of the partition get smaller and smaller, the volume approaches the definite integral

$$\int_0^h A(x)\, dx = \int_0^h b\left(\frac{x}{h}\right)^2 dx.$$

We can easily evaluate this integral to get our volume:

$$\int_0^h b\left(\frac{x}{h}\right)^2 dx = \frac{b}{h^2} \int_0^h x^2\, dx = \frac{b}{h^2} \cdot \frac{h^3}{3} = \frac{1}{3}bh.$$

$\square$

We can use the method of Problem 5.41 to compute volumes of more general regions. The only essential property that we used was the existence of a function $A(x)$ for the cross-sectional area at $x$. Thus, we can generalize:

**Problem 5.42:** Suppose that we have a three-dimensional solid bounded by the planes $x = a$ and $x = b$, such that $A(x)$ is the area of the cross-section at $x$. What is the volume of the solid?

*Solution for Problem 5.42:* We can divide the interval $[a, b]$ into a partition

$$a = x_0 < x_1 < \cdots < x_n = b.$$

We'll use this partition to break up our solid into smaller prisms, where the $i^{\text{th}}$ prism has its bases in the planes $x = x_i$ and $x = x_{i+1}$. If we choose a point $w_i \in [x_i, x_{i+1}]$, then we can approximate the volume of the piece of the solid lying within the interval $[x_i, x_{i+1}]$ as the volume of the prism with height $x_{i+1} - x_i$ and cross-sectional area $A(w_i)$. Thus, the volume of the solid is approximated by

$$\sum_{i=0}^{n-1} (x_{i+1} - x_i)A(w_i).$$

But this is a Riemann sum! As we let the sizes of the pieces of the partition get smaller and smaller, this Riemann sum approaches a definite integral. Thus, the volume of our region is given by the definite integral

$$\int_a^b A(x)\, dx.$$

□

> **Important:** The volume of a solid between the planes $x = a$ and $x = b$, with cross-sectional area given by the function $A(x)$, is
>
> $$\int_a^b A(x)\, dx.$$
>
> This should be thought of as "summing the areas" over the interval $[a, b]$.

This method of computing a volume is sometimes called **slicing**. We are essentially summing up the areas of cross-sectional slices. This technique is very flexible and can be used in a variety of different volume computations. For example:

**Problem 5.43:** Find the volume of a sphere of radius $r$.

*Solution for Problem 5.43:* We can think of the sphere as sitting with its center at the origin of three-dimension space. As $x$ varies from $-r$ to $r$, the cross-section of the sphere is a circle with radius $\sqrt{r^2 - x^2}$, and thus has area $\pi(r^2 - x^2)$. Thus, the volume of the sphere is given by the definite integral

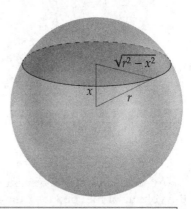

$$\int_{-r}^r \pi(r^2 - x^2)\, dx = \pi\left(r^2 x - \frac{x^3}{3}\right)\Bigg|_{-r}^r = \pi\left(\left(r^3 - \frac{r^3}{3}\right) - \left(r^2(-r) - \frac{(-r)^3}{3}\right)\right) = \frac{4}{3}\pi r^3.$$

□

There are a couple of common scenarios in which we use the graph of a function to get a three-dimensional solid.

**Problem 5.44:** Suppose that we start with the graph of $y = f(x)$ between $[a, b]$. We rotate this graph, in three dimensions, around the $x$-axis to get the surface of a three-dimensional solid. Find the volume of this **solid of revolution**.

*Solution for Problem 5.44:* The cross-section of the solid at any given value of $x$ is a circle of radius $f(x)$. Thus, the cross-section has area $\pi(f(x))^2$. Therefore, using our general principle of "summing the areas" to get volume, we conclude that the volume is given by the definite integral

$$\pi \int_a^b (f(x))^2 \, dx.$$

□

| **Important:** | The volume of the **solid of revolution** given by revolving the graph of $y = f(x)$, on the interval $[a, b]$, around the $x$-axis is $$\pi \int_a^b (f(x))^2 \, dx.$$ |
| --- | --- |

| **Concept:** | Most calculus courses teach the formula for the volume of a solid of revolution as a formula to be memorized. However, if you understand this formula as just a special case of the general slicing method, then you won't need to memorize it—it should be obvious to you! |
| --- | --- |

There is another commonly-used type of rotation that results in a solid of revolution:

**Problem 5.45:** Suppose that we start with the graph of $y = f(x)$ between $[a, b]$, where $0 < a < b$. We rotate the region under graph around the $y$-axis to get a three-dimensional solid. Find the volume of this solid.

*Solution for Problem 5.45:* The solid is a bit difficult to visualize—an example is shown to the left below. The $y$-axis is the axis of rotation, and passes through the hollow center of the solid. A "cross-section" of this object, for a specific value of $x$, is the surface of a cylinder. Two such cylinders are in the picture to the right below.

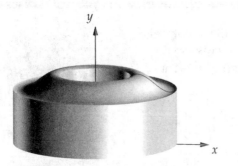
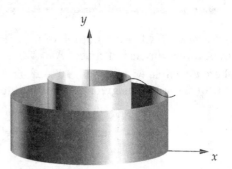

At each value of $x$, the cylinder has circumference $2\pi x$ and height $f(x)$, so it has surface area $2\pi x f(x)$. Hence, the volume of the solid (as $x$ ranges from $a$ to $b$) equals the definite integral of the cross-sectional surface areas as $x$ ranges from $a$ to $b$, and is thus

$$2\pi \int_a^b x f(x) \, dx.$$

□

This method of computing volume is sometimes called the **cylindrical shell** method.

> **Important:** The volume of the **solid of revolution** given by revolving the area under the graph of $y = f(x)$, on the interval $[a, b]$, around the $y$-axis is
>
> $$2\pi \int_a^b x f(x)\, dx.$$

> **Problem 5.46:** A hole of radius $a$ is drilled through the center of a solid sphere of radius $r$ (with $a < r$). Find the volume of the remaining object.

*Solution for Problem 5.46:* We can imagine our sphere with the hole cut along the $y$-axis, as shown in the picture to the right. The top edge of the hole produces a right triangle with hypotenuse $r$ (the radius of the sphere) and leg $a$ (the radius of the hole), so the distance from the center of the sphere to the top edge of the hole is $\sqrt{r^2 - a^2}$. Thus, our integral will sum the areas of the cross-sectional slices of the solid, perpendicular to the direction of the hole, from $-\sqrt{r^2 - a^2}$ to $\sqrt{r^2 - a^2}$ (where this quantity measures the distance of the cross-section from the center of the sphere). We can make the calculation slightly simpler by noticing that the top half of the object has the same volume as the bottom half of the object, so the total volume is just twice the volume from $y = 0$ to $y = \sqrt{r^2 - a^2}$.

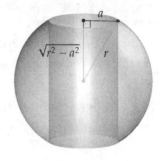

To find the cross-sectional area of the slice at height $y$, we observe that this cross-section is an **annulus**: a circle with a smaller circle removed. The smaller circle has radius $a$. The radius of the larger circle is the leg of a right triangle with hypotenuse $r$ and other leg $y$, so its radius is $\sqrt{r^2 - y^2}$. Thus, the area of the annular cross-section at height $y$ is the difference in the areas of the two circles, which is:

$$\pi \left( \sqrt{r^2 - y^2} \right)^2 - \pi a^2 = \pi (r^2 - a^2 - y^2).$$

The total volume is the sum of the areas of the annular cross-sections, given by the definite integral

$$2 \int_0^{\sqrt{r^2 - a^2}} \pi (r^2 - a^2 - y^2)\, dy.$$

(Don't forget the factor of 2, since the given integral is only for the top half of the object.) This evaluates to

$$2\pi \left( (r^2 - a^2) y - \frac{1}{3} y^3 \right) \Big|_0^{\sqrt{r^2 - a^2}} = 2\pi \left( (r^2 - a^2)^{\frac{3}{2}} - \frac{1}{3}(r^2 - a^2)^{\frac{3}{2}} \right) = \frac{4}{3} \pi (r^2 - a^2)^{\frac{3}{2}}.$$

As a check, note that when $a = 0$, we get the entire sphere's volume of $\frac{4}{3}\pi r^3$, and when $a = r$, we get 0, as expected.
□

> **Concept:** All of these volume methods are essentially the same. They all depend on the idea that to compute volume, we sum the areas of cross-sections along an interval. So you don't need to memorize any of the "special" volume formulas, since they all derive from the same basic principle.

### 5.4.3  Length of a curve

Let's now look at the problem of computing the length of the graph of $y = f(x)$ on the interval $[a, b]$. If the curve is sufficiently simple, then this is easy. For example:

**Problem 5.47:** Compute the length of the graph of $y = 2x - 3$ on the interval $[1, 4]$.

*Solution for Problem 5.47:*  This curve is just the line segment from $(1, -1)$ to $(4, 5)$, which has length

$$\sqrt{3^2 + 6^2} = \sqrt{45} = 3\sqrt{5}.$$

$\square$

**Problem 5.48:** Compute the length of the graph of $y = \sqrt{4 - x^2}$ on the interval $[1, 2]$.

*Solution for Problem 5.48:* The domain of the function is $[-2, 2]$, and the entire graph (for $x \in [-2, 2]$) is a semicircle of radius 2. The circumference of the semicircle is $2\pi$. This might lead to a quick "solution":

> **Bogus Solution:**   The interval in question, $[1, 2]$, is $\frac{1}{4}$ of the entire domain, so the length of the curve on $[1, 2]$ is $\frac{1}{4}$ of the total length on $[-2, 2]$, or $\frac{1}{4}(2\pi) = \frac{\pi}{2}$.

This is not correct! Just because $[1, 2]$ is one-quarter of the domain does not mean we get $\frac{1}{4}$ of the total length of the curve. If we look more carefully at the diagram at right, we will see the correct procedure. The section of the circle from $x = 1$ to $x = 2$ is the arc subtended by the angle $\theta$ as shown in the diagram. This angle satisfies $\cos \theta = \frac{1}{2}$ (using the triangle shown), so $\theta = \frac{\pi}{3}$. This implies that the arc is $\frac{1}{3}$ of the complete semicircle. Thus, the correct answer is that the length for $x \in [1, 2]$ is $\frac{1}{3}$ of the circumference of the semicircle, or $\frac{2\pi}{3}$. $\square$

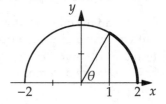

In general, it is hard to compute the length of an arbitrary curve. But we know that computing the lengths of line segments is really easy, as in Problem 5.47. Thus, our strategy will be to break up the curve into small pieces, approximate each small piece of the curve with a line segment, measure the lengths of the line segments, and sum these segment lengths.

**Problem 5.49:** Let $f$ be a differentiable function on $[a, b]$. We wish to determine the length of the curve $y = f(x)$ from $x = a$ to $x = b$.

(a)  Partition the interval $[a, b]$ as
$$a = x_0 < x_1 < \cdots < x_n = b.$$

What quantity approximates the length from $(x_i, f(x_i))$ to $(x_{i+1}, f(x_{i+1}))$? Sum these approximate lengths to get an expression that approximates the length of the curve.

(b)  We'd like the sum from part (a) to look like a Riemann sum of the form

$$\sum_{i=0}^{n-1} g(w_i)(x_{i+1} - x_i)$$

for some function $g$ and some $w_i \in [x_i, x_{i+1}]$. How can we manipulate our sum to be in this form?

(c)  Write a definite integral for the length of $y = f(x)$ from $x = a$ to $x = b$.

*Solution for Problem 5.49:*

(a) As usual, we'll start by partitioning the interval $[a, b]$ into smaller pieces:

$$a = x_0 < x_1 < \cdots < x_n = b.$$

For each interval $[x_i, x_{i+1}]$ with $0 \le i < n$, a close approximation to the curve is the straight line between $(x_i, f(x_i))$ and $(x_{i+1}, f(x_{i+1}))$. Its length is

$$\sqrt{(f(x_{i+1}) - f(x_i))^2 + (x_{i+1} - x_i)^2}.$$

Thus, our total arc length can be approximated as a sum:

$$\sum_{i=0}^{n-1} \sqrt{(f(x_{i+1}) - f(x_i))^2 + (x_{i+1} - x_i)^2}.$$

(b) Unfortunately, our sum above doesn't exactly look like a Riemann sum, so it's not immediately clear that this quantity becomes a definite integral as we let the partition pieces get smaller and smaller.

Here's the trick: what do we know about the difference of $f(x_{i+1})$ and $f(x_i)$? How can we approximate it or otherwise express it? We can use the Mean Value Theorem! Specifically, there is a point $w_i \in [x_i, x_{i+1}]$ such that

$$f'(w_i) = \frac{f(x_{i+1}) - f(x_i)}{x_{i+1} - x_i},$$

which gives

$$(x_{i+1} - x_i) f'(w_i) = f(x_{i+1}) - f(x_i).$$

We can substitute this into our sum:

$$\sum_{i=0}^{n-1} \sqrt{(f(x_{i+1}) - f(x_i))^2 + (x_{i+1} - x_i)^2} = \sum_{i=0}^{n-1} \sqrt{(f'(w_i)(x_{i+1} - x_i))^2 + (x_{i+1} - x_i)^2}.$$

We factor the $(x_{i+1} - x_i)$ term out of the square root:

$$\sum_{i=0}^{n-1} \left( \sqrt{(f'(w_i))^2 + 1} \right)(x_{i+1} - x_i).$$

Now it looks exactly like a Riemann sum!

(c) The expression above is a Riemann sum of the function $\sqrt{(f'(x))^2 + 1}$ along the interval $[a, b]$. Thus, as the partition widths approach 0, the sum becomes a definite integral. Therefore, the length of the curve $y = f(x)$ along the interval $[a, b]$ is

$$\int_a^b \sqrt{(f'(x))^2 + 1} \, dx.$$

□

---

**Important:** The length of the graph of $y = f(x)$ from the point $(a, f(a))$ to the point $(b, f(b))$ is given by

$$\int_a^b \sqrt{(f'(x))^2 + 1} \, dx.$$

---

Let's go back to our circle example from Problem 5.48 and verify that this gives what we expect:

**Problem 5.50:** Use a definite integral to compute the length of the graph of $y = \sqrt{4 - x^2}$ on the interval $[1, 2]$.

*Solution for Problem 5.50:* Let $f(x) = \sqrt{4 - x^2}$. Then $f'(x) = -\dfrac{x}{\sqrt{4 - x^2}}$, and the length is given by the integral

$$\int_1^2 \sqrt{\left(-\frac{x}{\sqrt{4 - x^2}}\right)^2 + 1}\, dx.$$

This simplifies to

$$\int_1^2 \sqrt{\frac{x^2}{4 - x^2} + 1}\, dx$$

Writing the integrand with a common denominator, we get:

$$\int_1^2 \sqrt{\frac{4}{4 - x^2}}\, dx = \int_1^2 \sqrt{\frac{1}{1 - \left(\frac{x}{2}\right)^2}}\, dx.$$

The antiderivative of $\dfrac{1}{\sqrt{1 - u^2}}$ is $\sin^{-1} u$, so our definite integral is

$$\int_1^2 \sqrt{\frac{1}{1 - \left(\frac{x}{2}\right)^2}}\, dx = 2\sin^{-1}\left(\frac{x}{2}\right)\Big|_1^2 = 2\left(\sin^{-1}(1) - \sin^{-1}\left(\frac{1}{2}\right)\right) = 2\left(\frac{\pi}{2} - \frac{\pi}{6}\right) = \frac{2\pi}{3}.$$

$\square$

Unfortunately, for most functions $f$, the integral $\int_a^b \sqrt{(f'(x))^2 + 1}\, dx$ is rather difficult to compute. This indicates that arc length is often a difficult quantity to deal with (although it can be analyzed using the integral approximation techniques that we will study in Section 5.5).

### 5.4.4   Average value of a function

A key way to think of a definite integral is as a "continuous sum." (That's why the integral sign looks like an elongated letter S.) We have already used this interpretation a number of times—for instance, to compute volume as a sum of cross-sectional areas, or to compute arc length as a sum of lengths of line segments. This general viewpoint of "a definite integral as a sum" gives us some other uses for the definite integral. For example, we know that when we have discrete data—that is, we have $n$ data points for some positive integer $n$—then the average value is the sum of the values of the data points divided by the number of data points. We can use the definite integral as a sum to extend this to an average of continuous data:

**Problem 5.51:** Suppose $f$ is a continuous function defined on an interval $[a, b]$ (with $a < b$). What expression could be interpreted as the average value of $f$ on $[a, b]$?

*Solution for Problem 5.51:* For a continuous function $f$, we think of the definite integral as performing a "sum" of the values of the function, and we use the length of the interval as the analog of the "number of data points" that we must divide by to get the average. So our candidate for the average value of $f$ on $[a, b]$ is:

$$\frac{1}{b - a} \int_a^b f(x)\, dx.$$

We can see why this makes sense by thinking in terms of a Riemann sum. As usual, suppose that we partition the interval $[a, b]$ into $n$ pieces:

$$a = x_0 < x_1 < \cdots < x_n = b,$$

and for simplicity, suppose that the pieces are equal sized, so that $x_{i+1} - x_i = \frac{b-a}{n}$ for all $0 \leq i < n$. We can approximate the average value of $f$ by choosing some $w_i \in [x_i, x_{i+1}]$ and then averaging (in the usual discrete sense) the values $f(w_i)$. This gives us

$$\text{Average of } f \approx \frac{1}{n} \sum_{i=0}^{n-1} f(w_i).$$

Let's make this look more like a Riemann sum by multiplying inside the sum by $(x_{i+1} - x_i)$, and dividing outside the sum by the same quantity, which we assumed was equal to $\frac{b-a}{n}$ for all $i$:

$$\text{Average of } f \approx \frac{n}{b-a} \cdot \frac{1}{n} \sum_{i=0}^{n-1} (x_{i+1} - x_i) f(w_i).$$

As the widths of the partition get smaller, the Riemann sum approaches a definite integral, and the $n$'s outside the sum cancel; therefore we are justified in writing

$$\text{Average of } f = \frac{1}{b-a} \int_a^b f(x) \, dx.$$

Geometrically, you can think of the average of $f$ as the "average" height of the region under $f$. That is, taking the area of a rectangle with base $[a, b]$ and height the average value of $f$ gives us:

$$\text{Area} = (b-a) \cdot (\text{Average value of } f) = (b-a) \cdot \frac{1}{b-a} \int_a^b f(x) \, dx = \int_a^b f(x) \, dx,$$

which is the area under $f$ on $[a, b]$. $\square$

In summary, we have

**Definition:** The **average value** of a continuous function $f$ along an interval $[a, b]$ (with $a < b$) is

$$\frac{1}{b-a} \int_a^b f(x) \, dx.$$

Here's a simple application:

**Problem 5.52:** The temperature at time $t$ (given in hours from 0 to 24 after midnight) in downtown Aopsville is given by $T = 10 - 5 \sin\left(\frac{t\pi}{12}\right)$ (degrees Celsius). What is the average temperature between noon and midnight?

*Solution for Problem 5.52:* By definition, the quantity we seek is

$$\frac{1}{12} \int_{12}^{24} \left(10 - 5 \sin\left(\frac{t\pi}{12}\right)\right) dt.$$

This gives us

$$\frac{1}{12} \left(10t + \frac{12}{\pi} 5 \cos\left(\frac{t\pi}{12}\right)\right)\Bigg|_{12}^{24}.$$

This is

$$10 + \frac{5}{\pi}(\cos 2\pi - \cos \pi) = 10 + \frac{10}{\pi} \approx 13.18.$$

This is reasonable: at noon the temperature is 10, at 6:00 it is 15, and at midnight it is 10 again. But the temperature stays closer to 15 for a longer period of time. So an average of 13.18 over the time period makes sense. □

Note that, in Problem 5.52, if we had asked for the average temperature between 6 a.m. and 6 p.m., we wouldn't need to write an integral: the symmetry of the temperature function about $t = 12$ shows that the average is 10.

Closely related to the idea of average value is another interpretation of the definite integral that goes back to the Fundamental Theorem of Calculus. If $f$ is differentiable, then for any $a \leq b$ we can write

$$f(b) = f(a) + \int_a^b f'(t)\,dt.$$

That is, the definite integral of $f'$ sums up the accumulated rate of change of $f$. In particular, when we rearrange this and divide by $b - a$ (assuming that $a < b$), we get:

$$\frac{f(b) - f(a)}{b - a} = \frac{1}{b - a}\int_a^b f'(t)\,dt = \text{average value of } f'(x) \text{ on } [a, b]$$

That is, $\dfrac{f(b) - f(a)}{b - a}$ is equal to the average rate of change of the function on $[a, b]$, as we expect.

> **Concept:**  All of the interpretations of the definite integral that we have discussed are interrelated! They all follow from the general idea of the definite integral as a continuous sum.

## EXERCISES

**5.4.1**   Find the areas of the following regions:

(a)   The bounded region between $y = x^2$ and $y = x^3$.

(b)   The bounded region between $y = \log x$ and the line segment connecting $(e, 1)$ and $(e^2, 2)$.

(c)   The region bounded by the $y$-axis, $y = x^2$, and $y = \cos x$. Express the area in terms of the positive constant $\alpha$ such that $\cos \alpha = \alpha^2$.

**5.4.2**   Find the volumes of the following:

(a)   The region enclosed by the surface resulting when the curve $y = x^3$ on $[0, 2]$ is rotated about the $x$-axis.

(b)   The solid consisting of the region under the curve $y = x^3$ along $[0, 2]$, rotated about the $y$-axis.

(c)   The region enclosed by the surface resulting when the curve $y = \cos x$ on $[0, \pi/2]$ is rotated about the $x$-axis.

(d)   The region $y^2 \leq x^2 - 1$ for $x \in [2, 3]$, rotated about the $y$-axis.

(e)   The ellipsoid obtained by rotating the ellipse $\left(\frac{x}{a}\right)^2 + \left(\frac{y}{b}\right)^2 = 1$ about the $x$-axis.

**5.4.3**   Find the lengths of the following curves: (a) $y = \dfrac{x^5}{20} + \dfrac{1}{3x^3}$ between $x = 2$ and $x = 4$.      (b) $y = 3x^{\frac{3}{2}} - 1$ between $(0, -1)$ and $(4, 23)$.

**5.4.4★**   Compute the volume of a torus of radius $a$ with cross-sectional radius $b$, with $a > b$. (The **torus** is the donut-shaped object that results when a circle of radius $b$ rotated around a line in the same plane as the circle, where $a$ is the distance between the line and the center of the circle.) **Hints:** 194, 137

**5.4.5★**

(a) Let $f$ be a continuous function defined on $[a, b]$. Show that there exists $c \in [a, b]$ such that

$$\int_a^b f(x)\, dx = f(c)(b - a).$$

**Hints:** 155

(b) Suppose that $g$ is also a continuous function defined on $[a, b]$ whose range is nonnegative. Show that there exists $c \in [a, b]$ such that

$$\int_a^b f(x)g(x)\, dx = f(c) \int_a^b g(x)\, dx.$$

**Hints:** 78

(c) Find an example of continuous functions $f$ and $g$ defined on $[a, b]$, for which the equation in part (b) is not satisfied for any $c \in [a, b]$. **Hints:** 152

## 5.5 APPROXIMATION TECHNIQUES

Many integrals, such as

$$\int_0^1 e^{-x^2}\, dx \qquad \text{and} \qquad \int_1^2 \frac{\sin t}{t}\, dt,$$

cannot be explicitly evaluated. For these and other integrals, it is important to have a technique for approximating them via numerical methods. This basically amounts to manually computing an approximation of the area under the curve.

As an example, we will approximate the definite integral

$$\int_{-1}^2 \left(-\frac{1}{5}x^2 + 2\right) dx.$$

Of course, we can easily compute this integral explicitly:

$$\int_{-1}^2 \left(-\frac{1}{5}x^2 + 2\right) dx = \left(-\frac{1}{15}x^3 + 2x\right)\Big|_{-1}^2 = \left(-\frac{8}{15} + 4\right) - \left(\frac{1}{15} - 2\right) = \frac{27}{5} = 5.4.$$

This is the area under the curve $y = -\frac{1}{5}x^2 + 2$ between $x = -1$ and $x = 2$.

There are a number of approximation techniques using rectangles. As you know by now, we defined the definite integral as a limit of sums of areas of rectangles. We can thus approximate an integral as a sum of areas of rectangles. There are several different ways that we can perform this approximation, based on different ways that we choose the rectangles.

Let's do a bunch of different approximations with $n = 6$ rectangles. (Of course, the more rectangles that we use, the greater the accuracy of the estimate should be.) For simplicity, we'll partition $[a, b]$ into subintervals of equal length, so that each rectangle will have width $\frac{b-a}{n}$. We then get a partition

$$a = x_0 < x_1 < x_2 < x_3 < x_4 < x_5 < x_6 = b,$$

where $x_i = a + i\left(\frac{b-a}{n}\right)$. In our example, $[a, b] = [-1, 2]$ and $n = 6$, so $x_0 = -1$, $x_1 = -0.5$, $x_2 = 0$, and so on up to $x_6 = 2$.

We can use the left endpoint of each interval to determine the height:

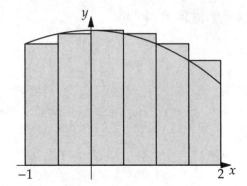

$$\text{Area} \approx \frac{b-a}{n} \sum_{i=0}^{5} f(x_i)$$
$$= (0.5)(f(-1) + f(-0.5) + f(0) + f(0.5) + f(1) + f(1.5))$$
$$= (0.5)(1.8 + 1.95 + 2 + 1.95 + 1.8 + 1.55)$$
$$= (0.5)(11.05)$$
$$= 5.525.$$

The general formula is

$$\frac{b-a}{n} \sum_{i=0}^{n-1} f(x_i),$$

but don't memorize this formula: think of it in terms of the rectangles.

Similarly, we can use the right endpoint of each interval to determine the height:

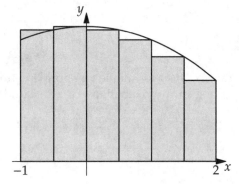

$$\text{Area} \approx \frac{b-a}{n} \sum_{i=1}^{6} f(x_i)$$
$$= (0.5)(f(-0.5) + f(0) + f(0.5) + f(1) + f(1.5) + f(2))$$
$$= (0.5)(1.95 + 2 + 1.95 + 1.8 + 1.55 + 1.2)$$
$$= (0.5)(10.45)$$
$$= 5.225.$$

The general formula for a right-side rectangular estimate is

$$\frac{b-a}{n} \sum_{i=1}^{n} f(x_i).$$

Notice that the only difference in the formulas for the left-side rectangular estimate and the right-side rectangular estimate is the limits of the summation: for the left-side estimate, we sum from $i = 0$ to $n - 1$, but for the right-side estimate, we sum from $i = 1$ to $n$. Also note the similarity of these sums to our average value computation from Problem 5.51; in particular, if we divide these sums by $b - a$, we get our usual discrete estimate for the average value $\frac{1}{b-a} \int_a^b f$, as expected.

We also note that the average of these two estimates is $(5.525 + 5.225)/2 = 5.375$, which is a lot closer to the actual value of 5.4 than either of the original estimates. Geometrically, what does this "average" represent?

If we average the left-endpoint and right-endpoint estimates, we get:

$$\frac{b-a}{n} \sum_{i=0}^{n-1} \frac{f(x_i) + f(x_{i+1})}{2},$$

which is sum of the area of *trapezoids*. This formula is usually written by pulling out the $\frac{1}{2}$ and combining the other terms:

$$\frac{1}{2}\left(\left(\frac{b-a}{n}\sum_{i=0}^{n-1}f(x_i)\right)+\left(\frac{b-a}{n}\sum_{i=1}^{n}f(x_i)\right)\right)=\frac{b-a}{2n}\left(f(x_0)+\left(2\sum_{i=1}^{n-1}f(x_i)\right)+f(x_n)\right),$$

and it is called the **Trapezoid Rule**.

Let's see it explicitly with our example:

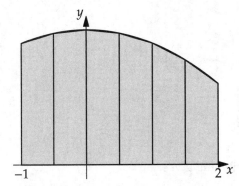

$$\text{Area}\approx\frac{b-a}{2n}\left(f(x_0)+\left(2\sum_{i=1}^{5}f(x_i)\right)+f(x_6)\right)$$

$$=(0.25)(f(-1)+2f(-0.5)+2f(0)+2f(0.5)$$
$$+2f(1)+2f(1.5)+f(2))$$

$$=(0.25)(1.8+3.9+4+3.9+3.6+3.1+1.2)$$

$$=(0.25)(21.5)$$

$$=5.375.$$

This is very close to the actual value of 5.4, and we can see in the picture that the trapezoids very closely fill the entire area under the curve.

There are two other important approximation methods. One of these methods is to use rectangles where the height is determined by the midpoint of each interval. That is,

$$\frac{b-a}{n}\sum_{i=0}^{n-1}f\left(\frac{x_i+x_{i+1}}{2}\right).$$

Here's the picture and computation with our example:

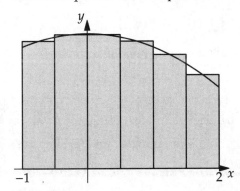

$$\text{Area}\approx\frac{b-a}{n}\sum_{i=0}^{n-1}f\left(\frac{x_i+x_{i+1}}{2}\right)$$

$$=(0.5)(f(-0.75)+f(-0.25)+f(0.25)+f(0.75)$$
$$+f(1.25)+f(1.75))$$

$$=(0.5)(1.8875+1.9875+1.9875+1.8875+1.6875+1.3875)$$

$$=(0.5)(10.825)$$

$$=5.4125.$$

This is also a pretty good estimate.

Finally, we can make an even more accurate estimate by using parabolas, instead of rectangles or trapezoids, to approximate the area under the curve. The details of this construction are a bit technical, so we will defer these details to Section 5.B. The surprising result is that this estimate turns out to be a weighted average of the midpoint estimate and the trapezoid estimate: we weight the midpoint estimate by $\frac{2}{3}$ and the trapezoid estimate by $\frac{1}{3}$. Specifically, in our example, this gives us

$$\frac{2}{3}(5.4125)+\frac{1}{3}(5.375)=5.4,$$

which happens to exactly match the value of the integral! In general we won't get the exact answer, but this estimate tends to be the most accurate.

In practice, we execute this approximation by "overlapping" the two rules via a partition with twice as many components. So our new partition uses $m = 2n$ intervals, giving

$$a = x'_0 < x'_1 < x'_2 < \cdots < x'_m = b.$$

Note that this new partition just splits all of the intervals in our old partition in half: if $i$ is even, then our "new" $x'_i$ is equal to the "old" $x_{i/2}$, and if $i$ is odd, then our "new" $x'_i$ is the midpoint between the "old" $x_{(i-1)/2}$ and $x_{(i+1)/2}$.

The trapezoid rule with the old partition gives

$$\frac{b-a}{2n}\left(f(x_0) + \left(2\sum_{i=1}^{n-1} f(x_i)\right) + f(x_n)\right) = \frac{b-a}{2n}\left(f(x'_0) + \left(2\sum_{i=1}^{n-1} f(x'_{2i})\right) + f(x'_{2n})\right).$$

The midpoint rule with the old partition gives

$$\frac{b-a}{n}\sum_{i=0}^{n-1} f\left(\frac{x_i + x_{i+1}}{2}\right) = \frac{b-a}{n}\sum_{i=0}^{n-1} f(x'_{2i+1}).$$

Weighting the trapezoid rule by $\frac{1}{3}$ and the midpoint rule by $\frac{2}{3}$ and combining gives

$$\frac{b-a}{3n}\left(\frac{1}{2}\left(f(x'_0) + \left(2\sum_{i=1}^{n-1} f(x'_{2i})\right) + f(x'_{2n})\right) + 2\sum_{i=0}^{n-1} f(x'_{2i+1})\right).$$

It is more clear what is going when we pull $\frac{1}{2}$ outside:

$$\frac{b-a}{6n}\left(f(x'_0) + \left(2\sum_{i=1}^{n-1} f(x'_{2i})\right) + f(x'_{2n}) + 4\left(\sum_{i=0}^{n-1} f(x'_{2i+1})\right)\right).$$

This is ugly, but it's clearer if we write it without the summation symbols, write it in terms of $m$ instead of $n$, and list the terms in order:

$$\frac{b-a}{3m}\left(f(x'_0) + 4f(x'_1) + 2f(x'_2) + 4f(x'_3) + 2f(x'_4) + \cdots + 4f(x'_{m-1}) + f(x'_m)\right).$$

This is called **Simpson's Rule**, and it generally has the smallest error of all the approximation techniques.

Let's use all of these techniques on another example:

**Problem 5.53:** Compute approximations for the integral $\int_0^1 e^{-x^2}\, dx$ (to 4 decimal places) using $n = 4$ via: (a) left-side rectangles, (b) right-side rectangles, (c) the Trapezoid Rule, (d) midpoint rectangles, and (e) Simpson's Rule (with $m = 2n = 8$).

*Solution for Problem 5.53:* Let $f(x) = e^{-x^2}$. Here is a chart of the computations:

| Method | Computation | Result |
|---|---|---|
| Left-side rectangles | $\frac{1}{4}(f(0) + f(0.25) + f(0.5) + f(0.75))$ | 0.8220 |
| Right-side rectangles | $\frac{1}{4}(f(0.25) + f(0.5) + f(0.75) + f(1))$ | 0.6640 |
| Trapezoid Rule | $\frac{1}{8}(f(0) + 2f(0.25) + 2f(0.5) + 2f(0.75) + f(1))$ | 0.7430 |
| Midpoint rectangles | $\frac{1}{4}(f(0.125) + f(0.375) + f(0.625) + f(0.875))$ | 0.7487 |
| Simpson's Rule | $\frac{1}{24}(f(0) + 4f(0.125) + 2f(0.25) + 4f(0.375) + 2f(0.5)$ $+ 4f(0.625) + 2f(0.75) + 4f(0.875) + f(1))$ | 0.7468 |

The Simpson's Rule estimate above is accurate to 4 decimal places. In fact, if we carried out the calculation to 6 decimal places, the Simpson's Rule estimate is 0.746826 and the actual value of the integral is 0.746824. □

> **Concept:** Problem 5.53 shows the usefulness of the various approximation methods. The integral $\int_0^1 e^{-x^2}\,dx$ is not directly computable: no integration technique will allow us to get an exact answer for this integral. So we are forced to use some sort of approximation method. Many functions that are very useful to mathematics and engineering are in the same boat: their integrals are important, but uncomputable except by numerical approximation.

## Exercises

**5.5.1** Compute (to 4 decimal places) the different estimates on the integral $\int_1^2 \frac{\sin t}{t}\,dt$, using $n = 4$ (and $m = 8$ for Simpson's Rule).

## Review Problems

**5.54** Compute the following integrals:

(a) $\int_2^4 \frac{x^2 - 1}{\frac{1}{x^2} - 1}\,dx$

(b) $\int_0^8 2\sqrt[3]{x^2}\,dx$

(c) $\int_{-1}^1 x^2\sqrt[3]{x^3 + 1}\,dx$

(d) $\int \frac{x^2}{x - 3}\,dx$

(e) $\int_{\pi/6}^{\pi/3} \tan\theta\,d\theta$

(f) $\int_0^2 \frac{x}{e^x}\,dx$

(g) $\int x^2 \sin x\,dx$

(h) $\int \sqrt{1 - x^2}\,dx$

(i) $\int_3^5 \frac{x + 1}{x^2 - 4}\,dx$

(j) $\int \frac{x^3 + x + 2}{x^4 + 2x^2 + 1}\,dx$

(k) $\int \frac{1}{\sqrt{1 + e^x}}\,dx$

**Hints:** (c) 259 (d) 109 (e) 275, 179 (f) 77 (g) 100 (h) 81 (j) 204, 297, 36 (k) 233

**5.55** Let $f$ be continuous on $[a, b]$, and let $c$ be a nonzero real number.

(a) Show that $\int_a^b f(x)\,dx = \int_{a+c}^{b+c} f(x - c)\,dx$.

(b) Show that $\int_a^b f(x)\,dx = \frac{1}{c}\int_{ca}^{cb} f\left(\frac{x}{c}\right)\,dx$.

**5.56** Let $f(x)$ be an antiderivative of $e^{-x^2}$. (This function is very important to statistics, but is not expressible in terms of "nice" functions that we know.) Determine $\int x^2 e^{-x^2}\,dx$ in terms of $f(x)$.

**5.57** Find a general formula for $\int e^{ax} \sin(bx)\,dx$, where $a$ and $b$ are real numbers. **Hints:** 92, 13

**5.58** Suppose $f(x)$ is an even function (so that $f(-x) = f(x)$) such that $\int_{-1}^1 f(x)\,dx = 8$ and $\int_{-2}^2 f(x)\,dx = 12$. Find $\int_1^2 f(x)\,dx$. **Hints:** 8

**5.59** The horizontal line $y = c$ intersects the curve $y = 2x - 3x^3$ in the first quadrant as shown at right. Find $c$ so that the areas of the two shaded regions are equal. *(Source: Putnam)* **Hints:** 301

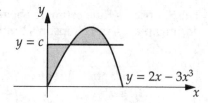

**5.60** Let $u$ and $v$ be differentiable functions. Determine an expression for

$$\frac{d}{dx} \int_{u(x)}^{v(x)} f(t)\, dt.$$

**5.61** Write a definite integral for the length of one period of the graph of the sine function. (Don't try to evaluate the integral: it's not possible to evaluate it in terms of elementary functions.)

**5.62** Find the volumes of the following:

(a) The region enclosed by the surface resulting when the curve $y = x^2 - x$ on $[1, 2]$ is rotated about the $x$-axis.

(b) The solid consisting of the region between $y = \cos x$ and the $x$-axis along $\left[0, \frac{\pi}{2}\right]$, rotated about the $y$-axis.

(c) A truncated cone with height 6, whose top is a circle of radius 2 and whose bottom is a circle of radius 5.

**5.63** Consider a sphere of radius 2 centered at the origin. Find the volume of the portion of the sphere lying between the planes $x = 0$ and $x = 1$. **Hints:** 167

**5.64** Find a formula (in terms of a definite integral) for the surface area of the volume of revolution (about the $x$-axis) of the graph $y = f(x)$ along the interval $[a, b]$, assuming that $f(x) \geq 0$ on $[a, b]$. (As a test, the surface area of a sphere of radius $r$ is $4\pi r^2$, so your formula should work with the function $f(x) = \sqrt{r^2 - x^2}$ on $[-r, r]$ to give $4\pi r^2$.) **Hints:** 31

**5.65** Let $f(x)$ be a cubic polynomial and let $a > 0$ be a positive real number. Show that the average value of $f(x)$ on the interval $[-a, a]$ can be computed by taking the average of $f\left(\frac{a}{\sqrt{3}}\right)$ and $f\left(-\frac{a}{\sqrt{3}}\right)$. *(Source: Putnam)* **Hints:** 291, 63

## CHALLENGE PROBLEMS

**5.66** The following integrals are all from the first two rounds of the 2007 MIT Integration Bee (see description on page 147). Try them for yourself!

(a) $\displaystyle\int \left(2\log x + (\log x)^2\right) dx$   **Hints:** 102, 286

(b) $\displaystyle\int \frac{2x^3 - 1}{x^4 + x}\, dx$   **Hints:** 290

(c) $\displaystyle\int \sin(\sqrt[3]{x})\, dx$   **Hints:** 197

(d) $\displaystyle\int \frac{x^{-\frac{1}{2}}}{1 + x^{\frac{1}{3}}}\, dx$   **Hints:** 198, 94

**5.67** Compute the following definite integrals:

(a) $\displaystyle\int_0^1 \frac{x^4(1 - x)^4}{1 + x^2}\, dx$   **Hints:** 256

(b) $\displaystyle\int_0^{\pi/2} \frac{\sin^3 x}{\sin^3 x + \cos^3 x}\, dx$   **Hints:** 108, 238

(c) $\displaystyle\int_0^1 \binom{207}{7} x^{200}(1 - x)^7\, dx$   **Hints:** 157, 46, 177

(d) $\displaystyle\int_1^2 \frac{9x + 4}{x^5 + 3x^2 + x}\, dx$   **Hints:** 300, 1

*(Source: (a) Putnam, (b) Rice, (c) Texas A&M, (d) HMMT)*

**5.68** Find a general formula for $\displaystyle\int \frac{dx}{(x - a)(x - b)}$, where $a$ and $b$ are real numbers.

**5.69** Compute the length of the curve $y = \log(\sin x)$ between the points $\left(\frac{\pi}{4}, \log \frac{\sqrt{2}}{2}\right)$ and $\left(\frac{\pi}{2}, 0\right)$. **Hints:** 292, 101

**5.70** The **hyperbolic cosine** function is given by

$$\cosh x = \frac{e^x + e^{-x}}{2}.$$

Find the length of the graph of $y = \cosh x$ from $x = 0$ to $x = 2$. **Hints: 236**

**5.71** Recall that the **error function** is defined by

$$\text{erf}(x) = \frac{2}{\sqrt{\pi}} \int_0^x e^{-t^2} \, dt.$$

Compute the following (your answer may be expressed in terms of $\text{erf}(x)$):

(a) $\dfrac{1}{2\sqrt{\pi}} \displaystyle\int_{-x}^x e^{-\frac{t^2}{2}} \, dt$ (b) $\dfrac{d}{dx} \displaystyle\int_0^{x^2} e^{-t^2} \, dt$ (c) $\dfrac{d}{dx}(\sqrt{x}\,\text{erf}(x))$ (d) $\displaystyle\int \text{erf}(x) \, dx$ **Hints: 79**

**5.72★** Suppose that $f$ is a monotonic continuous function defined on a closed interval $[a, b]$. Prove that $\displaystyle\int_a^b f$ is defined. (Hint: show that for any $\epsilon > 0$, we can find a partition $\mathcal{P}$ such that $u(f, \mathcal{P}) - l(f, \mathcal{P}) < \epsilon$.) **Hints: 83, 241**

**5.73★** Find all continuous positive functions $f(x)$, for $0 \le x \le 1$, such that

$$\int_0^1 f(x) \, dx = 1, \quad \int_0^1 f(x) x \, dx = \alpha, \quad \int_0^1 f(x) x^2 \, dx = \alpha^2$$

where $\alpha$ is a given real number. *(Source: Putnam)* **Hints: 45, 130, 105**

**5.74★** Find the volume of the intersection of two infinitely-long cylinders of radius 1, whose axes intersect at a right angle. **Hints: 73, 190, 273**

**5.75★** Make a reasonable definition of a 4-dimensional unit sphere (of radius 1), and compute its volume. **Hints: 11, 144, 178**

---

# 5.A FORMAL DEFINITIONS OF LOG AND EXP

Throughout the book, we have been forced to have imprecise "definitions" of the exponential and natural logarithm functions. Now that we have defined the definite integral and proved the Fundamental Theorem of Calculus, we are finally able to make rigorous definitions of these functions. We start by defining the natural logarithm function:

> **Definition:** The **natural logarithm** function is the function $\log : (0, +\infty) \to \mathbb{R}$ defined for any $x > 0$ as
>
> $$\log x = \int_1^x \frac{1}{t} \, dt.$$

Note that the Fundamental Theorem of Calculus tells us that $\dfrac{d}{dx} \log x = \dfrac{1}{x}$.

We can prove all of the nice properties of the natural logarithm that we were forced to assume earlier in the book. In particular:

**Problem 5.76:** Let $a, b$ be positive real numbers, and let $n$ be an integer. Show that:

(a) $\log 1 = 0$

(b) $\log ab = \log a + \log b$

(c) $\log \frac{a}{b} = \log a - \log b$

(d) $\log a^n = n \log a$

*Solution for Problem 5.76:*

(a) We just apply the definition: $\log 1 = \int_1^1 \frac{1}{t} dt = 0$, since $\int_1^1 f = 0$ for any function $f$.

(b) Pretend that $b$ is constant, and we'll differentiate the function $\log ab$ with respect to $a$, using the Chain Rule:

$$\frac{d}{da} \log ab = \frac{1}{ab} \cdot \frac{d}{da}(ab) = \frac{1}{ab} \cdot b = \frac{1}{a}.$$

Thus, we conclude that $\log a$ and $\log ab$, thought of as functions of $a$, have the same derivative, and thus must differ by a constant. That is,

$$\log ab = \log a + C$$

for some constant $C$. But plugging in $a = 1$ gives $\log b = \log 1 + C = C$, so $C = \log b$, and we have reached our conclusion that

$$\log ab = \log a + \log b.$$

(c) We simply rearrange part (b):

$$\log a = \log \left( b \cdot \frac{a}{b} \right) = \log b + \log \frac{a}{b},$$

and then subtracting $\log b$ from both sides gives the desired result.

(d) First, assume $n > 0$. Then the result is an easy consequence of part (b):

$$\log a^n = \log \left( \underbrace{a \cdot a \cdots \cdot a}_{n \text{ times}} \right) = \underbrace{(\log a) + (\log a) + \cdots + (\log a)}_{n \text{ times}} = n \log a.$$

If $n = 0$, then the result is just $\log a^0 = \log 1 = 0 = 0 \cdot \log a$. Finally, if $n < 0$, we use part (c):

$$\log a^n = \log \left( \frac{1}{a} \right)^{-n} = -n \log \frac{1}{a} = -n(\log 1 - \log a) = n \log a.$$

$\square$

We now would like to be able to take the inverse function of the logarithm and get the exponential function. Since $\frac{1}{t} > 0$ for all $t > 0$, we know that $\log x = \int_1^x \frac{1}{t} dt$ is a strictly increasing function, so it has an inverse whose domain is the range of log. By part (c) of Problem 5.76, we have $\log a^n = n \log a$ for any integer $n$ and positive $a$, and the quantity $n \log a$ is clearly unbounded as $n$ ranges over all the integers (for any $a \neq 1$). Thus, since log is continuous and has unbounded range, its range must be $\mathbb{R}$, and hence log must have an inverse with domain $\mathbb{R}$:

**Definition:** The **exponential** function is the function $\exp : \mathbb{R} \to (0, +\infty)$ defined as the inverse of the natural logarithm function. We usually write $\exp x = e^x$, where $e = \exp 1$.

Using the properties of inverse functions, we can prove the properties corresponding to Problem 5.76 for the exponential function:

**Problem 5.77:** Let $a, b$ be real numbers and let $n$ be an integer. Show that:

(a) $e^{a+b} = e^a e^b$

(b) $e^{a-b} = \frac{e^a}{e^b}$

(c) $e^{an} = (e^a)^n$

*Solution for Problem 5.77:* All of these result from taking the exponential of the corresponding fact from Problem 5.76.

(a) Note that
$$\log e^{a+b} = a + b = \log e^a + \log e^b = \log e^a e^b.$$
Taking the exponential of both sides gives the desired result.

(b) We do essentially the same as part (a):
$$\log e^{a-b} = a - b = \log e^a - \log e^b = \log \frac{e^a}{e^b}.$$
Taking the exponential of both sides gives the desired result.

(c) We have
$$\log e^{an} = an = n \log e^a = \log(e^a)^n,$$
and again, taking the exponential of both sides gives the desired result.

$\square$

We can also easily show that exp is its own derivative:

**Problem 5.78:** Show that $\frac{d}{dx} e^x = e^x$.

*Solution for Problem 5.78:* We use the Inverse Function Rule for derivatives:
$$(f^{-1})'(x) = \frac{1}{f'(f^{-1}(x))},$$
where here $f(x) = \log x$, so that $f'(x) = \frac{1}{x}$, and $f^{-1}(x) = e^x$. This gives
$$\frac{d}{dx} e^x = \frac{1}{\frac{1}{e^x}} = e^x,$$
as desired. $\square$

We can further define exponential functions with any positive base:

**Definition:** Let $a$ be a positive real number. Define the function $a^x : \mathbb{R} \to (0, +\infty)$ by
$$a^x = e^{x \log a}.$$

Note that this definition even works for $a = e$, since $\log e = 1$. We quickly see that
$$a^0 = e^{0 \log a} = e^0 = 1$$
and
$$a^1 = e^{\log a} = a.$$

We can also show that $a^x$ has all the properties that we expect for exponentials:

**Problem 5.79:** Let $a$ be a positive real number, and $b, c \in \mathbb{R}$. Show that:

(a) $a^{bc} = (a^b)^c$

(b) $a^{b+c} = a^b a^c$

*Solution for Problem 5.79:* We simply use the definition of $a^x$ and apply the properties that we know about the function $e^x$.

(a) It's easier if we start from the right side and write, by definition,

$$(a^b)^c = e^{c \log a^b}.$$

But again we can apply the definition and get

$$(a^b)^c = e^{c \log a^b} = e^{c \log e^{b \log a}}.$$

Using the fact that log and exp are inverses gives

$$(a^b)^c = e^{c \log a^b} = e^{c \log e^{b \log a}} = e^{c(b \log a)}.$$

And now we just apply the definition one final time:

$$(a^b)^c = e^{c \log a^b} = e^{c \log e^{b \log a}} = e^{c(b \log a)} = e^{bc \log a} = a^{bc}.$$

(b) This is easier than part (a):

$$a^{b+c} = e^{(b+c) \log a} = e^{b \log a + c \log a} = (e^{b \log a})(e^{c \log a}) = a^b a^c.$$

$\square$

We could go on and define $\log_a x$ as the inverse of $a^x$, and prove its properties, and compute the derivatives of $a^x$ and $\log_a x$, but you get the idea. The point is that the definitions of exponentials and logarithms can be made rigorous and all of their relevant properties can be proved. So we weren't really cheating in Chapters 1-4 when we used these properties.

## 5.B  SIMPSON'S RULE

**Simpson's Rule** is an approximation technique used to estimate $\int_a^b f$, in which we form a Riemann sum of areas under parabolas. As with the other approximation methods that we studied in Section 5.5, we first choose a positive integer $n$, and we partition $[a, b]$ into $n$ pieces of size $\frac{b-a}{n}$:

$$a = x_0 < x_1 < x_2 < \cdots < x_n = b,$$

where $x_i = a + i\left(\dfrac{b-a}{n}\right)$.

We will approximate the area under $f$ on each interval $[x_i, x_{i+1}]$ of the partition by constructing the parabola that passes through the same points as the graph of $f$ at each end of the interval and at the midpoint of the interval. That is, for each $0 \le i < n$, we wish to find a quadratic $q_i(x)$ such that

$$q(x_i) = f(x_i), \quad q\left(\frac{x_i + x_{i+1}}{2}\right) = f\left(\frac{x_i + x_{i+1}}{2}\right), \quad q(x_{i+1}) = f(x_{i+1}).$$

Then, since quadratics are easy to integrate, we will approximate the integral by the sum of the integrals of the quadratic pieces:

$$\int_a^b f(x)\, dx \approx \sum_{i=0}^{n-1} \int_{x_i}^{x_{i+1}} q_i(x)\, dx. \tag{5.B.1}$$

Our next step is to investigate the integrals of these quadratics:

**Problem 5.80:** Suppose that $q(x)$ is a quadratic function, and $c < d$ are real numbers. Let $m = \dfrac{c+d}{2}$ be the midpoint of $[c, d]$. Compute $\displaystyle\int_c^d q(x)\, dx$ in terms of $c, d, q(c), q(d),$ and $q(m)$.

*Solution for Problem 5.80:* Since $q$ is quadratic, we can write it as $q(x) = a_2 x^2 + a_1 x + a_0$ for some coefficients $a_0, a_1, a_2$. We can now compute:

$$
\begin{aligned}
\int_c^d (a_2 x^2 + a_1 x + a_0)\, dx &= \left. \left( \frac{1}{3} a_2 x^3 + \frac{1}{2} a_1 x^2 + a_0 x \right) \right|_c^d \\
&= \frac{1}{3} a_2 (d^3 - c^3) + \frac{1}{2} a_1 (d^2 - c^2) + a_0 (d - c) \\
&= \frac{d - c}{6} \left( 2 a_2 (d^2 + dc + c^2) + 3 a_1 (d + c) + 6 a_0 \right). 
\end{aligned} \tag{5.B.2}
$$

We want to write this expression in terms of $q(c), q(d),$ and $q(m)$. We have

$$
\begin{aligned}
q(c) &= a_2 c^2 + a_1 c + a_0, \\
q(m) &= \frac{1}{4} a_2 (d^2 + 2dc + c^2) + \frac{1}{2} a_1 (d + c) + a_0, \\
q(d) &= a_2 d^2 + a_1 d + a_0.
\end{aligned}
$$

In particular, note that

$$q(c) + 4q(m) + q(d) = a_2(c^2 + d^2 + 2dc + c^2 + d^2) + a_1(c + 2d + 2c + d) + a_0(1 + 4 + 1) = 2a_2(d^2 + dc + c^2) + 3a_1(d + c) + 6a_0.$$

This exactly matches the expression in parentheses in (5.B.2), so we conclude that

$$\int_c^d (a_2 x^2 + a_1 x + a_0)\, dx = \frac{d - c}{6}\left(2a_2(d^2 + dc + c^2) + 3a_1(d + c) + a_0\right) = \frac{d - c}{6}(q(c) + 4q(m) + q(d)).$$

$\square$

Using the result from Problem 5.80 in equation (5.B.1), where $c = x_i$, $d = x_{i+1}$, and $m = \left( \dfrac{x_i + x_{i+1}}{2} \right)$, we get

$$
\begin{aligned}
\int_a^b f(x)\, dx &\approx \sum_{i=0}^{n-1} \int_{x_i}^{x_{i+1}} q_i(x)\, dx \\
&= \sum_{i=0}^{n-1} \frac{x_{i+1} - x_i}{6} \left( f(x_i) + 4f\left( \frac{x_i + x_{i+1}}{2} \right) + f(x_{i+1}) \right) \\
&= \frac{b - a}{6n} \sum_{i=0}^{n-1} \left( f(x_i) + 4f\left( \frac{x_i + x_{i+1}}{2} \right) + f(x_{i+1}) \right). 
\end{aligned} \tag{5.B.3}
$$

As discussed in Section 5.5, we usually apply this approximation by constructing a new partition with $m = 2n$ pieces

$$a = x'_0 < x'_1 < x'_2 < \cdots < x'_m = b,$$

where the even terms are the terms of the original partition (so that $x'_{2i} = x_i$) and the odd terms are the midpoints of the intervals in the original partition $\left(\text{so that } x'_{2i+1} = \dfrac{x_i + x_{i+1}}{2}\right)$. Then the Simpson's Rule approximation in (5.B.3) becomes

$$\frac{b-a}{3m}(f(x'_0) + 4f(x'_1) + 2f(x'_2) + 4f(x'_3) + 2f(x'_4) + \cdots + 4f(x'_{m-1}) + f(x'_m)).$$

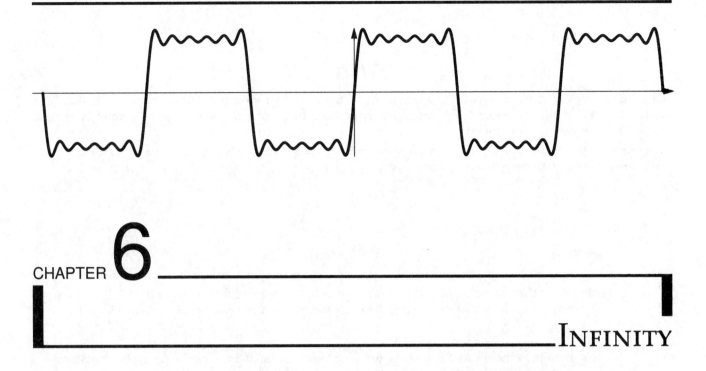

# CHAPTER 6

# INFINITY

**Infinity** is a concept that you probably have an intuitive feel for. Informally, some of the meanings of infinity are "larger than finite" and "grows without bound" and "arbitrarily large." But what does "infinity" really mean? How do we rigorously work with infinity?

In calculus, we have different meanings for infinity and for the infinity symbol ∞ depending on the context. Sometimes ∞ represents a number or quantity that grows arbitrarily large (and similarly −∞ represents a number or quantity that grows arbitrarily negative). In other places, ∞ will be a placeholder for a quantity that is unbounded—for example, the interval $[2, \infty)$ that has no upper bound.

In this chapter, we will explore different notions of ∞ as they occur in calculus.

## 6.1 LIMITS TOWARDS INFINITY

Let's recall our definition of limit: if $f$ is a real-valued function, then we say that

$$\lim_{x \to a} f(x) = L$$

if, for all $\epsilon > 0$, there exists $\delta > 0$ such that

$$0 < |x - a| < \delta \quad \Rightarrow \quad |f(x) - L| < \epsilon.$$

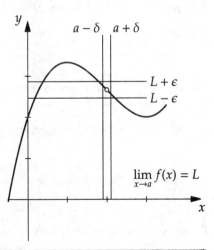

Also recall the graphical representation of this, shown at right. In words, this says that we can get $f(x)$ to be as close to $L$ as we want by making $x$ sufficiently close to $a$. Graphically, this means that given any pair of horizontal lines, we can find a sufficiently narrow set of vertical lines so that the graph of $f$ between the vertical lines lies entirely inside the horizontal strip between the given horizontal lines.

How can we modify this concept to define

$$\lim_{x \to \infty} f(x) = L?$$

We want to "make $x$ arbitrarily close to infinity," but what does that mean? What makes sense is that "$x$ is arbitrarily close to infinity" means "$x$ is arbitrarily large"—getting closer to infinity means getting larger and larger. This motivates our definition:

---

**Definition:** Let $f$ be a real-valued function. We say

$$\lim_{x \to \infty} f(x) = L$$

if, for all $\epsilon > 0$, there exists $N$ such that

$$x > N \quad \Rightarrow \quad |f(x) - L| < \epsilon.$$

---

In words, this states that we can make $f(x)$ arbitrarily close to $L$—meaning that we want $|f(x) - L| < \epsilon$ for some given $\epsilon > 0$—by restricting $x$ to be "arbitrarily close" to $\infty$—meaning that we have $x > N$ for some large $N$.

---

**Concept:** In the usual limit definition, we have the condition $0 < |x - a| < \delta$, signifying that $x$ is sufficiently close to $a$. In the definition of a limit towards infinity, we have the condition $x > N$, signifying that $x$ is sufficiently close to $\infty$.

---

We can also see what this looks like graphically. In the picture to the right, we see that all values of $x > N$ make the function be within $\epsilon$ of our limit $L$. If we make $\epsilon$ smaller, as in the second picture, we can move $N$ to the right to still "squeeze" the function within $\epsilon$ of $L$:

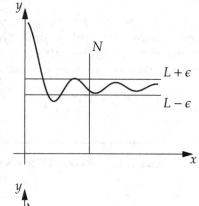

The definition of $\lim_{x \to -\infty} f(x)$ is similar, except now we have $x$ "arbitrarily close" to $-\infty$, meaning that $x < N$ for some $N$:

---

**Definition:** Let $f$ be a real-valued function. We say

$$\lim_{x \to -\infty} f(x) = L$$

if, for all $\epsilon > 0$, there exists $N$ such that

$$x < N \quad \Rightarrow \quad |f(x) - L| < \epsilon.$$

---

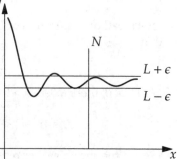

As with limits at positive infinity, the condition $x < N$ in the definition above is interpreted to mean that $x$ is arbitrarily close to $-\infty$. We will leave it to you to draw the corresponding picture.

We also use the following terminology that describes the graph $y = f(x)$:

---

**Definition:** We say that the graph of a function $f$ has a **horizontal asymptote** at $L$ if

$$\lim_{x \to \infty} f(x) = L \quad \text{or} \quad \lim_{x \to -\infty} f(x) = L.$$

---

This means that the graph of $f$ becomes arbitrarily close to the graph of $y = L$ as $x$ gets arbitrarily large (or arbitrarily negative).

Let's practice using the definition of a limit at infinity.

**Problem 6.1:** Find $\lim\limits_{x \to \infty} \dfrac{1}{x}$.

*Solution for Problem 6.1:* Let $f(x) = \frac{1}{x}$. It seems that the limit should be 0, as the value of $f(x)$ gets closer and closer to 0 as $x$ gets larger and larger. But how do we prove it?

As usual, in limit-definition computations, we start with a given $\epsilon > 0$, and we need to find a corresponding value of $N$ so that the definition is satisfied. Specifically, we want $N$ such that

$$x > N \quad \Rightarrow \quad |f(x) - 0| < \epsilon \quad \Rightarrow \quad \left|\frac{1}{x}\right| < \epsilon.$$

But $\left|\frac{1}{x}\right| < \epsilon \Leftrightarrow |x| > \frac{1}{\epsilon}$, so we can choose $N = \frac{1}{\epsilon}$. Then, reversing the argument, we note that if $x > N$, then $\frac{1}{x} < \frac{1}{N}$ and

$$|f(x) - 0| = |f(x)| = \left|\frac{1}{x}\right| < \left|\frac{1}{\frac{1}{\epsilon}}\right| = \epsilon.$$

Thus, $x > N$ implies $|f(x) - 0| < \epsilon$, and hence, by definition, $\lim\limits_{x \to \infty} f(x) = 0$. $\square$

One thing that should not surprise you is that limits at infinity satisfy all the same nice algebraic properties that other limits do:

$$\lim_{x \to \infty}(f + g)(x) = \lim_{x \to \infty} f(x) + \lim_{x \to \infty} g(x),$$

$$\lim_{x \to \infty}(fg)(x) = \left(\lim_{x \to \infty} f(x)\right)\left(\lim_{x \to \infty} g(x)\right),$$

$$\lim_{x \to \infty}(f/g)(x) = \frac{\lim\limits_{x \to \infty} f(x)}{\lim\limits_{x \to \infty} g(x)} \quad (\text{if } \lim_{x \to \infty} g(x) \neq 0),$$

$$\lim_{x \to \infty}(cf)(x) = c\left(\lim_{x \to \infty} f(x)\right),$$

provided all of the above limits exist. The same properties also hold for limits towards $-\infty$. We will leave the proofs of these properties as exercises.

Next, we study the behavior approaching infinity of **rational functions**: functions that are quotients of polynomial functions.

**Problem 6.2:** Find $\lim\limits_{x \to \infty} \dfrac{2x^3 - 4x + 1}{3x^3 + 2x^2 - x + 3}$.

*Solution for Problem 6.2:* You may already intuitively believe that the answer should be $\frac{2}{3}$, because the $x^3$ terms "dominate" the others as $x$ grows arbitrarily large. But how can we more rigorously see this?

Let's call the function $f(x)$ and divide numerator and denominator by $x^3$:

$$f(x) = \frac{2 - \frac{4}{x^2} + \frac{1}{x^3}}{3 + \frac{2}{x} - \frac{1}{x^2} + \frac{3}{x^3}}.$$

Now it is clear what is happening: when $x \to \infty$, all of the terms with powers of $x$ in the denominator will approach 0. So we are left with just $\frac{2}{3}$. Hence

$$\lim_{x \to \infty} \frac{2x^3 - 4x + 1}{3x^3 + 2x^2 - x + 3} = \frac{2}{3}.$$

$\square$

We can see the horizontal asymptote at $\frac{2}{3}$ by drawing the graph of

$$y = \frac{2x^3 - 4x + 1}{3x^3 + 2x^2 - x + 3},$$

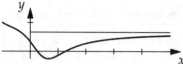

shown at right. As $x$ grows large, we see that this graph approaches the line $y = \frac{2}{3}$; this the graphical representation of

$$\lim_{x \to \infty} \frac{2x^3 - 4x + 1}{3x^3 + 2x^2 - x + 3} = \frac{2}{3}.$$

This sort of thing generalizes to any rational function:

**Problem 6.3:** Describe how to find the limit as $x \to \infty$ of $h(x) = \dfrac{f(x)}{g(x)}$, where $f(x)$ and $g(x)$ are polynomials. How does this limit depend on the degrees of $f$ and $g$?

*Solution for Problem 6.3:* For notational sake, let's suppose $f$ has degree $m$ and $g$ has degree $n$. So we write

$$h(x) = \frac{a_m x^m + a_{m-1} x^{m-1} + \cdots + a_0}{b_n x^n + b_{n-1} x^{n-1} + \cdots + b_0},$$

where $a_m \neq 0$ and $b_n \neq 0$.

In keeping with our technique for Problem 6.2, we divide by the highest power of $x$ present in either polynomial.

This leads to 3 cases:

*Case 1: $m > n$.* If the polynomial in the numerator is higher degree than the polynomial in the denominator, we get, after division by $x^m$:

$$h(x) = \frac{a_m + \frac{a_{m-1}}{x} + \cdots + \frac{a_0}{x^m}}{\frac{b_n}{x^{m-n}} + \frac{b_{n-1}}{x^{m-n+1}} + \cdots + \frac{b_0}{x^m}}.$$

We see that as $x \to \infty$, the numerator approaches $a_m$, which is nonzero, but the denominator approaches 0. So the fraction as a whole becomes arbitrarily large (positive if $\frac{a_m}{b_n} > 0$, negative if $\frac{a_m}{b_n} < 0$), since the numerator approaches $a_m$ while the denominator becomes arbitrarily small. Therefore the limit does not exist. Although, in this situation, we sometimes write

$$\lim_{x \to \infty} h(x) = \infty \text{ or } -\infty,$$

which we will say more about in Section 6.2.

*Case 2: $m < n$.* We again divide by the highest power of $x$, which in this case is $x^n$:

$$h(x) = \frac{\frac{a_m}{x^{n-m}} + \frac{a_{m-1}}{x^{n-m+1}} + \cdots + \frac{a_0}{x^n}}{b_n + \frac{b_{n-1}}{x} + \cdots + \frac{b_0}{x^n}}.$$

Now the numerator approaches 0 while the denominator approaches $b_n$. So the limit is $0/b_n = 0$.

*Case 3: $m = n$.* This is the case in our earlier example from Problem 6.2. We divide by $x^m$:

$$h(x) = \frac{a_m + \frac{a_{m-1}}{x} + \cdots + \frac{a_0}{x^m}}{b_m + \frac{b_{m-1}}{x} + \cdots + \frac{b_0}{x^m}}.$$

As $x$ approaches infinity, all the terms with powers of $x$ in the denominator approach 0. So we have

$$\lim_{x \to \infty} h(x) = \frac{a_m}{b_m}.$$

To summarize:

- If the numerator has higher degree, the rational function grows without bound.

- If the denominator has higher degree, the rational function has a horizontal asymptote at 0.

- If they have the same degree, the rational function has a horizontal asymptote equal to the ratio of the leading coefficients.

□

Limits as $x$ approaches $\infty$ are not all that mysterious, and can be restated in terms of a finite limit:

**Problem 6.4:** Suppose $f$ is a function whose domain includes $(0, \infty)$. Show that

$$\lim_{x \to \infty} f(x) = \lim_{z \to 0^+} f\left(\frac{1}{z}\right),$$

provided either limit is defined.

*Solution for Problem 6.4:* Intuitively, we see that $x$ grows arbitrarily large as $\frac{1}{x} > 0$ gets arbitrarily close to 0, and vice versa, so the result seems plausible. The proof is a matter of plowing through the $\delta$-$\epsilon$ definitions.

First, suppose that $\lim_{x \to \infty} f(x) = L$, and let $\epsilon > 0$ be given. We know that we can choose $N > 0$ such that

$$x > N \quad \Rightarrow \quad |f(x) - L| < \epsilon.$$

Let $\delta = \frac{1}{N}$. Then

$$0 < z < \delta \quad \Rightarrow \quad \frac{1}{z} > N \quad \Rightarrow \quad \left|f\left(\frac{1}{z}\right) - L\right| < \epsilon.$$

But this last statement is exactly the definition of $\lim_{z \to 0^+} f\left(\frac{1}{z}\right) = L$.

Conversely, suppose that $\lim_{z \to 0^+} f\left(\frac{1}{z}\right) = L$, and let $\epsilon > 0$ be given. We know that we can choose $\delta > 0$ such that

$$0 < z < \delta \quad \Rightarrow \quad \left|f\left(\frac{1}{z}\right) - L\right| < \epsilon.$$

Let $N = \frac{1}{\delta}$. Then

$$x > N \quad \Rightarrow \quad 0 < \frac{1}{x} < \delta \quad \Rightarrow \quad \left|f\left(\frac{1}{\frac{1}{x}}\right) - L\right| < \epsilon \quad \Rightarrow \quad |f(x) - L| < \epsilon.$$

This is the definition of $\lim_{x \to \infty} f(x) = L$.

Therefore, the two limits are equal (provided they are defined). □

A statement similar to that of Problem 6.4 exists for limits as $x$ approaches $-\infty$; we will leave this as an exercise.

There is a special case of a function $f$ in which we know that $\lim_{x \to \infty} f(x)$ must exist. If $f$ is an increasing function and $f(x)$ is bounded above, then $f$ cannot continue increasing forever, but must approach some value as

$x$ approaches $\infty$. Not surprisingly, the value that $f$ must approach is the least upper bound of $f(x)$. We can make this statement more precise:

**Problem 6.5:** Suppose that $f$ is a monotonically increasing function and $f(x)$ is bounded above—that is, there exists some $M$ such that $f(x) \leq M$ for all $x$. Show that $\lim\limits_{x \to \infty} f(x)$ exists and is equal to $\sup \text{Rng}(f)$, the least upper bound of the range of $f$.

*Solution for Problem 6.5:* Let $L = \sup \text{Rng}(f)$: we know that $L$ must exist since $\text{Rng}(f)$ is a subset of $\mathbb{R}$ that has an upper bound (namely $M$), so by the axioms of the real numbers (from Chapter 1), $\text{Rng}(f)$ must have a least upper bound. We wish to show that $\lim\limits_{x \to \infty} f(x) = L$. This means, by definition, that for any $\epsilon > 0$, we must find $N > 0$ such that

$$x > N \quad \Rightarrow \quad |f(x) - L| < \epsilon.$$

Because $L$ is an upper bound, we have $f(x) - L < 0$ for all $x \in \text{Dom}(f)$, so the above statement is equivalent to

$$x > N \quad \Rightarrow \quad f(x) > L - \epsilon.$$

We simply choose any $N$ such that $f(N) > L - \epsilon$. Such an $N$ must exist, because if it doesn't, then $L - \epsilon$ is an upper bound for $f$, contradicting the fact that $L$ is the *least* upper bound for $f$. Then, because $f$ is increasing, we have $f(x) \geq f(N) > L - \epsilon$ for any $x > N$, as desired. $\square$

Essentially the same argument shows that if $f$ is monotonically decreasing and is bounded below, then

$$\lim_{x \to \infty} f(x) = \inf \text{Rng}(f).$$

## EXERCISES

**6.1.1** Compute the following limits:

(a) $\lim\limits_{x \to \infty} \dfrac{5x^3 - x^2 + 3x - 2}{2x^3 + 3x^2 - x + 6}$ 
(b) $\lim\limits_{x \to \infty} \dfrac{2x^4 + x^2 - 3}{-3x^5 - x^3 + 2x - 7}$ 
(c) $\lim\limits_{x \to \infty} \dfrac{x^2 + \sin x}{2x^2 + \sin x}$ **Hints: 175**

**6.1.2** Suppose $f, g$ are functions with $\lim\limits_{x \to \infty} f = L$ and $\lim\limits_{x \to \infty} g = M$. Prove that

(a) $\lim\limits_{x \to \infty} (f + g) = L + M$ 
(b) $\lim\limits_{x \to \infty} (cf) = cL$ for any $c \in \mathbb{R}$

**6.1.3** Show that $\lim\limits_{x \to -\infty} f(x) = \lim\limits_{z \to 0^-} f\left(\dfrac{1}{z}\right)$. **Hints: 142**

**6.1.4★** If $f(x)$ is differentiable and $\lim\limits_{x \to \infty} f(x) = c$, then what can we say about $\lim\limits_{x \to \infty} f'(x)$? **Hints: 121, 43, 251**

## 6.2 LIMITS OF INFINITY

In Section 6.1, we discussed what it means for there to be a limit of $f(x)$ as $x$ approaches $\infty$ or $-\infty$. Here, we discuss the related question of what it means for the *value* of the function to approach $\infty$; that is, the meaning of

$$\lim_{x \to a} f(x) = \infty,$$

for some $a \in \mathbb{R}$. Informally, this should mean that as $x$ gets close to $a$, the value of $f(x)$ approaches $\infty$, meaning the value of $f(x)$ grows arbitrarily large. But of course we want to define this rigorously.

**Definition:** Let $f$ be a real-valued function and $a \in \mathbb{R}$. We say

$$\lim_{x \to a} f(x) = \infty$$

if, for all $N$, there exists $\delta > 0$ such that

$$0 < |x - a| < \delta \quad \Rightarrow \quad f(x) > N.$$

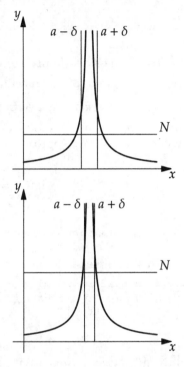

In words, this means that we can make $f(x)$ become arbitrarily close to $\infty$—that is, we can require $f(x) > N$ for any given $N$—by choosing $x$ sufficiently close to $a$—that is, by choosing $\delta$ such that $0 < |x - a| < \delta$.

We can also represent this definition graphically, as in the picture to the right. Given any value of $N$, we can find a value of $\delta$ so that the entire graph between $x = a - \delta$ and $x = a + \delta$ lies above $y = N$. If we increase $N$, then we can always find a smaller $\delta$, as shown in the lower picture. Everything between the vertical lines at $x = a - \delta$ and $x = a + \delta$ lies above the horizontal line $y = N$.

There's a similar definition for

$$\lim_{x \to a} f(x) = -\infty,$$

but we will leave the statement of this definition as an exercise.

**WARNING!!** $\lim_{x \to a} f(x) = \infty$ is just a convenient notation. It is important not to think of $\infty$ as a number. $\lim_{x \to a} f(x) = \infty$ means that $f(x)$ grows arbitrarily large as $x$ approaches $a$. At no point does $f(x)$ "equal" $\infty$.

Let's look at a quick example of the definition.

**Problem 6.6:** Show that $\lim_{x \to 2} \dfrac{1}{(x-2)^2} = \infty$.

*Solution for Problem 6.6:* Let $f(x) = \frac{1}{(x-2)^2}$. Intuitively, we see that as $x$ gets close to 2, the denominator is positive but very close to 0, so the value of the $f(x)$ gets very large. To show this rigorously, we have to show that, given any $N$, we can find a $\delta$ satisfying the definition.

So, given $N$, we need to find $\delta$ such that

$$0 < |x - 2| < \delta \quad \Rightarrow \quad \frac{1}{(x-2)^2} > N.$$

Note that if $N \leq 0$, then any $\delta$ will work, since $f(x)$ is positive-valued. Thus we can assume that $N > 0$. The condition $\dfrac{1}{(x-2)^2} > N$ means that $(x-2)^2 < \dfrac{1}{N}$, so $|x - 2| < \sqrt{\dfrac{1}{N}} = \dfrac{1}{\sqrt{N}}$.

So we simply choose $\delta = \dfrac{1}{\sqrt{N}}$, and we're done. $\square$

We can also define one-sided limits that approach $\infty$ or $-\infty$, in the obvious way that is analogous to one-sided finite limits:

**Definition:** Let $f$ be a real-valued function and $a \in R$.

- $\lim\limits_{x \to a^+} f(x) = \infty$ means that for all $N$, there exists $\delta > 0$ such that

$$0 < x - a < \delta \quad \Rightarrow \quad f(x) > N.$$

- $\lim\limits_{x \to a^-} f(x) = \infty$ means that for all $N$, there exists $\delta > 0$ such that

$$0 < a - x < \delta \quad \Rightarrow \quad f(x) > N.$$

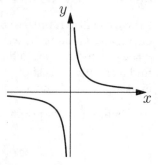

These one-sided limits are useful for a function such as $f(x) = \dfrac{1}{x}$, shown to the right. The graph of this function approaches the line $x = 0$, so we want to think of this function as having a vertical asymptote at $x = 0$. But $\lim\limits_{x \to 0} \dfrac{1}{x}$ is undefined, since the function grows without bound as $x$ approaches 0 from the right, but decreases without bound as $x$ approaches 0 from the left. Instead, we can write

$$\lim_{x \to 0^+} \frac{1}{x} = \infty \quad \text{and} \quad \lim_{x \to 0^-} \frac{1}{x} = -\infty.$$

Again, note that $\lim\limits_{x \to 0} \dfrac{1}{x}$ does not exist.

This example motivates our definition of vertical asymptote:

**Definition:** We say that the graph of a function $f$ has a **vertical asymptote** at $x = a$ if

$$\lim_{x \to a^+} f(x) = \pm\infty \quad \text{or} \quad \lim_{x \to a^-} f(x) = \pm\infty.$$

(Note that $\pm\infty$ means that the limit is $\infty$ or $-\infty$.)

Geometrically, this means that the graph of $f$ approaches the line $x = a$ as $x$ approaches $a$ from one side.

In Problem 6.3, we determined the horizontal asymptote (if any) of a rational function. Next, we examine the vertical asymptotes of such a function:

**Problem 6.7:** What are the vertical asymptotes of $h(x) = \dfrac{f(x)}{g(x)}$, where $f$ and $g$ are polynomials?

*Solution for Problem 6.7:* Clearly, if $a$ is such that $g(a) \neq 0$, then $x = a$ cannot be a vertical asymptote, since then

$$\lim_{x \to a} \frac{f(x)}{g(x)} = \frac{f(a)}{g(a)} \in \mathbb{R}.$$

We might we tempted to "conclude" that:

**Bogus Solution:** If $r$ is a root of $g(x)$ (so that $g(r) = 0$), then there will be a vertical asymptote at $x = r$.

But this is not necessarily the case. For example, the function

$$h(x) = \frac{x^2 - 1}{x - 1}$$

does not have a vertical asymptote at $x = 1$, since

$$\lim_{x \to 1} h(x) = \lim_{x \to 1}(x + 1) = 2.$$

It is true that if $r$ is a root of $g$ (the denominator of the rational function) but not of $f$ (the numerator of the function), then $h = f/g$ will have a vertical asymptote at $x = r$. However, if $r$ is a root of the numerator and denominator, then we divide both by the common factor $(x - r)$ and recompute. $\square$

---

**Concept:** To find vertical asymptotes of a rational function $\dfrac{f(x)}{g(x)}$, first cancel out all factors corresponding to common roots of $f$ and $g$. Then, any remaining roots of $g$ will be vertical asymptotes of $\frac{f}{g}$.

---

## Exercises

**6.2.1**

(a)  Write a definition of $\lim\limits_{x \to a} f(x) = -\infty$.

(b)  Write a definition of $\lim\limits_{x \to \infty} f(x) = \infty$.

**6.2.2**  Compute the following limits:

(a)  $\lim\limits_{x \to 2^+} \dfrac{1}{x^2 - 3x + 2}$    (b)  $\lim\limits_{x \to 1^-} \dfrac{x - 1}{x^3 - x^2 + x - 1}$    (c)  $\lim\limits_{x \to \frac{\pi}{2}^-} \tan x$

**6.2.3**  Find a continuous function $f$ such that $\lim\limits_{x \to \infty} f(x)$ is undefined (in particular, this limit is neither $a$ for any $a \in \mathbb{R}$ nor $\pm\infty$). **Hints:** 293

---

## 6.3  Rational indeterminate forms and l'Hôpital's Rule

In Problems 6.3 and 6.7, we determined the asymptotes of rational functions—functions that are quotients of polynomials. We'd like to be able to study more generally functions of the form $\frac{f(x)}{g(x)}$, where $f$ and $g$ are arbitrary functions, and in particular describe their behavior as $x$ approaches $\infty$ or $-\infty$.

For example, you probably already believe that exponentials "dominate" polynomials. This means that

$$\lim_{x \to \infty} \frac{f(x)}{e^x} = 0$$

for any polynomial function $f$. However, why do we believe this? We have an idea that exponentials "grow faster" than polynomials, but how do we make this limit computation precise?

Let us first examine a related question that is slightly more tractable. Suppose $f$ and $g$ are differentiable functions such that $f(a) = g(a) = 0$ at some point $a$. How can we compute

$$\lim_{x \to a} \frac{f(x)}{g(x)}?$$

We immediately see the difficulty: although the function $(f/g)$ is continuous where it is defined, it is not defined at $x = a$, since $g(a) = 0$. So we can't just "plug in" $x = a$ to compute the limit.

But the key here is that the functions are not just continuous—they are *differentiable*, and that gives us an additional tool to work with—specifically, we have the tool of tangent line approximation. See if you can work it out from here:

**Problem 6.8:** Let $f$ and $g$ be differentiable functions at $a$ with $f(a) = g(a) = 0$ and $g'(a) \neq 0$. Our goal is to compute

$$\lim_{x \to a} \frac{f(x)}{g(x)}.$$

Replace $f(x)$ and $g(x)$ with their tangent line approximations at $x = a$, and explain why we can conclude that

$$\lim_{x \to a} \frac{f(x)}{g(x)} = \frac{f'(a)}{g'(a)}.$$

*Solution for Problem 6.8:* The tangent line approximation of $f$ at $x = a$ is

$$f(x) \approx f(a) + f'(a)(x - a),$$

and similarly the tangent line approximation of $g$ at $x = a$ is

$$g(x) \approx g(a) + g'(a)(x - a).$$

This gives us the approximation

$$\lim_{x \to a} \frac{f(x)}{g(x)} \approx \lim_{x \to a} \frac{f(a) + f'(a)(x - a)}{g(a) + g'(a)(x - a)}$$

But recall that $f(a) = g(a) = 0$. So we're left with

$$\lim_{x \to a} \frac{f(x)}{g(x)} \approx \lim_{x \to a} \frac{f'(a)(x - a)}{g'(a)(x - a)}.$$

If $x \neq a$, we can cancel the $x - a$ terms and we have

$$\lim_{x \to a} \frac{f(x)}{g(x)} \approx \lim_{x \to a} \frac{f'(a)}{g'(a)} = \frac{f'(a)}{g'(a)}.$$

The above argument is only informal and is not rigorous, because we approximated the limit with the tangent line approximations of $f$ and $g$. Specifically, we'd like to get rid of that "$\approx$" symbol and say

$$\lim_{x \to a} \frac{f(x)}{g(x)} = \frac{f'(a)}{g'(a)}.$$

It turns out this is OK to do. Recall that in Problem 4.22, we defined

$$E_f(x) = f(x) - (f(a) + f'(a)(x - a))$$

to be the error of the linear approximation of $f$, and we also showed that $\lim\limits_{x \to a} \dfrac{E_f(x)}{x - a} = 0$. Thus, defining $E_g(x)$ similarly as the error of the linear approximation of $g$, we have

$$\lim_{x \to a} \frac{f(x)}{g(x)} = \lim_{x \to a} \frac{f(a) + f'(a)(x - a) + E_f(x)}{g(a) + g'(a)(x - a) + E_g(x)} = \lim_{x \to a} \frac{f'(a) + \frac{E_f(x)}{x - a}}{g'(a) + \frac{E_g(x)}{x - a}} = \frac{f'(a)}{g'(a)}.$$

$\square$

Putting this all together gives us:

> **Important:** ⚠️ Basic version of **l'Hôpital's Rule**: If $f, g$ are differentiable functions with $f(a) = g(a) = 0$, and $g'(a) \neq 0$, then
> $$\lim_{x \to a} \frac{f(x)}{g(x)} = \frac{f'(a)}{g'(a)}.$$

In fact, l'Hôpital's Rule works with $g'(a) = 0$ too! But then the quotient of the derivatives becomes a limit too. We have:

> **Important:** ⚠️ More general version of l'Hôpital's Rule: If $f, g$ are differentiable functions with $f(a) = g(a) = 0$, then
> $$\lim_{x \to a} \frac{f(x)}{g(x)} = \lim_{x \to a} \frac{f'(x)}{g'(x)}.$$

In this more general version, if $f'(a) = g'(a) = 0$, then we can apply l'Hôpital's Rule again if necessary. We will show the details of the proof in Section 6.A.

Here's a basic example of l'Hôpital's Rule in practice:

**Problem 6.9:** Compute $\lim_{x \to 0} \dfrac{\sin x}{x}$.

*Solution for Problem 6.9:* We've seen this limit before, but having l'Hôpital's Rule in the toolbox makes it easy.

If we let $f(x) = \sin x$ and $g(x) = x$, then $f(0) = g(0) = 0$. L'Hôpital's Rule says that we can evaluate $\frac{f'(0)}{g'(0)}$ to find the limit.

We see that $f'(x) = \cos x$, so $f'(0) = 1$, and $g'(x) = 1$, so $g'(0) = 1$. Thus, the limit is $\frac{f'(0)}{g'(0)} = \frac{1}{1} = 1$. □

A function $\frac{f(x)}{g(x)}$ where $f(a) = g(a) = 0$ is called a $\frac{0}{0}$ **indeterminate form** at $x = a$. We can use l'Hôpital's Rule to compute limits that are $\frac{0}{0}$ indeterminate forms. Let's do one more example:

**Problem 6.10:** Compute $\lim_{t \to 0} \dfrac{e^{3t} - 3t - 1}{4t^2}$.

*Solution for Problem 6.10:* The numerator and denominator are 0 at $t = 0$, so this limit is a $\frac{0}{0}$ indeterminate form, and we can use l'Hôpital's Rule by taking the derivative of both the numerator and the denominator:

$$\lim_{t \to 0} \frac{e^{3t} - 3t - 1}{4t^2} = \lim_{t \to 0} \frac{3e^{3t} - 3}{8t}.$$

We try to compute the limit by plugging in $t = 0$, but we see that this is still a $\frac{0}{0}$ indeterminate form at $t = 0$. No problem, we can use l'Hôpital's Rule again:

$$\lim_{t \to 0} \frac{e^{3t} - 3t - 1}{4t^2} = \lim_{t \to 0} \frac{3e^{3t} - 3}{8t} = \lim_{t \to 0} \frac{9e^{3t}}{8}.$$

Now we plug in $t = 0$, and see that the limit is $\frac{9}{8}$. □

A very nice feature of l'Hôpital's Rule is that it is flexible, so that it can be used in many situations other than $\frac{0}{0}$ indeterminate forms. One such situation is to compute a limit of a quotient of functions towards $\infty$.

**Problem 6.11:** Suppose $f, g$ are differentiable functions with

$$\lim_{x \to \infty} f(x) = \lim_{x \to \infty} g(x) = 0.$$

Use the substitution $z = \frac{1}{x}$ to show that l'Hôpital's Rule applies "at infinity"; that is,

$$\lim_{x \to \infty} \frac{f(x)}{g(x)} = \lim_{x \to \infty} \frac{f'(x)}{g'(x)},$$

provided this last limit is defined.

*Solution for Problem 6.11:* We use the result of Problem 6.4: if we substitute $z = \frac{1}{x}$, then

$$\lim_{x \to \infty} \frac{f(x)}{g(x)} = \lim_{z \to 0^+} \frac{f\left(\frac{1}{z}\right)}{g\left(\frac{1}{z}\right)}.$$

But $\lim_{z \to 0^+} f\left(\frac{1}{z}\right) = \lim_{x \to \infty} f(x) = 0$, and similarly $\lim_{z \to 0^+} g\left(\frac{1}{z}\right) = \lim_{x \to \infty} g(x) = 0$. So l'Hôpital's Rule applies, and we have

$$\lim_{z \to 0^+} \frac{f\left(\frac{1}{z}\right)}{g\left(\frac{1}{z}\right)} = \lim_{z \to 0^+} \frac{\frac{d}{dz} f\left(\frac{1}{z}\right)}{\frac{d}{dz} g\left(\frac{1}{z}\right)} = \lim_{z \to 0^+} \frac{-\frac{1}{z^2} f'\left(\frac{1}{z}\right)}{-\frac{1}{z^2} g'\left(\frac{1}{z}\right)} = \lim_{z \to 0^+} \frac{f'\left(\frac{1}{z}\right)}{g'\left(\frac{1}{z}\right)}.$$

Putting this all together gives

$$\lim_{x \to \infty} \frac{f(x)}{g(x)} = \lim_{z \to 0^+} \frac{f\left(\frac{1}{z}\right)}{g\left(\frac{1}{z}\right)} = \lim_{z \to 0^+} \frac{f'\left(\frac{1}{z}\right)}{g'\left(\frac{1}{z}\right)} = \lim_{x \to \infty} \frac{f'(x)}{g'(x)},$$

as desired. □

Of course, essentially the same argument works for limits as $x$ approaches $-\infty$; we will leave the details as an exercise.

Yet another flavor of l'Hôpital's Rule deals with infinite limits:

> **Important:** **L'Hôpital's Rule** for infinite limits: if $f, g$ are differentiable functions with
>
> $$\lim_{x \to a} f(x) = \lim_{x \to a} g(x) = \pm\infty,$$
>
> then
>
> $$\lim_{x \to a} \frac{f(x)}{g(x)} = \lim_{x \to a} \frac{f'(x)}{g'(x)},$$
>
> provided this last limit is defined. This also works as $x$ approaches $\pm\infty$: if
>
> $$\lim_{x \to \pm\infty} f(x) = \lim_{x \to \pm\infty} g(x) = \pm\infty,$$
>
> then
>
> $$\lim_{x \to \pm\infty} \frac{f(x)}{g(x)} = \lim_{x \to \pm\infty} \frac{f'(x)}{g'(x)},$$

These statements are considerably harder to prove, so we will leave the proofs to section 6.A. Not surprisingly, a function $\frac{f(x)}{g(x)}$ where $\lim_{x \to a} f(x) = \lim_{x \to a} g(x) = \infty$ is called an $\frac{\infty}{\infty}$ **indeterminate form** at $x = a$. We can use l'Hôpital's

Rule to compute limits at $\frac{\infty}{\infty}$ indeterminate forms, and in particular we can use it to address the question posed at the beginning of this section:

**Problem 6.12:** Suppose $f$ is a polynomial function. Compute $\lim\limits_{x \to \infty} \dfrac{f(x)}{e^x}$.

*Solution for Problem 6.12:* We know that $\lim\limits_{x \to \infty} f(x) = \pm\infty$ for any non-constant polynomial $f$, and also $\lim\limits_{x \to \infty} e^x = \infty$. Thus $\frac{f(x)}{e^x}$ is an $\frac{\infty}{\infty}$ indeterminate form as $x$ approaches $\infty$, and we can apply l'Hôpital's Rule, noting that $\frac{d}{dx} e^x = e^x$:

$$\lim_{x \to \infty} \frac{f(x)}{e^x} = \lim_{x \to \infty} \frac{f'(x)}{e^x}.$$

This helps because the degree of $f'$ is one less than the degree of $f$. If $f'$ is non-constant, then this is still an $\frac{\infty}{\infty}$ indeterminate form, and we can continue to apply l'Hôpital's Rule. The denominator will stay $e^x$, but the degree of the numerator will decrease by 1 again. Repeating this process will eventually lead to a polynomial with degree 0 in the numerator, which is a constant. Specifically, if $\deg f = n$, then

$$\lim_{x \to \infty} \frac{f(x)}{e^x} = \lim_{x \to \infty} \frac{f'(x)}{e^x} = \cdots = \lim_{x \to \infty} \frac{f^{(n)}(x)}{e^x} = \lim_{x \to \infty} \frac{c}{e^x},$$

for some constant $c$. But this limit is 0, since the denominator grows without bound while the numerator is constant. Thus

$$\lim_{x \to \infty} \frac{f(x)}{e^x} = 0.$$

$\square$

Problem 6.12 is a special case of a more general property that we examine for a quotient of functions:

**Definition:** We say that a function $g$ **dominates** a function $f$ if

$$\lim_{x \to \infty} \frac{f(x)}{g(x)} = 0.$$

Informally, this means that $g(x)$ "grows faster" than $f(x)$ as $x$ grows arbitrary large. In our previous examples, we have seen that higher degree polynomials dominate lower degree polynomials, and that exponential functions dominate all polynomials. As an exercise, you will show that all polynomials dominate the sine and cosine functions.

We often have to be a little careful using l'Hôpital's Rule, as in the following example:

**Problem 6.13:** Compute $\lim\limits_{x \to \infty} \dfrac{x + \sin x}{2x + 3}$.

*Solution for Problem 6.13:* This function is an $\frac{\infty}{\infty}$ indeterminate form. So we use l'Hôpital's Rule to compute the limit. We take the derivatives of numerator and denominator:

$$\lim_{x \to \infty} \frac{x + \sin x}{2x + 3} = \lim_{x \to \infty} \frac{1 + \cos x}{2}.$$

However, this latter limit is undefined, since cosine oscillates and does not approach any value. This might lead to the wrong conclusion:

> **Bogus Solution:**  L'Hôpital's Rule tells us that
> $$\lim_{x\to\infty} \frac{x + \sin x}{2x + 3} = \lim_{x\to\infty} \frac{1 + \cos x}{2}.$$
> Since this latter limit is undefined, the original limit is also undefined.

No! This just means that we can't apply l'Hôpital's Rule to compute the original limit. Then, how do we calculate the original limit? We do it in the way that we first computed limits at $\infty$ for rational functions, by dividing by the highest power of $x$:

$$\lim_{x\to\infty} \frac{x + \sin x}{2x + 3} = \lim_{x\to\infty} \frac{1 + \frac{\sin x}{x}}{2 + \frac{3}{x}}.$$

Now the answer is clear: the two terms with $x$ in the denominator approach $0$ as $x$ approaches $\infty$, and thus the limit is $\frac{1}{2}$. □

---

## EXERCISES

**6.3.1** Compute the following limits:

(a) $\displaystyle \lim_{x\to 0} \frac{1 - \cos x}{x^2}$
(b) $\displaystyle \lim_{x\to\pi} \frac{\sin 3x}{\sin 4x}$
(c) $\displaystyle \lim_{x\to 0} \frac{xe^x}{1 - e^x}$
(d) $\displaystyle \lim_{x\to 0^+} \sqrt{\frac{\log x}{x^4 - 1}}$

**6.3.2** Show that if $f$ is a non-constant polynomial, then $f$ dominates the sine and cosine functions. **Hints:** 176

**6.3.3** Show that any non-constant polynomial dominates the function $f(x) = \sqrt{x}$. **Hints:** 196

**6.3.4** If we apply l'Hôpital's Rule to

$$\lim_{h\to 0} \frac{f(x + h) - f(x)}{h},$$

what happens?

**6.3.5** Show that l'Hôpital's Rule works for $\dfrac{0}{0}$ indeterminate forms as $x \to -\infty$.

---

## 6.4 EXPONENTIAL INDETERMINATE FORMS

As we saw in the last section, l'Hôpital's Rule is a very useful tool for computing limits of quotients of functions that produce indeterminate forms. But l'Hôpital's Rule has even more powerful uses than in the examples we have already seen.

Our motivation is the following classic limit:

> **Problem 6.14:** Our goal is to compute
> $$\lim_{x\to\infty} \left(1 + \frac{1}{x}\right)^x.$$
>
> (a) Let $y = \left(1 + \frac{1}{x}\right)^x$. Write $\log y$ as a quotient of functions of $x$.
> (b) Use l'Hôpital's Rule to compute $\displaystyle \lim_{x\to\infty} \log y$.
> (c) Compute the original limit.

*Solution for Problem 6.14:* At first glance, this doesn't really look like a limit for which we can use l'Hôpital's Rule. But taking the logarithm is the key to converting it into a more traditional indeterminate form.

> **Concept:** We can often eliminate unpleasant exponential terms by taking logarithms.

(a) We let $y = \left(1 + \frac{1}{x}\right)^x$. Then

$$\log y = x \log\left(1 + \frac{1}{x}\right).$$

But this can be rewritten as a quotient of functions:

$$\log y = \frac{\log\left(1 + \frac{1}{x}\right)}{\frac{1}{x}}.$$

Now we see that as $x \to \infty$, this limit goes to $\frac{0}{0}$, so we have a $\frac{0}{0}$ indeterminate form.

(b) We can apply l'Hôpital's Rule:

$$\lim_{x \to \infty} \log y = \lim_{x \to \infty} \frac{\frac{1}{1 + \frac{1}{x}}\left(-\frac{1}{x^2}\right)}{-\frac{1}{x^2}}.$$

This looks ugly, but the $-\frac{1}{x^2}$ terms cancel, and we have

$$\lim_{x \to \infty} \log y = \lim_{x \to \infty} \frac{1}{\left(1 + \frac{1}{x}\right)} = \frac{1}{1 + 0} = 1.$$

(c) We can undo the logarithm by taking the exponential of both sides of the above equation, and this preserves the limit because the exponential function is continuous. Thus, we have

$$\lim_{x \to \infty} y = e^1 = e,$$

and hence

$$\lim_{x \to \infty} \left(1 + \frac{1}{x}\right)^x = e.$$

$\square$

This produces one of the classical formulas for the magic number $e$:

> **Important:**
> $$\lim_{x \to \infty} \left(1 + \frac{1}{x}\right)^x = e.$$

Problem 6.14 is an example that shows that l'Hôpital's Rule is useful for more than just $\frac{0}{0}$ and $\frac{\infty}{\infty}$ indeterminate forms. Let's look at a more complicated example:

> **Problem 6.15:** Compute $\lim_{x \to 0^+} x^{\sin x}$.

*Solution for Problem 6.15:* We write $f(x) = x^{\sin x}$. Taking the logarithm of both sides, we get

$$\log f(x) = \log\left(x^{\sin x}\right) = (\sin x)(\log x).$$

We'd like this in a form to which we can apply l'Hôpital's Rule, so write this as

$$\log f(x) = \frac{\log x}{\csc x}.$$

Now it is an $\frac{\infty}{\infty}$ indeterminate form as $x \to 0^+$, so we apply l'Hôpital's Rule:

$$\lim_{x \to 0^+} \log f(x) = \lim_{x \to 0^+} \frac{\log x}{\csc x} = \lim_{x \to 0^+} \frac{\frac{1}{x}}{-\csc x \cot x} = -\lim_{x \to 0^+} \frac{\sin^2 x}{x \cos x}.$$

This is now a $\frac{0}{0}$ indeterminate form, so we apply l'Hôpital's Rule again:

$$\lim_{x \to 0^+} (\log f(x)) = -\lim_{x \to 0^+} \frac{2 \sin x \cos x}{\cos x - x \sin x}.$$

At $x = 0$, the numerator of the last expression is 0 and the denominator is 1, so the limit is 0. Thus,

$$\lim_{x \to 0^+} \log f(x) = 0,$$

and hence $\lim_{x \to 0^+} f(x) = e^0 = 1.$ $\square$

---

**Concept:** Converting exponential indeterminate forms into $\frac{0}{0}$ or $\frac{\infty}{\infty}$ indeterminate forms uses the fact that "exponentials commute with limits," by which we mean

$$e^{\lim f} = \lim e^f$$

for any function $f$. This works precisely because the exponential function is continuous. Specifically, we start with

$$h(x) = f(x)^{g(x)}$$

and take logs to get

$$\log h(x) = \log\left(f(x)^{g(x)}\right) = g(x)(\log f(x)).$$

If we find that the limit of the rightmost expression above is $L$, then

$$\lim \log h(x) = L,$$

which gives $\lim h(x) = e^L$.

---

## EXERCISES

**6.4.1** Compute the following limits:

(a) $\displaystyle\lim_{x \to 0^+} x \log x$    (b) $\displaystyle\lim_{x \to \infty} x \sin\left(\frac{1}{x}\right)$    (c) $\displaystyle\lim_{x \to 1} x^{\left(\frac{x}{\sin(1-x)}\right)}$ **Hints:** 61, 50 *(Source: HMMT)*

**6.4.2** Show that $e = \displaystyle\lim_{x \to 0^+} (1 + x)^{\frac{1}{x}}$.

**6.4.3** Compute $\lim_{x \to 0^+} (1 + kx)^{\frac{1}{x}}$, where $k > 0$ is a positive constant. **Hints:** 125

**6.4.4** Suppose $f$ and $g$ are functions such that $\lim_{x \to \infty} f(x) = \lim_{x \to \infty} g(x) = \infty$. Explain how we can use l'Hôpital's Rule as a tool to compute $\lim_{x \to \infty} (f(x) - g(x))$. **Hints:** 161, 156, 162

## 6.5 IMPROPER INTEGRALS

As we've seen, we use the definite integral $\int_a^b f$ to compute the area of the region under the graph of $y = f(x)$ along the interval $[a, b]$. By definition, these integrals can only be used to compute areas of bounded regions. In some situations, however, we are interested in *unbounded* regions—these are regions that extend "towards infinity" in at least one direction. Yet, many unbounded regions still have finite area.

We start with a basic example of this phenomenon:

**Problem 6.16:** What is the area of the region bordered by the curve $y = \dfrac{1}{x^2}$, the line $x = 1$, and the $x$-axis?

*Solution for Problem 6.16:* We sketch a picture of this region at right. Notice that this region is unbounded: the region extends towards $+\infty$ as $x$ grows large. Even though this region is unbounded, we can attempt to determine its area. We certainly can compute the area of the portion of the region to the left of $x = b$ (for any $b > 1$) as the definite integral

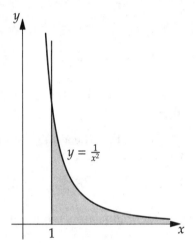

$$\int_1^b \frac{1}{x^2}\, dx.$$

As $b$ grows larger, we expect that the area under the curve on $[1, b]$ approaches the area of the entire region under the curve on $[1, +\infty)$. Specifically, this area is

$$\lim_{b \to \infty} \int_1^b \frac{1}{x^2}\, dx.$$

The integral is easy to evaluate:

$$\int_1^b \frac{1}{x^2}\, dx = \left. -\frac{1}{x} \right|_1^b = 1 - \frac{1}{b}.$$

Thus, when we take the limit, we get that the area of the region is

$$\lim_{b \to \infty} \int_1^b \frac{1}{x^2}\, dx = \lim_{b \to \infty} \left( 1 - \frac{1}{b} \right) = 1 - 0 = 1.$$

$\square$

Note the "paradox" here: even though the region is unbounded, it has finite area. Problem 6.16 suggests a logical definition:

**Definition:** Let $f$ be a continuous function and $a \in \mathbb{R}$ such that $(a, \infty) \subseteq \mathrm{Dom}(f)$. We define the **improper integral**

$$\int_a^\infty f(x)\, dx = \lim_{b \to \infty} \int_a^b f(x)\, dx,$$

provided the limit is defined. If the limit is defined and is not $\pm\infty$, we say that the improper integral **converges**. Otherwise, we say that the improper integral **diverges**.

There's an obviously similar definition for improper integrals in the other direction:

> **Definition:** Let $f$ be a continuous function and $b \in \mathbb{R}$ such that $(-\infty, b) \subseteq \mathrm{Dom}(f)$. We define the **improper integral**
>
> $$\int_{-\infty}^{b} f(x)\, dx = \lim_{a \to -\infty} \int_{a}^{b} f(x)\, dx,$$
>
> provided the limit is defined. If the limit is defined and is not $\pm\infty$, we say that the improper integral **converges**. Otherwise, we say that the improper integral **diverges**.

**Problem 6.17:** Let $r$ be a real number. Compute

$$\int_{1}^{\infty} \frac{1}{x^r}\, dx.$$

*Solution for Problem 6.17:* By definition, we compute the improper integral by writing a limit. If $r \neq 1$, then we have:

$$\lim_{b \to \infty} \int_{1}^{b} \frac{1}{x^r}\, dx = \lim_{b \to \infty} \left. -\frac{1}{(r-1)x^{r-1}} \right|_{1}^{b}.$$

This equals

$$\lim_{b \to \infty} \frac{1}{r-1}\left(1 - \frac{1}{b^{r-1}}\right).$$

If $r > 1$, then the term $\frac{1}{b^{r-1}}$ approaches $0$ as $b$ approaches $\infty$. Thus, in this case, the improper integral converges to $\frac{1}{r-1}$.

If $r < 1$, then the term $\frac{1}{b^{r-1}}$ grows without bound as $b$ approaches $\infty$. Thus, the integral diverges. We might also write

$$\int_{1}^{\infty} \frac{1}{x^r}\, dx = \infty \qquad \text{if } r < 1.$$

Our original integration was not valid for $r = 1$, so we have to do that case separately:

$$\lim_{b \to \infty} \int_{1}^{b} \frac{1}{x}\, dx = \lim_{b \to \infty} \left. (\log x) \right|_{1}^{b} = \lim_{b \to \infty} (\log b).$$

As $b$ goes towards infinity, this grows without bound, so the integral diverges.

In summary:

$$\int_{1}^{\infty} \frac{1}{x^r}\, dx = \begin{cases} \frac{1}{r-1} & \text{if } r > 1, \\ \text{diverges} & \text{if } r \leq 1. \end{cases}$$

$\square$

**Problem 6.18:** Compute $\displaystyle\int_{0}^{\infty} e^{ax}\, dx$, where $a$ is a real number.

*Solution for Problem 6.18:* We compute, for $a \neq 0$ (we'll investigate $a = 0$ at the end):

$$\lim_{b \to \infty} \int_{0}^{b} e^{ax}\, dx = \lim_{b \to \infty} \frac{1}{a}(e^{ab} - 1) = \frac{1}{a} \lim_{b \to \infty} (e^{ab} - 1).$$

If $a$ is positive, then $\lim_{b \to \infty} e^{ab} = \infty$, so the integral diverges. If $a$ is negative, then $\lim_{b \to \infty} e^{ab} = 0$, so the integral equals $-\frac{1}{a}$. (Note this is a positive number when $a$ is negative, so this answer makes sense.) Finally, if $a = 0$, then the integral is $\int_0^\infty 1 \, dx$, which clearly diverges.

Thus, the integral diverges for nonnegative exponents, and converges for negative exponents. □

The result of Problem 6.18 is typically written as follows: if $r > 0$, then

$$\int_0^\infty e^{-rx} \, dx = \frac{1}{r}.$$

**Problem 6.19:** Suppose $f$ and $g$ are continuous functions on $[a, \infty)$ and $f(x) \le g(x)$ for all $x \ge a$.

(a)  Show that, if $\int_a^\infty f$ and $\int_a^\infty g$ both converge, then

$$\int_a^\infty f \le \int_a^\infty g.$$

(b)  Show that if both functions are positive, and $\int_a^\infty g$ converges, then $\int_a^\infty f$ converges.

(c)  Show that if both functions are positive, and $\int_a^\infty f$ diverges, then $\int_a^\infty g$ diverges.

*Solution for Problem 6.19:*

(a)  For any $b \ge a$, we have $(g - f)(x) \ge 0$ for all $x \in [a, b]$, thus

$$\int_a^b (g - f)(x) \, dx \ge 0.$$

Therefore,

$$\int_a^b f(x) \, dx \le \int_a^b g(x) \, dx,$$

and since limits preserve non-strict inequalities, we conclude that

$$\int_a^\infty f(x) \, dx = \lim_{b \to \infty} \int_a^b f(x) \, dx \le \lim_{b \to \infty} \int_a^b g(x) \, dx = \int_a^\infty g(x) \, dx.$$

(b)  Define a function

$$F(x) = \int_a^x f(t) \, dt.$$

Note that $F$ is an increasing function (since $f(x) \ge 0$ for all $x \ge a$), and that $\int_a^\infty f(x) \, dx = \lim_{x \to \infty} F(x)$, if this limit exists. Also, since $0 \le f(x) \le g(x)$ for all $x \ge a$, we have

$$0 \le F(x) = \int_a^x f(t) \, dt \le \int_a^x g(t) \, dt \le \int_a^\infty g(t) \, dt.$$

Thus $F$ is increasing and has an upper bound (namely, $\int_a^\infty g(t) \, dt$, which by assumption converges), so by the result of Problem 6.5, the limit

$$\lim_{x \to \infty} F(x) = \int_a^\infty f(t) \, dt$$

exists, so the integral converges.

(c)   This is just the contrapositive statement to part (b), so there is nothing additional to prove.

□

> **WARNING!!**  We can only use the comparison tests in parts (b) and (c) of Problem 6.19 if both functions are positive. As a trivial example, if $f(x) = -1$ and $g(x) = 0$, then for any $a \in \mathbb{R}$, $\int_a^\infty g = 0$, so $\int_a^\infty g$ converges, but $\int_a^\infty f$ diverges.

Thus far in this section, we have looked at improper integrals that compute areas of regions that are unbounded in the $x$-direction. There is another type of improper integral that occurs when the region that we are examining is unbounded in the $y$-direction, as in the following example:

**Problem 6.20:** Compute $\int_0^1 \dfrac{1}{\sqrt{x}}\,dx$.

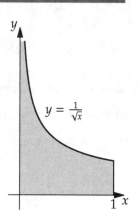

*Solution for Problem 6.20:* Sketching the graph will immediately show the issue. We have $\lim\limits_{x\to 0^+} \dfrac{1}{\sqrt{x}} = \infty$. So the area under $y = \dfrac{1}{\sqrt{x}}$ is potentially infinite (and in fact the function is not even defined at 0).

We can do essentially the same thing we did for improper integrals with a limit of integration of $\pm\infty$. We define

$$\int_0^1 \frac{1}{\sqrt{x}}\,dx = \lim_{c\to 0^+} \int_c^1 \frac{1}{\sqrt{x}}\,dx.$$

Note the "$0^+$"—since we only care about the interval $(0,1]$, we only care about what happens to the right of 0.

This integral is now easy to compute:

$$\int_c^1 \frac{1}{\sqrt{x}}\,dx = 2\sqrt{x}\,\Big|_c^1 = 2 - 2\sqrt{c}.$$

As $c \to 0^+$, this approaches 2. Hence

$$\int_0^1 \frac{1}{\sqrt{x}}\,dx = 2.$$

Once again, a seemingly infinite area turns out to be finite. □

We can generalize the definition from Problem 6.20:

> **Definition:** Suppose $f$ is a function, continuous on $(a, b]$, such that $\lim\limits_{x\to a^+} f(x) = \pm\infty$. We define the **improper integral**
>
> $$\int_a^b f(x)\,dx = \lim_{c\to a^+} \int_c^b f(x)\,dx,$$
>
> provided this limit is defined. If the limit is defined, we say that this improper integral **converges**, and if it is undefined, we say that the improper integral **diverges**.

Of course, we can do the same thing if the function has a limit of $\pm\infty$ at the "$b$" end of $[a, b)$. (We will omit writing out the formal definition.)

> **Sidenote:**
>
> ♪
>
> Note that the above definition is consistent with our usual (non-improper) integrals. In particular, if $\int_a^b f$ is defined, then by the Fundamental Theorem of Calculus, the function
>
> $$g(x) = \int_x^b f(t)\,dt$$
>
> is differentiable, hence continuous, and thus
>
> $$\int_a^b f(t)\,dt = g(a) = \lim_{x \to a^+} g(x) = \lim_{x \to a^+} \int_x^b f(t)\,dt.$$

We know that for regular (not improper) integrals, we can break them apart at any point into two separate integrals. Specifically, if $c \in (a, b)$, then

$$\int_a^b f = \int_a^c f + \int_c^b f.$$

This is also how we evaluate integrals that are improper at both ends, as in the following example:

**Problem 6.21:** Compute $\displaystyle\int_0^\infty \frac{1}{x^r}\,dx$ for all $r > 0$ (or determine when it diverges).

*Solution for Problem 6.21:* The correct thing to do with an integral that is improper at both ends is to split it somewhere in the middle. For example, we can write

$$\int_0^\infty \frac{1}{x^r}\,dx = \int_0^1 \frac{1}{x^r}\,dx + \int_1^\infty \frac{1}{x^r}\,dx.$$

(We didn't have to pick $x = 1$ as the point at which to split them, but it seems convenient since $x^r$ is nicely behaved at $x = 1$.) We already know by Problem 6.17 that $\int_1^\infty \frac{1}{x^r}\,dx$ converges if and only if $r > 1$. The other integral is

$$\int_0^1 \frac{1}{x^r}\,dx = \lim_{a \to 0+} \int_a^1 \frac{1}{x^r}\,dx = \lim_{a \to 0+}\left(-\frac{1}{(r-1)x^{r-1}}\Big|_a^1\right) = \frac{1}{r-1}\lim_{a \to 0+}\left(\frac{1}{a^{r-1}} - 1\right).$$

If $r > 1$, then the fraction gets arbitrarily large, so the limit is infinite. Thus $\int_0^1 \frac{1}{x^r}\,dx$ diverges for $r > 1$.

Hence our original doubly-improper integral is never convergent: the integral on $(0, 1]$ diverges for $r > 1$, and the integral on $[1, \infty)$ diverges for $r \le 1$. □

> **Important:**
>
> ⚠
>
> If $(a, b) \subseteq \text{Dom}(f)$ and $\int_a^b f(t)\,dt$ is improper at both ends of $(a, b)$, then
>
> $$\int_a^b f(t)\,dt = \lim_{x \to a^+} \int_x^c f(t)\,dt + \lim_{x \to b^-} \int_c^x f(t)\,dt,$$
>
> for any $c \in (a, b)$.

As noted in the solution to Problem 6.21, it doesn't matter at which point we break up the doubly-improper integral.

**Concept:** We can break an integral apart as

$$\int_a^b f = \int_a^c f + \int_c^b f$$

at any $c \in (a, b)$ that we choose. Thus, choose $c$ to be as convenient as possible.

We will leave it as an exercise to prove this. Also, it is not correct to try to take a shortcut and deal with both ends of a double-improper integral at once. In particular:

**WARNING!!** $\displaystyle\int_{-\infty}^{\infty} f(x)\,dx$ is not the same as $\displaystyle\lim_{a \to \infty} \int_{-a}^{a} f(x)\,dx$.

The correct way to evaluate an integral over all of $\mathbb{R}$ is to choose $c \in \mathbb{R}$, and then compute

$$\int_{-\infty}^{\infty} f(x)\,dx = \int_{-\infty}^{c} f(x)\,dx + \int_{c}^{\infty} f(x)\,dx = \lim_{a \to -\infty} \int_{a}^{c} f(x)\,dx + \lim_{b \to +\infty} \int_{c}^{b} f(x)\,dx.$$

We will leave it as an exercise to explore this further.

We also have to be a bit cautious when dealing with functions with domains that are not all of $\mathbb{R}$. Integrals of such functions might be improper but not immediately appear so. For example:

**Problem 6.22:** Compute $\displaystyle\int_{-2}^{3} \frac{1}{x^2}\,dx$.

*Solution for Problem 6.22:* If you weren't paying close attention, you might do this:

**Bogus Solution:**

$$\int_{-2}^{3} \frac{1}{x^2}\,dx = -\frac{1}{x}\bigg|_{-2}^{3} = -\frac{1}{3} + \frac{1}{2} = \frac{1}{6}.$$

We can't do this, because the function is not defined at 0! To be a little more precise, the function $\frac{1}{x^2}$ does not have an antiderivative on the interval $[-2, 3]$, because it is not defined at $x = 0$, so we cannot apply the Fundamental Theorem of Calculus.

In order to evaluate the integral, we need to break it up into a sum of two improper integrals at the point at which the function is undefined:

$$\int_{-2}^{3} \frac{1}{x^2}\,dx = \int_{-2}^{0} \frac{1}{x^2}\,dx + \int_{0}^{3} \frac{1}{x^2}\,dx.$$

As we saw in Problem 6.21, both of these diverge. Thus, the original integral itself diverges. $\square$

More generally, when computing something like $\displaystyle\int_{-1}^{1} \frac{dx}{x}$, it might be tempting to say "$\frac{1}{x}$ is an odd function, so the integral from $-1$ to 0 will cancel out the integral from 0 to 1, and thus the overall integral is 0." This is also the result that naive calculation will give:

**Bogus Solution:**

$$\int_{-1}^{1} \frac{dx}{x} = \log|x|\bigg|_{-1}^{1} = \log(1) - \log(1) = 0.$$

But this is not correct! The only way legally to evaluate this integral is to break it up into its improper parts.

$$\int_{-1}^{1} \frac{dx}{x} = \int_{-1}^{0} \frac{dx}{x} + \int_{0}^{1} \frac{dx}{x}.$$

Neither part converges, so the integral diverges.

## EXERCISES

**6.5.1**  Compute the following improper integrals:

(a) $\displaystyle\int_{3}^{\infty} \frac{1}{(2x-1)^2}\, dx$
(b) $\displaystyle\int_{2}^{\infty} \frac{1}{x(\log x)^2}\, dx$
(c) $\displaystyle\int_{0}^{\infty} xe^{-x^2}\, dx$
(d) $\displaystyle\int_{0}^{2} \frac{1}{4-x^2}\, dx$

**6.5.2**

(a)  Compute $\displaystyle\int_{0}^{\infty} \frac{1}{1+x^2}\, dx$.

(b)  Compute $\displaystyle\int_{-\infty}^{\infty} \frac{1}{1+x^2}\, dx$.

**6.5.3**  Compute $\displaystyle\int_{0}^{\infty} x^2 e^{-x}\, dx$.

**6.5.4**  Show that it doesn't matter at which point we break up a doubly-improper integral. Specifically, show that, for any $c, d \in (a, b)$, if $\int_{a}^{c} f$ and $\int_{c}^{b} f$ converge, then $\int_{a}^{d} f$ and $\int_{d}^{b} f$ also converge, and

$$\int_{a}^{c} f + \int_{c}^{b} f = \int_{a}^{d} f + \int_{d}^{b} f.$$

**Hints:** 230, 97

**6.5.5★**

(a)  Show that if $\displaystyle\int_{-\infty}^{\infty} f(x)\, dx$ converges, then $\displaystyle\int_{-\infty}^{\infty} f(x)\, dx = \lim_{a \to \infty} \int_{-a}^{a} f(x)\, dx$. **Hints:** 165

(b)  Show that the converse of part (a) is not true; that is, it is possible that $\displaystyle\lim_{a \to \infty} \int_{-a}^{a} f(x)\, dx$ converges but that $\displaystyle\int_{-\infty}^{\infty} f(x)\, dx$ diverges. **Hints:** 82, 225

## REVIEW PROBLEMS

**6.23**  Compute the following:

(a) $\displaystyle\lim_{x \to 1} \frac{x^2 - 1}{\log x}$
(b) $\displaystyle\lim_{x \to 0} \frac{\cos^2 x - 1}{x^2}$
(c) $\displaystyle\lim_{x \to 0} \frac{10x^2 - \frac{1}{2}x^3}{e^{4x^2} - 1}$ (Source: Rice)

**6.24**  Suppose $a$ and $b$ are nonzero real numbers. Find $\displaystyle\lim_{t \to 0} \frac{\sin at}{\sin bt}$ and $\displaystyle\lim_{t \to 0} \frac{\tan at}{\tan bt}$. **Hints:** 32

**6.25**  Compute

(a) $\displaystyle\int_{1}^{\infty} e^{-2x}\, dx$
(b) $\displaystyle\int_{0}^{2} \frac{1}{x^3}\, dx$
(c) $\displaystyle\int_{-\infty}^{\infty} \frac{1}{x^2 + 2x + 2}\, dx$ **Hints:** 72

**6.26** Compute $\int_0^1 \dfrac{dx}{\sqrt{x} + \sqrt[3]{x}}$. *(Source: HMMT)* **Hints:** 29, 265, 44

**6.27** Compute $\lim\limits_{x\to\infty} \left( \sqrt{x^2 + x} - x \right)$. *(Source: [Sp])* **Hints:** 135

**6.28** Sometimes, "little-o" notation is used to describe the growth rates of functions. Specifically, if $f$ is a function, then $o(f)$ is the set of functions defined as:

$$o(f) = \left\{ g \ \Big| \ \lim_{x\to\infty} \frac{g(x)}{f(x)} = 0 \right\}.$$

Prove the following:

(a)  $o(f)o(g) \subseteq o(fg)$ (This means that if $h_1 \in o(f)$ and $h_2 \in o(g)$, then $h_1 h_2 \in o(fg)$)

(b)  $o(o(f)) \subseteq o(f)$ (This means that if $h_1 \in o(f)$ and $h_2 \in o(h_1)$, then $h_2 \in o(f)$)

(c)  If $f$ is a polynomial and $g(x) = e^x$, then $f \in o(g)$

**6.29** For any $a \le b$, show that $\lim\limits_{m\to\infty} \int_a^b \sin mx \, dx = 0$.

(In fact, it's true that if $f$ is continuous on $[a, b]$, then $\lim\limits_{m\to\infty} \int_a^b f(x) \sin mx \, dx = 0$, but this is much more difficult to prove.)

## CHALLENGE PROBLEMS

**6.30** The **gamma function** is defined for a positive real number $z$ as

$$\Gamma(z) = \int_0^\infty x^{z-1} e^{-x} \, dx.$$

(a)  Compute $\Gamma(1)$.

(b)  Show that $\Gamma(z + 1) = z\Gamma(z)$ for any $z > 0$. **Hints:** 195

(c)  Use (a) and (b) to find a simple formula for $\Gamma(n)$, where $n$ is a positive integer. **Hints:** 212

**6.31** Suppose $a,b,x,y$ are all positive and $a + b = 1$. Compute $\lim\limits_{t\to0^+} (ax^t + by^t)^{\frac{1}{t}}$.

**6.32** Recall from page 140 the **error function**, defined by

$$\operatorname{erf}(x) = \frac{2}{\sqrt{\pi}} \int_0^x e^{-t^2} \, dt.$$

It has that weird constant in the front because

$$\int_0^\infty e^{-t^2} \, dt = \frac{\sqrt{\pi}}{2}.$$

(We'll prove this later in the book.) Using this fact, compute

$$\int_{-\infty}^\infty e^{-\frac{(x-a)^2}{b}} \, dx,$$

where $a, b$ are real numbers with $b \ne 0$.

**6.33★** Let $f$ be a continuous function on $[0,1]$. Evaluate $\displaystyle\lim_{x\to0^+} x \int_x^1 \frac{f(t)}{t}\, dt$. *(Source: [Sp])* **Hints:** 193, 244, 228, 98

**6.34★** Evaluate $\displaystyle\int_1^\infty \frac{dx}{e^{x+1} + e^{3-x}}$. *(Source: Putnam)* **Hints:** 271, 133, 169, 283

---

# 6.A  PROOF OF L'HÔPITAL'S RULE

Before we can rigorously prove l'Hôpital's Rule, we need to have a more general version of the Mean Value Theorem.

> **Problem 6.35:** Let $f, g$ be continuous functions on an interval $[a, b]$ and differentiable on $(a, b)$. Show that there exists $c \in (a, b)$ such that
> $$f'(c)(g(b) - g(a)) = g'(c)(f(b) - f(a)).$$

Note that if $g(x) = x$, then $g'(c) = 1$ for all $c$, and the above expression can be rearranged as

$$f'(c) = \frac{f(b) - f(a)}{b - a},$$

which is just the Mean Value Theorem.

*Solution for Problem 6.35:* Define a function $h$ as

$$h(x) = f(x)(g(b) - g(a)) - g(x)(f(b) - f(a)).$$

Notice that

$$h(a) = h(b) = f(a)g(b) - f(b)g(a),$$

thus by Rolle's Theorem, there exists $c \in (a, b)$ such that $h'(c) = 0$. Therefore,

$$0 = h'(c) = f'(c)(g(b) - g(a)) - g'(c)(f(b) - f(a)),$$

which can be rearranged to $f'(c)(g(b) - g(a)) = g'(c)(f(b) - f(a))$, as desired. $\square$

The result of Problem 6.35 is called the **Extended Mean Value Theorem**.

> **Important:**  **General statement of l'Hôpital's Rule:** In the following statement,
>
> - $\heartsuit$ can be a real number, a "one-sided real number" (for example, $\displaystyle\lim_{x\to1^+}$), or $\pm\infty$, and
>
> - $\spadesuit$ can be 0 or $\pm\infty$.
>
> Let $f, g$ be differentiable functions such that
> $$\lim_{x\to\heartsuit} f(x) = \lim_{x\to\heartsuit} g(x) = \spadesuit.$$
>
> Then
> $$\lim_{x\to\heartsuit} \frac{f(x)}{g(x)} = \lim_{x\to\heartsuit} \frac{f'(x)}{g'(x)},$$
>
> provided this latter limit exists.

We will first rigorously prove the "basic" case of l'Hôpital's Rule.

> **Problem 6.36:** Prove l'Hôpital's Rule where $\spadesuit = 0$, $\heartsuit = a$ for some $a \in \mathbb{R}$, and
>
> $$\lim_{x \to a} \frac{f'(x)}{g'(x)} = L$$
>
> for some $L \in \mathbb{R}$.

Note: The modifications to the following proof in the cases that $\heartsuit = a^+$ or $\heartsuit = a^-$ should be clear, and we will not present them.

*Solution for Problem 6.36:*  We alter $f$ (if necessary) by setting $f(a) = 0$; note that since $\lim_{x \to a} f(x) = 0$ by assumption, this makes $f$ continuous at $a$. Similarly alter $g$ if necessary so that $g(a) = 0$.

We are assuming that $\lim_{x \to a} \dfrac{f'(x)}{g'(x)} = L$. This means that by definition, for any $\epsilon > 0$, we can choose $\delta > 0$ such that

$$0 < |x - a| < \delta \quad \Rightarrow \quad \left| \frac{f'(x)}{g'(x)} - L \right| < \epsilon. \tag{6.A.1}$$

Note that this implies that $g'(x) \neq 0$ for all $0 < |x - a| < \delta$. This further implies that $g(x) \neq 0$ for all $0 < |x - a| < \delta$, since if $g(x) = 0 = g(a)$, then by the Mean Value Theorem there is some $\xi$ between $x$ and $a$ such that $g'(\xi) = 0$, a contradiction.

We wish to show that

$$0 < |x - a| < \delta \quad \Rightarrow \quad \left| \frac{f(x)}{g(x)} - L \right| < \epsilon.$$

But $f(a) = g(a) = 0$, so we can write

$$\left| \frac{f(x)}{g(x)} - L \right| = \left| \frac{f(x) - f(a)}{g(x) - g(a)} - L \right|.$$

Now we apply the Extended Mean Value Theorem: there exists $z$ between $x$ and $a$ such that

$$f'(z)(g(x) - g(a)) = g'(z)(f(x) - f(a)).$$

Furthermore, since we know that $g'(z) \neq 0$ and $g(x) \neq g(a)$, we may divide by $g'(z)(g(x) - g(a))$ to get

$$\frac{f(x) - f(a)}{g(x) - g(a)} = \frac{f'(z)}{g'(z)},$$

and since $0 < |z - a| < |x - a| < \delta$, we have by (6.A.1) that

$$\epsilon > \left| \frac{f'(z)}{g'(z)} - L \right| = \left| \frac{f(x) - f(a)}{g(x) - g(a)} - L \right| = \left| \frac{f(x)}{g(x)} - L \right|.$$

Thus, by the $\delta$-$\epsilon$ definition of limit, we conclude that

$$\lim_{x \to a} \frac{f(x)}{g(x)} = L,$$

as desired.  $\square$

> **Problem 6.37:** Modify the solution to Problem 6.36 to prove l'Hôpital's Rule where $\spadesuit = 0$, $\heartsuit = a$ for some $a \in \mathbb{R}$, and
>
> $$\lim_{x \to a} \frac{f'(x)}{g'(x)} = \pm\infty.$$

*Solution for Problem 6.37:* If $L$ is $\pm\infty$, then all the statements in the solution to Problem 6.36 of the form

$$\left|\text{something} - L\right| < \epsilon$$

get replaced by statements of the form

$$\left|\text{something}\right| > N \text{ (if } L = +\infty) \quad \text{or} \quad \left|\text{something}\right| < N \text{ (if } L = -\infty),$$

but all of the same arguments hold. $\square$

**Problem 6.38:** Use Problem 6.4 to prove l'Hôpital's Rule for the case where $\heartsuit = \pm\infty$ and $\spadesuit = 0$.

*Solution for Problem 6.38:* By Problems 6.36 and 6.37, we know that l'Hôpital's Rule is true for $\heartsuit = 0$. Thus, we can prove the case where $\heartsuit = \pm\infty$ by replacing $f(x)$ and $g(x)$ by $f(1/x)$ and $g(1/x)$, respectively. In particular:

$$\lim_{x\to\pm\infty} \frac{f(x)}{g(x)} = \lim_{u\to 0^\pm} \frac{f(1/u)}{g(1/u)}$$
$$= \lim_{u\to 0^\pm} \frac{\frac{d}{du}f(1/u)}{\frac{d}{du}g(1/u)}$$
$$= \lim_{u\to 0^\pm} \frac{(-1/u^2)f'(1/u)}{(-1/u^2)g'(1/u)}$$
$$= \lim_{u\to 0^\pm} \frac{f'(1/u)}{g'(1/u)}$$
$$= \lim_{x\to\pm\infty} \frac{f'(x)}{g'(x)}.$$

$\square$

The previous problems prove l'Hôpital's Rule in all cases where $\spadesuit = 0$. Unfortunately, the case where $\spadesuit = \pm\infty$ is considerably harder. We will prove one specific case of this, and leave it to the reader to extend it to other cases in a similar manner as above.

We first prove the following lemma:

**Problem 6.39:** Let $f$ be a function such that $\lim\limits_{x\to\infty} f(x) = \infty$, and let $a \in \mathbb{R}$. Show that

$$\lim_{x\to\infty} \frac{f(x) + a}{f(x)} = 1.$$

*Solution for Problem 6.39:* We simply compute:

$$\lim_{x\to\infty} \frac{f(x) + a}{f(x)} = \lim_{x\to\infty} \left(1 + \frac{a}{f(x)}\right) = 1 + 0 = 1.$$

$\square$

**Problem 6.40:** Let $f, g$ be differentiable functions such that

$$\lim_{x \to \infty} f(x) = \lim_{x \to \infty} g(x) = \infty,$$

and

$$\lim_{x \to \infty} \frac{f'(x)}{g'(x)} = L$$

for some $L \in \mathbb{R}$. Prove that

$$\lim_{x \to \infty} \frac{f(x)}{g(x)} = L.$$

**WARNING!!**    The proof is quite difficult.

*Solution for Problem 6.40:*  By definition, for any $\epsilon > 0$, there exists some $M > 0$ such that

$$x > M \quad \Rightarrow \quad \left| \frac{f'(x)}{g'(x)} - L \right| < \frac{\epsilon}{4}. \tag{6.A.2}$$

(The reason that we use $\frac{\epsilon}{4}$ rather than $\epsilon$ will become more clear later in the proof.) Also, for all $x > M$, there exists, via the Extended Mean Value Theorem, some $z \in (M, x)$ such that

$$\frac{f(x) - f(M)}{g(x) - g(M)} = \frac{f'(z)}{g'(z)}.$$

(We have $g'(z) \neq 0$ and $g(x) \neq g(M)$ for essentially the same reason as in Problem 6.36; we will not repeat the details here.) This, combined with (6.A.2), means that

$$x > M \quad \Rightarrow \quad \left| \frac{f(x) - f(M)}{g(x) - g(M)} - L \right| < \frac{\epsilon}{4}.$$

However, we want to be able to compare $\frac{f(x)}{g(x)}$ to $L$, so we introduce some algebraic sleight-of-hand. Define a new function

$$j(x) = \frac{f(x)}{f(x) - f(M)} \cdot \frac{g(x) - g(M)}{g(x)},$$

so that

$$\frac{f(x)}{g(x)} = \frac{f(x) - f(M)}{g(x) - g(M)} \cdot j(x).$$

By Problem 6.39, we know that

$$\lim_{x \to \infty} j(x) = \lim_{x \to \infty} \left( \frac{f(x)}{f(x) - f(M)} \right) \cdot \lim_{x \to \infty} \left( \frac{g(x) - g(M)}{g(x)} \right) = 1 \cdot 1 = 1.$$

Thus, we can choose $N > M$ sufficiently large so that for all $x > N$,

$$|j(x) - 1| < \min \left\{ 1, \frac{\epsilon}{2|L|} \right\}.$$

Then for all $x > N$, we have $|j(x)| < 2$, and we compute (for $L \neq 0$):

$$
\begin{aligned}
\left| \frac{f(x)}{g(x)} - L \right| &= \left| \left( \frac{f(x) - f(M)}{g(x) - g(M)} \right) j(x) - L \right| \\
&\leq \left| \left( \frac{f(x) - f(M)}{g(x) - g(M)} \right) j(x) - L j(x) \right| + |L j(x) - L| \\
&= |j(x)| \left| \frac{f(x) - f(M)}{g(x) - g(M)} - L \right| + |L||j(x) - 1| \\
&< 2 \left( \frac{\epsilon}{4} \right) + |L| \left( \frac{\epsilon}{2|L|} \right) \\
&\leq \epsilon.
\end{aligned}
$$

(If $L = 0$, then we only require $N$ sufficiently large so that $|j(x) - 1| < 1$ for all $x > N$, and in the above computation, the second term on the next-to-last line will be 0.)

In summary, we have shown that for any $\epsilon > 0$, there exists $N$ such that

$$
x > N \quad \Rightarrow \quad \left| \frac{f(x)}{g(x)} - L \right| < \epsilon,
$$

thus we have established $\lim\limits_{x \to \infty} \dfrac{f(x)}{g(x)} = L$. $\square$

The proof that l'Hôpital's Rule holds as in Problem 6.40 for $L = \pm\infty$ will be left to the reader.

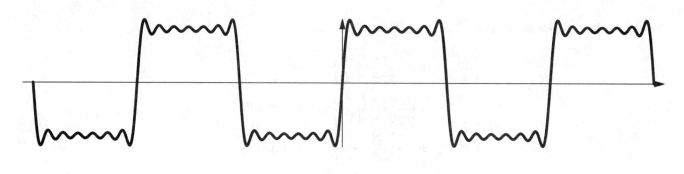

CHAPTER **7**

Series

## 7.1 Infinite sequences

> **Definition:** A **sequence** is a list of numbers.

Occasionally this list will be finite, but most often in calculus we deal with infinite sequences. We may write an infinite sequence as a list of numbers separated by commas, with an ellipsis (...) to indicate that the sequence is infinite, assuming the pattern is clear. For example,

$$1, 2, 4, 8, 16, 32, \ldots$$

is the infinite sequence consisting of all the positive powers of 2.

However, more often we refer to elements of a sequence using variables, like so:

$$a_1, a_2, a_3, \ldots,$$

where the **index** of each term in the sequence is denoted using a subscript. We would denote the entire sequence as $\{a_n\}_{n=1}^{\infty}$. Sequences need not start at $n = 1$. For instance, some sequences might start at $n = 0$ rather than $n = 1$; we would write such as sequence as $\{a_n\}_{n=0}^{\infty}$.

Note, however, that a sequence is not the same as a set (despite the similar-looking notation), because a key facet of a sequence is that the terms are ordered: there is a first term, then a second term, then a third term, and so on. We often omit the bounds ($n = 1$ and $\infty$) if the context makes clear that $\{a_n\}$ is a sequence (and not a set). And, of course, if the sequence is finite rather than infinite, we replace $\infty$ with the index of the last term.

A very common and useful type of sequence is a **geometric sequence**, which is a sequence in which the ratio between every two consecutive terms is constant. For example, the sequence

$$3, 6, 12, 24, 48, \ldots$$

is a geometric sequence with first term 3 and common ratio 2.

Naturally, there is a more formal definition:

---

**Definition:** A sequence $\{a_n\}_{n=1}^{\infty}$ is a **geometric sequence** if there exists a real number $r$ such that $a_{k+1} = ra_k$ for all $k \geq 1$. The number $r$ is called the **common ratio** of the geometric sequence.

---

**Problem 7.1:** Suppose $\{a_n\}_{n=1}^{\infty}$ is a geometric sequence with common ratio $r$. Write a formula for $a_n$ in terms of $a_1$ and $r$.

---

*Solution for Problem 7.1:* To reach $a_n$ in the sequence, we start with the first term $a_1$ and multiply by the common ratio $r$ a total of $n-1$ times (since we must move $n-1$ terms forward in the sequence to get from $a_1$ to $a_n$). Thus, the formula is $a_n = r^{n-1}a_1$. $\square$

---

**WARNING!!** It is a common mistake to write $a_n = r^n a_1$ for the $n^{\text{th}}$ term of the geometric series starting at $a_1$ with common ratio $r$. We need to multiply $a_1$ by $r$ only $n-1$ times to get the $n^{\text{th}}$ term, so the formula is $a_n = r^{n-1}a_1$.

---

Sequences can also be defined **recursively**, meaning that each term is defined in terms of one or more previous terms.

For example, a geometric sequence $\{a_n\}_{n=1}^{\infty}$ with common ratio $r$ can be defined recursively by

$$a_k = ra_{k-1}$$

for all $k \geq 2$. Note that this **recursive formula** does not tell us anything about the first term $a_1$—it must be given or assumed—but all subsequent terms can then be expressed recursively.

An advantage of the recursive method of defining a sequence is that it gives us more flexibility to define other sequences that would be hard to define explicitly. For example, the **Fibonacci sequence** is the sequence that starts $1, 1, \ldots$ and where each subsequent term is the sum of the previous two terms:

$$1, 1, 2, 3, 5, 8, 13, 21, 34, \ldots.$$

This is recursively defined by $a_0 = a_1 = 1$ and $a_k = a_{k-1} + a_{k-2}$ for all $k \geq 2$. Note that this recursive formula defines each term $a_k$ (for $k \geq 2$) using the two previous terms (rather that just one term as in the recursive formula for a geometric sequence), and as such we must specify the first two terms of the sequence, $a_0$ and $a_1$, in order to completely define the sequence.

---

**Sidenote:** Although not used in calculus, the Fibonacci sequence occurs quite often in discrete mathematics. You can read more about the Fibonacci sequence and its applications in Art of Problem Solving's *Intermediate Counting & Probability* textbook.

---

Another way to define an infinite sequence is as a real-valued function whose domain is the positive integers (or possibly the nonnegative integers). Specifically, we think of $\{a_n\}_{n=1}^{\infty}$ as a function $a$ such that $a(n) = a_n$ for any positive integer $n$. This is sometimes called a **discrete function**, because its domain includes only the discrete values $1, 2, 3, \ldots$.

A natural question that we can ask about an infinite sequence $\{a_n\}_{n=1}^{\infty}$ is whether it **converges** to any number. In other words, we can try to compute $\lim\limits_{n \to \infty} a_n$. This has the same formal definition as $\lim\limits_{x \to \infty} a(x)$ does for a function $a$, except that our sequence is a discrete function and not a function defined on all of $\mathbb{R}$.

> **Definition:** We say that an infinite sequence $\{a_n\}_{n=1}^{\infty}$ **converges** to $L$, also written
>
> $$\lim_{n \to \infty} a_n = L,$$
>
> if for any $\epsilon > 0$ there exists a positive integer $N$ such that for any $n > N$, we have $|a_n - L| < \epsilon$.

In words, this means that we can choose $N$ sufficiently large so that all terms of the sequence after $a_N$ are within $\epsilon$ of $L$. Thus, the sequence gets "arbitrarily close" to $L$ as $n$ gets arbitrarily large.

If the sequence does not converge, we say it **diverges**.

Because the definition for the convergence of an infinite sequence is basically the same as that of the infinite limit of a function, we can often use our function tools to compute sequence convergence. Specifically, if we can write $a_n = f(n)$ for some function $f$ whose domain includes the positive real numbers, then

$$\lim_{n \to \infty} a_n = \lim_{x \to \infty} f(x),$$

assuming the limit of the function is defined.

> **WARNING!!** The sequence might converge even if the function doesn't, so be careful! For example, the sequence $a_n = 0$ trivially converges to 0, but the function $f(x) = \sin \pi x$ does not have a limit as $x \to \infty$, even though $f(n) = a_n$ for all positive integers $n$.

> **Problem 7.2:** Let $\{a_n\}_{n=1}^{\infty}$ be a geometric sequence with common ratio $r$. When does this sequence converge, and to what value (in terms of $a_1$ and $r$)?

*Solution for Problem 7.2:* If $r = 0$, then the sequence is $a_1, 0, 0, 0, \ldots$, which clearly converges to 0. If $r \neq 0$, then we have $a_n = r^{n-1}a_1$, and we compute

$$\lim_{x \to \infty} r^{x-1} a_1 = \frac{a_1}{r} \lim_{x \to \infty} r^x.$$

If $a_1 = 0$, then the limit is 0, and the sequence is the constant sequence in which every term is 0. Otherwise, if $a_1 \neq 0$, then the sequence converges if and only if $r^x$ converges. This will converge if and only if $r \in (-1, 1]$. Note that if $r = 1$, then the sequence is constant, and if $|r| < 1$, then the sequence converges to 0. Also note that the sequence does not converge if $r = -1$, since $(-1)^x$ does not converge as $x \to \infty$, but instead the sequence alternates between $a_1$ and $-a_1$. $\square$

Some sequences are a lot trickier to analyze. For example:

> **Problem 7.3:** Does the sequence $a_n = \left(1 + \frac{1}{n}\right)^n$ converge?

*Solution for Problem 7.3:* This sequence consists of the values at positive integers of the function $f(x) = \left(1 + \frac{1}{x}\right)^x$. We computed the limit of this function in Problem 6.14, and thus

$$\lim_{n \to \infty} a_n = \lim_{x \to \infty} f(x) = e.$$

$\square$

In many instances, we don't really care what value a particular infinite sequence converges to; we'd just like to know whether it converges or not. In these cases, we can examine sequences a bit more qualitatively, as in the following examples.

> **Problem 7.4:** Suppose that we have a sequence $\{a_n\}$ that is **increasing**: that is, $a_k \leq a_{k+1}$ for all $k \geq 1$. Show that the sequence converges if and only if it is bounded above, meaning that there is some number $M$ such that $a_n \leq M$ for all positive integers $n$.

An example of such a sequence is

$$0, \frac{1}{2}, \frac{2}{3}, \frac{3}{4}, \dots,$$

that is, the sequence given by $a_n = 1 - \dfrac{1}{n}$ for all positive integers $n$. This sequence is increasing, and clearly converges to 1.

*Solution for Problem 7.4:* First, we assume that the sequence is bounded above; we will prove that it converges. Thinking back to Chapter 1, what do we know about a nonempty set of real numbers that has an upper bound? We know that the set has a least upper bound, called the **supremum** of the set. As you recall, this is one of the defining axioms of the real numbers.

We claim that if $\{a_n\}$ is increasing and bounded, then

$$\lim_{n \to \infty} a_n = \sup\{a_n\}.$$

Note that when we write $\sup\{a_n\}$, we are thinking of the elements of the sequence merely as a set and not as an ordered list.

To prove our claim, let $A = \sup\{a_n\}$, and let $\epsilon > 0$ be given. Choose $N$ such that $a_N > A - \epsilon$. Such an $N$ must exist, because if it does not, then $A - \epsilon$ is an upper bound for $\{a_n\}$, contradicting the fact that $A$ is the *least* upper bound for $\{a_n\}$. Then, since the sequence is increasing, we have

$$n > N \quad \Rightarrow \quad A \geq a_n \geq a_N > A - \epsilon \quad \Rightarrow \quad 0 \leq A - a_n < \epsilon.$$

Thus, by the definition of convergence, we conclude that $\{a_n\}$ converges to $A$.

We leave the opposite direction of the proof—that is, proving that if an increasing sequence converges, then it has an upper bound—as an exercise. $\square$

There is a similar statement for decreasing sequences: if a sequence $\{a_n\}_{n=1}^{\infty}$ is a decreasing sequence, so that $a_{k+1} \leq a_k$ for all $k \geq 1$, then the sequence converges if and only if it has a lower bound, and if this is the case, then the sequence converges to the greatest lower bound $\inf\{a_n\}$. The proof is virtually identical to the solution to Problem 7.4, so we will omit it.

> **Definition:**
>
> - A sequence $\{a_n\}_{n=1}^{\infty}$ is called **monotonically increasing** if $a_k \leq a_{k+1}$ for all $k \geq 1$.
> - A sequence $\{a_n\}_{n=1}^{\infty}$ is called **monotonically decreasing** if $a_k \geq a_{k+1}$ for all $k \geq 1$.
> - A sequence $\{a_n\}_{n=1}^{\infty}$ is called **strictly monotonically increasing** if $a_k < a_{k+1}$ for all $k \geq 1$.
> - A sequence $\{a_n\}_{n=1}^{\infty}$ is called **strictly monotonically decreasing** if $a_k > a_{k+1}$ for all $k \geq 1$.
> - In any of these cases, $\{a_n\}$ is called **monotonic**.

Thus our conclusion is:

> **Concept:** A bounded monotonic sequence converges.

Let's look at a couple more sequence convergence examples.

**Problem 7.5:** Consider the infinite sequence $a_n = \dfrac{n!}{n^n}$. Does this sequence converge, and if so, to what value?

*Solution for Problem 7.5:* It sometimes helps to list a few terms, to get some idea of what's going on:

$$a_1 = \frac{1!}{1^1} = 1,$$

$$a_2 = \frac{2!}{2^2} = \frac{1}{2},$$

$$a_3 = \frac{3!}{3^3} = \frac{2}{9},$$

$$a_4 = \frac{4!}{4^4} = \frac{3}{32}.$$

It seems that the sequence is strictly monotonically decreasing, and that 0 is the greatest lower bound. So we suspect that the sequence converges to 0. Let's try to prove both of these facts.

First, we want to show that $a_n > a_{n+1}$ for all $n \geq 1$. Since all the terms are positive, this is equivalent to showing that $\dfrac{a_{n+1}}{a_n} < 1$.

**Concept:** Examining the ratio of consecutive terms of a sequence is often a useful tool for getting information about the sequence.

Let's write out this expression:

$$\frac{a_{n+1}}{a_n} = \frac{\frac{(n+1)!}{(n+1)^{n+1}}}{\frac{n!}{n^n}} = \frac{(n+1)!}{n!} \cdot \frac{n^n}{(n+1)^{n+1}} = \frac{(n+1)n^n}{(n+1)^{n+1}} = \left(\frac{n}{n+1}\right)^n < 1.$$

So the sequence is strictly monotonically decreasing. Since it has a lower bound (namely, 0), we know it converges. We'd like to show that $0 = \inf\{a_n\}$ so that we can conclude that the sequences converges to 0.

**Concept:** Note the distinction between the previous two sentences. Knowing that a monotonic sequence is bounded is enough to prove that it converges, but if we want to know the value to which it converges, we need the greatest lower bound (for a decreasing sequence) or the least upper bound (for an increasing sequence).

To show that 0 is the greatest lower bound, we need to show that the sequence gets arbitrarily close to 0 as $n$ grows large. To see this, let's write $a_n$ in a slightly different way:

$$a_n = \frac{n!}{n^n} = \frac{1}{n} \cdot \frac{2}{n} \cdot \frac{3}{n} \cdot \ldots \cdot \frac{n}{n}.$$

The last term is $\frac{n}{n} = 1$, so we have

$$a_n = \frac{1}{n} \cdot \frac{2}{n} \cdot \ldots \cdot \frac{n-1}{n}.$$

We notice that at least half of these terms are less than or equal to $\frac{1}{2}$ (in particular, the terms where the numerator is at most $\frac{n}{2}$), and the rest of the terms are less than 1. Therefore,

$$a_n \leq \left(\frac{1}{2}\right)^{\frac{n-1}{2}} = \frac{1}{\left(\sqrt{2}\right)^{n-1}}.$$

Thus

$$0 < a_n \le \frac{1}{\left(\sqrt{2}\right)^{n-1}}$$

for all $n \ge 1$, and taking the limit as $n \to \infty$ and using the Squeeze Theorem, we have

$$0 \le \lim_{n \to \infty} a_n \le \lim_{n \to \infty} \frac{1}{\left(\sqrt{2}\right)^{n-1}} = 0.$$

Thus, $\inf\{a_n\} = \lim_{n \to \infty} a_n = 0.$ $\square$

**Problem 7.6:** Determine if the sequence $a_n = \sqrt[n]{n}$ converges, and if so, to what value.

*Solution for Problem 7.6:* As in the previous problem, experimenting (perhaps with your calculator) might convince you that this sequence is monotonically decreasing and that 1 is a lower bound. So we might guess that it converges to 1.

We can try computing

$$\lim_{x \to \infty} x^{\frac{1}{x}}.$$

If this limit exists, then it is also the limit of our sequence (although, recall the warning on page 222—the sequence might converge even if the above limit does not exist). Noticing that this function is an $\infty^0$ indeterminate form as $x \to \infty$, we try taking logs and using l'Hôpital's Rule. Specifically, we have that

$$\log x^{\frac{1}{x}} = \frac{\log x}{x}.$$

We see that $\frac{\log x}{x}$ is an $\frac{\infty}{\infty}$ indeterminate form, so we apply l'Hôpital's Rule, giving

$$\lim_{x \to \infty} \frac{\log x}{x} = \lim_{x \to \infty} \frac{\frac{1}{x}}{1} = \lim_{x \to \infty} \frac{1}{x} = 0.$$

Taking exponentials, we get $\lim_{x \to \infty} x^{\frac{1}{x}} = e^0 = 1$, and hence the original sequence converges to 1. $\square$

## EXERCISES

**7.1.1** In each of the following, determine if the sequence $\{a_n\}_{n=1}^{\infty}$ converges, and, if it converges, what it converges to.

(a) $\quad a_n = \dfrac{n^3 - 1}{n^3 + 3n^2 + 3n + 1}$
(b) $\quad a_n = \dfrac{3n^2 + 2e^n}{n - e^n}$
(c) $\quad a_n = \dfrac{n \sin n}{n^2 + 1}$ **Hints:** 234

(d) $\quad a_n = \sqrt[4]{n^2 + 1} - \sqrt{n + 1}$ **Hints:** 266 (e) $\quad a_n = \sqrt[n]{n^2 + 1}$ **Hints:** 18

**7.1.2** Prove that when each term in a geometric sequence is multiplied by a constant $k$, then the resulting sequence is also geometric.

**7.1.3**

(a) Show that nonzero numbers $x$, $y$, and $z$ are consecutive terms of a geometric sequence if and only if $y^2 = xz$.

(b) Is it true that nonzero numbers $x$, $y$ and $z$ are consecutive terms of a geometric sequence if and only if $y = \sqrt{xz}$?

**7.1.4** Prove a stronger version of the "only if" direction of Problem 7.4: if an infinite sequence converges, then it is bounded.

## 7.2 INFINITE SERIES

Summing the elements of a sequence results in a **series**. If the sequence is finite, this is pretty easy, although the technical details of the definition may be somewhat more complicated than you are used to:

---

**Definition:** The **series** corresponding to the finite sequence $\{a_n\}_{n=1}^k$ is the finite sequence of **partial sums** of the initial terms of the sequence:

$$a_1, \; a_1 + a_2, \; a_1 + a_2 + a_3, \; \ldots, \; a_1 + a_2 + \cdots + a_k.$$

The final term $a_1 + \cdots + a_k = \sum_{i=1}^k a_i$ is the **sum** of the series.

---

**WARNING!!** The terminology can be somewhat ambiguous. We often refer to the "series" as simply the sum $\sum_{i=1}^k a_i$, even though this is really a number. However, inherent in the definition of "series" is the *order* of the terms that we are summing, which is why it is more proper to consider a series as a sequence of partial sums. This is not much of a concern with finite series, but as we will soon see it is more of an issue for infinite series.

More generally, sometimes we say that a "series" is the sum of a sequence, and other times we "sum a series" to get a value. Usually the context makes it clear what we are talking about.

---

If our sequence is finite, then there's really no issue: we just sum the terms. In particular, if we have a finite sequence $\{a_n\}_{n=1}^k$, then the sum of the corresponding series is

$$a_1 + a_2 + \cdots + a_k = \sum_{i=1}^k a_i.$$

We see this with a basic example that you probably already know:

**Problem 7.7:** What is the sum of the series corresponding to the finite geometric sequence with $n$ terms, first term $a$, and common ratio $r$?

*Solution for Problem 7.7:* Let's write the sum explicitly:

$$\text{Sum} = a + ra + r^2 a + \cdots + r^{n-1} a$$
$$= a(1 + r + r^2 + \cdots + r^{n-1}).$$

There are two ways to finish from here. One way is to recall the factorization

$$r^n - 1 = (r-1)(r^{n-1} + r^{n-2} + \cdots + 1).$$

Thus we can write our sum as

$$\frac{a(r^n - 1)}{r - 1}.$$

Of course, we can't do this if $r = 1$. In that case, the sum is just $na$.

The other method is to denote the sum as

$$S = a(1 + r + r^2 + \cdots + r^{n-1}),$$

so that

$$rS = a(r + r^2 + r^3 + \cdots + r^n).$$

When we subtract, most of the terms cancel:

$$rS - S = a(r^n - 1),$$

and dividing by $r - 1$ (again assuming $r \neq 1$) gives

$$S = \frac{a(r^n - 1)}{r - 1}.$$

$\square$

> **Concept:** The sum of the series corresponding to the finite geometric sequence with $n$ terms, first term $a$, and common ratio $r$ is $\dfrac{a(r^n - 1)}{r - 1}$ if $r \neq 1$, and $na$ if $r = 1$.

Much more interesting, and more useful to calculus, are sums of terms of infinite sequences, and in particular the "sum" of an entire infinite sequence. Since we can't formally evaluate an infinite sum, we do the most logical alternative: we take the limit of finite sums.

> **Definition:** The **infinite series** corresponding to the infinite sequence $\{a_n\}_{n=1}^{\infty}$ is the infinite sequence of **partial sums** of the initial terms of the sequence:
>
> $$a_1, \ a_1 + a_2, \ a_1 + a_2 + a_3, \ \ldots.$$
>
> The **sum** of the series is defined as the limit of the terms of the series; that is,
>
> $$\sum_{i=1}^{\infty} a_i = \lim_{k \to \infty} \sum_{i=1}^{k} a_i.$$
>
> If this limit exists and is equal to some real number $S$, we say that the series **converges** to $S$; if the limit is $\pm\infty$ or does not exist, we say that the series **diverges**.

> **WARNING!!** The terminology tends to be a bit sloppy. We often refer to the "infinite series" as the "sum" $\displaystyle\sum_{i=1}^{\infty} a_i$, even though this is really a limit of the partial sums in our series.

Let's look at our basic example:

> **Problem 7.8:** What is the sum of the series corresponding to the infinite geometric sequence with first term $a$ and common ratio $r$?

*Solution for Problem 7.8:* If $r = 1$, then the geometric sequence is the constant sequence $a, a, a, \ldots$, and thus the corresponding series does not converge unless $a = 0$. So let's assume that $r \neq 1$. We need to compute

$$\lim_{n \to \infty} \frac{a(r^n - 1)}{r - 1}.$$

If $a = 0$, then the sum of the series is trivially 0, so let's further assume that $a$ is nonzero.

We can factor out the constants:

$$\frac{a}{r - 1} \lim_{n \to \infty} (r^n - 1).$$

We now have cases depending on the value of $r$.

If $|r| < 1$, then $r^n$ approaches 0, and the sum becomes $\frac{a}{1 - r}$. Note that this works regardless of whether $r$ is positive or negative.

If $r = -1$ or $|r| > 1$, then the limit of $r^n$ diverges. So the sum diverges. $\square$

> **Important:** Given an infinite geometric sequence with first term $a \neq 0$ and common ratio $r$, the corresponding series converges to $\frac{a}{1 - r}$ if $|r| < 1$, and diverges if $|r| \geq 1$.

Let's practice using this infinite series:

**Problem 7.9:** The sum of an infinite geometric series with common ratio $r$ such that $|r| < 1$ is 15, and the sum of the squares of the terms of this series is 45. What is the first term of the series? *(Source: AMC)*

*Solution for Problem 7.9:* We can sum an infinite geometric series if we know the first term and the common ratio, but in this problem the first term is not given to us. However, we can let the first term be $a$ and see if we can find any helpful equations to work with. The sum of the first series, in terms of $a$, is

$$\frac{a}{1 - r} = 15.$$

We can find the sum of the second series in terms of $a$ and $r$ in the same way. We note that the second series is geometric with first term $a^2$ and common ratio $r^2$, so we have the sum

$$\frac{a^2}{1 - r^2} = 45.$$

Thus, we now have two equations involving $r$ and $a$:

$$\frac{a}{1 - r} = 15,$$
$$\frac{a^2}{1 - r^2} = 45.$$

To solve this system of equations most easily, we can multiply through by the denominators:

$$a = 15(1 - r),$$
$$a^2 = 45(1 - r^2).$$

We notice that the first equation involves expressions that are both factors of the corresponding parts of the second equation. This gives us the idea to divide the second equation by the first equation, giving $a = 3(1 + r)$.

We now have two linear expressions for $a$, so we can equate these expressions and solve for $r$:

$$15 - 15r = 3 + 3r,$$

giving $12 = 18r$ and $r = \frac{2}{3}$.

To finish the problem, we need the first term of the original series, which is just $a$, so $a = 3 + 3r = 3 + 2 = 5$. □

## Exercises

**7.2.1** Suppose $\{a_n\}$ and $\{b_n\}$ are infinite sequences such that the corresponding infinite series converge:

$$\sum_{i=1}^{\infty} a_i = A \quad \text{and} \quad \sum_{i=1}^{\infty} b_i = B.$$

(a) Let $m \in \mathbb{R}$ and let $\{c_n\}$ be the sequence such that $c_n = ma_n$ for all $n$. Prove that

$$\sum_{i=1}^{\infty} c_i = mA.$$

(b) Let $\{d_n\}$ be the sequence such that $d_n = a_n + b_n$ for all $n$. Prove that

$$\sum_{i=1}^{\infty} d_i = A + B.$$

**Hints:** 158

**7.2.2** Sum each of the following infinite geometric series:

(a) $\dfrac{1}{6^1} + \dfrac{1}{6^2} + \dfrac{1}{6^3} + \cdots$

(b) $192 + 144 + 108 + \cdots$

(c) $2 - \sqrt{2} + 1 - \dfrac{\sqrt{2}}{2} + \dfrac{1}{2} - \cdots$

**7.2.3** Let $\{a_n\}_{n=1}^{\infty}$ be an infinite sequence, and suppose that $a_n = b_n - b_{n+1}$ (for all $n \geq 1$) for some sequence $\{b_n\}_{n=1}^{\infty}$.

(a) Show that, if $\lim_{n \to \infty} b_n = 0$, then $\sum_{n=1}^{\infty} a_n = b_1$. (We call this method of computing the sum **telescoping**.)

(b) Compute $\displaystyle\sum_{n=1}^{\infty} \dfrac{1}{n^2 + n}$. **Hints:** 205

(c) Compute $\displaystyle\sum_{n=1}^{\infty} \dfrac{6^n}{(3^{n+1} - 2^{n+1})(3^n - 2^n)}$. *(Source: Putnam)* **Hints:** 150, 116, 129

**7.2.4** Find the sum $\dfrac{1}{7} + \dfrac{2}{7^2} + \dfrac{1}{7^3} + \dfrac{2}{7^4} + \cdots$. *(Source: AHSME)* **Hints:** 239

## 7.3 Series convergence tests

The first question that we usually ask when presented with an infinite series is: does it converge? In this section, we will discuss a number of convergence tests that we can perform on infinite series. Most of the tests that we present in this section only work for infinite series corresponding to sequences with nonnegative values; in Section 7.4, we will discuss methods to study series with both positive and negative terms.

Before going on to more sophisticated convergence tests, we should note one basic fact about convergence that should be clear:

**Problem 7.10:** If $\displaystyle\sum_{n=1}^{\infty} a_n$ converges, then what do we know about $\displaystyle\lim_{n\to\infty} a_n$?

*Solution for Problem 7.10:*  Intuitively, we can reason as follows: "We're taking an infinite sum of terms of a sequence, so if that sum ends up being finite, then the terms that we are summing had better get arbitrarily close to 0. So the limit of the sequence must be 0 if the series converges."

This intuitive reasoning is absolutely correct. The proof, however, is a bit technical. If you are convinced of the intuitive reasoning, feel free to skip to the end of the solution; if you want to see the gory details, read on.

Let $L = \displaystyle\sum_{k=1}^{\infty} a_k$ be the sum of the series. Then we know that given any $\epsilon > 0$, there exists some $N$ so that for any $n \geq N$,

$$\left| L - \sum_{k=1}^{n} a_k \right| < \epsilon.$$

In particular, we can compute the sums for $n$ and $n + 1$:

$$\left| L - \sum_{k=1}^{n} a_k \right| < \epsilon \qquad \text{and} \qquad \left| L - \sum_{k=1}^{n+1} a_k \right| < \epsilon.$$

What happens when we add these inequalities? If we reverse the order inside one of the absolute values, then we can make most of the terms cancel when we apply the Triangle Inequality:

$$2\epsilon > \left| \sum_{k=1}^{n+1} a_k - L \right| + \left| L - \sum_{k=1}^{n} a_k \right| \geq \left| \sum_{k=1}^{n+1} a_k - \sum_{k=1}^{n} a_k \right| = |a_{n+1}|.$$

Thus we get $|a_{n+1}| < 2\epsilon$. But this is true for all $n > N$. So we have proved that, given any $2\epsilon > 0$, we can find $N > 0$ such that $|a_n| < 2\epsilon$ for any $n > N$. This, by definition, means that $\displaystyle\lim_{n\to\infty} a_n = 0$. $\square$

Taking the contrapositive of Problem 7.10 gives us our most basic test of convergence or divergence:

**Important:** The **Divergence Test**: if $\{a_n\}$ is a sequence such that $\displaystyle\lim_{n\to\infty} a_n \neq 0$ or $\displaystyle\lim_{n\to\infty} a_n$ does not exist, then $\sum a_n$ diverges.

One common infinite series that occurs in calculus (and indeed in higher mathematics in general) is:

$$\sum_{n=1}^{\infty} \frac{1}{n^p},$$

where $p > 0$ is some fixed real number. This is called a *p*-**series**. If $p = 1$, this is the **harmonic series**:

$$1 + \frac{1}{2} + \frac{1}{3} + \frac{1}{4} + \cdots.$$

**Problem 7.11:** Does the harmonic series converge, and if so, to what?

*Solution for Problem 7.11:* We can list the first few partial sums:

$$1 = 1,$$

$$1 + \frac{1}{2} = 1.5$$

$$1 + \frac{1}{2} + \frac{1}{3} = 1.8333\ldots$$

$$1 + \frac{1}{2} + \frac{1}{3} + \frac{1}{4} = 2.0833\ldots$$

$$1 + \frac{1}{2} + \frac{1}{3} + \frac{1}{4} + \frac{1}{5} = 2.2833\ldots$$

$$\vdots$$

It is clear that these sums form a monotonically increasing sequence, and because the growth rate of the sequence is slowing, we may suspect that it is bounded above, and thus converges.

However, it diverges, and there is a relatively simple yet ingenious proof. The clever idea is to group the terms by powers of 2:

$$\sum_{n=1}^{\infty} \frac{1}{n} = 1$$
$$+ \frac{1}{2}$$
$$+ \frac{1}{3} + \frac{1}{4}$$
$$+ \frac{1}{5} + \frac{1}{6} + \frac{1}{7} + \frac{1}{8}$$
$$+ \frac{1}{9} + \frac{1}{10} + \frac{1}{11} + \frac{1}{12} + \frac{1}{13} + \frac{1}{14} + \frac{1}{15} + \frac{1}{16}$$
$$+ \cdots$$

Note that we can continue this process indefinitely, and that each row (after the first) will be greater than $\frac{1}{2}$. Thus, the sum grows without bound, hence the series diverges. $\square$

The reasoning that we used in the previous solution is a basic example of the **Series Comparison Test**, which we explore in the next problem. In this problem, we also introduce the shorthand notation $\sum a_n$ for the sum of the series corresponding to the sequence $\{a_n\}_{n=1}^{\infty}$.

**Problem 7.12:** Suppose $\{a_n\}$ and $\{b_n\}$ are two sequences such that $0 \leq a_n \leq b_n$ for all $n$.
(a) If $\sum b_n$ converges, what can we conclude about $\sum a_n$?
(b) If $\sum a_n$ converges, what can we conclude about $\sum b_n$?
(c) What conclusions can we make about divergence?
(d) Why do we need the condition that the terms of the sequences are nonnegative?

*Solution for Problem 7.12:*

(a) The key idea is that the sequence of partial sums

$$a_1, a_1 + a_2, a_1 + a_2 + a_3, \ldots$$

is a monotonically increasing sequence (since all the $a_i$ are positive). So to prove it converges, we just need to show that it has an upper bound. Fortunately, we have a very likely candidate for an upper bound. Let

$$B = \lim_{n \to \infty} \sum_{k=1}^{n} b_k = \sup \left\{ \sum_{k=1}^{n} b_k \right\}.$$

We claim that $B$ is an upper bound for the sequence of partial sums of the $a_i$. This is clear, since for any positive integer $n$,

$$\sum_{k=1}^{n} a_k \le \sum_{k=1}^{n} b_k \le B.$$

So the partial sums of $\{a_n\}$ are bounded, and thus the monotonically increasing sequence of partial sums of $\{a_n\}$ converges, which by definition means that the series $\sum a_n$ converges.

(b) Part (a) does not work in the other direction. To take a simple example, let

$$\{a_n\} = 1, \frac{1}{2}, \frac{1}{4}, \frac{1}{8}, \cdots$$

and

$$\{b_n\} = 1, \frac{1}{2}, \frac{1}{3}, \frac{1}{4}, \cdots.$$

Note that $a_n = \dfrac{1}{2^n} \le \dfrac{1}{n} = b_n$ for all $n \ge 1$. Yet $\sum a_n$ converges whereas $\sum b_n$ diverges.

(c) We just take the contrapositive of part (a). That is, if $\{a_n\}$ diverges, then $\{b_n\}$ must diverge too (since if $\{b_n\}$ converged, we would have to have $\{a_n\}$ converge as well).

(d) None of this works if the sequences have negative terms, because then the sequences of partial sums of the series will not be monotonically increasing. However, the problem can be suitably modified if all of the terms of both sequences are nonpositive; we will leave this as an exercise.

$\square$

---

**Important:** The **Series Comparison Test**: suppose $\{a_n\}$ and $\{b_n\}$ are two sequences such that $0 \le a_n \le b_n$ for all $n$.

- If $\sum b_n$ converges, then $\sum a_n$ converges too.
- If $\sum a_n$ diverges, then $\sum b_n$ diverges too.

---

**Problem 7.13:** Prove that the $p$-series $\displaystyle\sum_{k=1}^{\infty} \frac{1}{k^p}$ diverges for all $0 \le p \le 1$.

---

*Solution for Problem 7.13:* We already saw in Problem 7.11 that the harmonic series (that is, the $p$-series for $p = 1$) diverges. But when $0 \le p \le 1$, we have $0 < k^p \le k$ for all $k \ge 1$, hence

$$\frac{1}{k^p} \ge \frac{1}{k}$$

for all positive integers $k$. Thus the terms of the $p$-series with $0 \le p \le 1$ are greater than or equal to the corresponding terms of the harmonic series. Therefore, by the Series Comparison Test, since the harmonic series diverges, so does the $p$-series. $\square$

> **Important:**
>
> The $p$-series $\displaystyle\sum_{k=1}^{\infty} \frac{1}{k^p}$ diverges if $0 \le p \le 1$.

We'll examine the $p$-series for $p > 1$ with our next tool.

Whenever we have a sum, we can try to express this sum as a Riemann sum of an appropriate function over an appropriate interval, and then use our knowledge of the corresponding definite integral to get information about the sum. For example, let's revisit the harmonic series:

$$1 + \frac{1}{2} + \frac{1}{3} + \frac{1}{4} + \cdots .$$

**Problem 7.14:**

(a) Write the (finite) sum

$$1 + \frac{1}{2} + \frac{1}{3} + \cdots + \frac{1}{n}$$

as an upper Darboux sum of an appropriate function on the interval $[1, n+1]$.

(b) Use (a) to show that

$$1 + \frac{1}{2} + \frac{1}{3} + \cdots + \frac{1}{n} > \log(n+1).$$

(c) Explain why this shows that the harmonic series diverges.

*Solution for Problem 7.14:*

(a) Writing the sum in summation notation might help to see it more clearly:

$$\sum_{k=1}^{n} \frac{1}{k}.$$

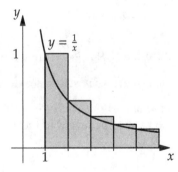

This is a Riemann sum of the function $f(x) = 1/x$ using boxes of width 1, as in the diagram to the right. Note that the first box has area 1, the second box has area $\frac{1}{2}$, the third box has area $\frac{1}{3}$, and so on. Thus, we have cleverly arranged it so that all of boxes have the maximum possible height; in other words, our Riemann sum is an upper Darboux sum of $f(x) = 1/x$ on the interval $[1, n+1]$.

(b) Using part (a), we see that the sum is strictly larger than the area under $y = \frac{1}{x}$ along $[1, n+1]$; that is,

$$\sum_{k=1}^{n} \frac{1}{k} > \int_1^{n+1} \frac{1}{x}\,dx = \log(n+1) - \log(1) = \log(n+1).$$

(c) As $n \to \infty$, we see that the partial sums grow without bound, since $\lim_{n \to \infty} \log(n+1) = \infty$. Therefore, the sum diverges.

$\square$

Problem 7.14 is an example of what is called (not surprisingly) the **Integral Test** for infinite series. But note the geometric feature of the graph that made it work: the function $f(x) = \frac{1}{x}$ is a *decreasing* function. That's what ensured that the boxes that make up our Riemann sum are larger than the area under the curve, so that the partial sum is in fact an upper Darboux sum that is an upper bound of the integral.

The test works for convergent series too (though we will leave the proof of this as an exercise). Here is the complete result:

> **Important:** The **Integral Test** for series: Suppose $a_n = f(n)$ for some positive decreasing continuous function $f$. Then
> $$\sum_{n=1}^{\infty} a_n$$
> has the same behavior as
> $$\int_1^{\infty} f(x)\,dx :$$
> they both converge or they both diverge.

> **WARNING!!** In the convergence case of the Integral Test, the value of the integral typically will not equal the sum of the series.

For example, the series

$$\frac{1}{2} + \frac{1}{4} + \frac{1}{8} + \frac{1}{16} + \cdots$$

converges to 1. If we apply the Integral Test, we get

$$\int_1^{\infty} \frac{1}{2^x}\,dx = \int_1^{\infty} (1/2)^x\,dx = \int_1^{\infty} e^{x\log(1/2)}dx = \left.\frac{1}{\log(1/2)}e^{x\log(1/2)}\right|_1^{\infty} = 0 - \frac{1/2}{\log(1/2)} = \frac{1}{2\log 2}.$$

However, in the exercises, you will be asked to explore how the value of the integral is related to the sum of the series.

We can now settle the remaining cases of $p$-series:

> **Problem 7.15:** Determine the values of $p \geq 0$ such that $\sum_{n=1}^{\infty} \frac{1}{n^p}$ converges.

*Solution for Problem 7.15:* In Problem 7.13, we showed that the $p$-series diverges for $0 \leq p \leq 1$. It is perhaps not too hard to believe that the $p$-series converges for $p > 1$. We can easily show this using the Integral Test:

$$\int_1^{\infty} \frac{1}{x^p}\,dx = \lim_{b\to\infty} \int_1^b \frac{1}{x^p}\,dx = \lim_{b\to\infty} \frac{1}{1-p}\left(\frac{1}{b^{p-1}} - 1\right).$$

If $p > 1$, then $\lim_{b\to\infty} \frac{1}{b^{p-1}} = 0$, so the integral converges, and hence by the Integral Test, the $p$-series converges. $\square$

> **Important:** The series $\sum_{n=1}^{\infty} \frac{1}{n^p}$ converges for $p > 1$, and diverges for $0 \leq p \leq 1$.

| Sidenote: ♪ | When we allow $p$ to be a complex number with real part greater than 1, the $p$-series generalizes to the **Riemann zeta function**, although traditionally it is written with the letter $s$ instead of $p$: $$\zeta(s) = \sum_{n=1}^{\infty} \frac{1}{n^s}.$$ The Riemann zeta function is the subject of perhaps the most famous unsolved problem in higher mathematics, the **Riemann Hypothesis**, which is well beyond the scope of this book. |
|---|---|

There are a couple of other series convergence tests that are important and useful. The first of these compares an unknown series to a known series that is "close to" the unknown series:

| Important: ⚠ | The **Limit Comparison Test**: Let $\{a_n\}$ and $\{b_n\}$ be positive sequences, and suppose that $$\lim_{n\to\infty} \frac{a_n}{b_n} = c \neq 0.$$ Then $\sum a_n$ and $\sum b_n$ either both converge or both diverge. |
|---|---|

Note that the key to this test is that $c$ is *nonzero*. We cannot use this test if the limit is 0 or does not exist.

We will leave the formal proof of the Limit Comparison Test as an exercise. The statement should make some intuitive sense: basically it means that $\{a_n\}$ and $\{b_n\}$ (up to a constant) behave the same as $n$ goes towards infinity. A more precise proof uses our earlier Series Comparison Test: if $\frac{a_n}{b_n} \to c$, then $a_n \leq 2cb_n$ for sufficiently large $n$, so $\sum a_n$ converges if $\sum b_n$ converges. Conversely, $b_n \leq \frac{2}{c}a_n$ for sufficiently large $n$, so $\sum b_n$ converges if $\sum a_n$ converges. (We leave it as an exercise to fill in the missing details.)

Let's see how we use the Limit Comparison Test:

| **Problem 7.16:** Does $\displaystyle\sum_{n=2}^{\infty} \frac{n^2 - n + 3}{n^3 + 3n^2 - 5n + 1}$ converge? |
|---|

*Solution for Problem 7.16:* Note that the limit of the terms is 0, so it might converge. But what we notice is that as $n$ gets large, this sequence approaches the harmonic sequence. So we suspect that the sum diverges. We can use the Limit Comparison Test to prove this.

We have $a_n = \dfrac{n^2 - n + 3}{n^3 + 3n^2 - 5n + 1}$. We want to compare it to the sequence $b_n = \dfrac{1}{n}$. This gives

$$\lim_{n\to\infty} \frac{a_n}{b_n} = \lim_{n\to\infty} \frac{n^3 - n^2 + 3n}{n^3 + 3n^2 - 5n + 1} = 1.$$

The limit of $\dfrac{a_n}{b_n}$ is indeed nonzero, so we may apply the Limit Comparsion Test. Therefore, since the harmonic series diverges, so does our given series. □

| Concept: 🔑 | We use the Limit Comparison Test to compare an unfamiliar series to a simpler series whose behavior we know. Usually, our "simpler" series is a geometric series or a $p$-series. |
|---|---|

We can use the Limit Comparison Test to make a general statement about a series whose terms are given by a rational function:

---

**Problem 7.17:** Suppose $f(n)$ and $g(n)$ are polynomials. When does $\displaystyle\sum_{n=1}^{\infty} \frac{f(n)}{g(n)}$ converge?

---

*Solution for Problem 7.17:* If $\deg f \geq \deg g$, then the series satisfies the Divergence Test $\left(\text{since } \displaystyle\lim_{n\to\infty} \frac{f(n)}{g(n)} \neq 0\right)$, so the series must diverge.

If $\deg f < \deg g$, then we compare the terms $a_n = \dfrac{f(n)}{g(n)}$ of our desired series with the terms $b_n = \dfrac{1}{n^{(\deg g - \deg f)}}$ of the $p$-series with $p = \deg g - \deg f$. We notice that

$$\frac{a_n}{b_n} = \frac{f(n) \cdot n^{(\deg g - \deg f)}}{g(n)}$$

is a ratio of polynomials (in terms of $n$) of degrees equal to $\deg g$, and thus $\displaystyle\lim_{n\to\infty} \frac{a_n}{b_n}$ is equal to the quotient of the leading coefficients of $f$ and $g$. In particular, this limit is nonzero, so we may compare the series using the Limit Comparison Test. Since the $p$-series diverges for $p = 1$ and converges for $p > 1$, we see that we must have $\deg g - \deg f > 1$ for the series to converge. $\square$

---

**Important:** If $f$ and $g$ are nonzero polynomials such that $g(k) \neq 0$ for all positive integers $k$, then the series

$$\sum_{k=1}^{\infty} \frac{f(k)}{g(k)}$$

converges if and only if the degree of $g$ is at least 2 more than the degree of $f$.

---

There's one more important convergence test for positive series, as we can see in the following example:

---

**Problem 7.18:** For what values of $c > 0$ does $\displaystyle\sum_{n=1}^{\infty} \frac{c^n}{n!}$ converge?

---

*Solution for Problem 7.18:* The denominator grows much faster than the numerator (and in particular the limit of the terms is 0), so we suspect that the series converges.

Let $a_n = \frac{c^n}{n!}$ be the $n^{\text{th}}$ term of the sequence. Looking more closely, we notice that the ratio between successive terms of the sequence is:

$$\frac{a_{n+1}}{a_n} = \frac{\frac{c^{n+1}}{(n+1)!}}{\frac{c^n}{n!}} = \frac{c}{n+1}.$$

In particular, once we have $n > c$, the ratio of successive terms is less than 1. In other words, after the first $c$ terms, the sequence "looks like" a geometric series with ratio less than 1.

To be a bit more specific, let $r = \dfrac{c}{c+1} < 1$. Then for all $n > c$, we have

$$\frac{a_{n+1}}{a_n} = \frac{c}{n+1} < \frac{c}{c+1} = r.$$

Hence, by induction, $a_{n+k} < r^k a_n$ for all $k > 0$.

Therefore, the series (after the first $n$ terms) is less than a geometric series with common ratio $r < 1$, which we know converges. Thus, by the Series Comparison Test, our given series converges for any positive value of $c$. □

In fact, the series of Problem 7.18 converges to $e^c - 1$; we'll see how to prove this in Section 7.6.

Extending the example from Problem 7.18 to more general series gives us a new test, called the **Ratio Test**. The basic idea is that we try to see how close our series is to a geometric series of common ratio $r$.

---

**Important:**

⚠️

The **Ratio Test** for series: Suppose $\sum a_n$ is a series with positive terms. Let $r = \lim\limits_{n \to \infty} \dfrac{a_{n+1}}{a_n}$ be the limit of the ratio of successive terms.

- If $r < 1$, then the series converges.

- If $r > 1$ (including $r = \infty$), then the series diverges.

- If $r = 1$, then this test doesn't give us any information.

---

It is important to note that the $r = 1$ case is inconclusive. For example, the series $\sum\limits_{n=1}^{\infty} \dfrac{1}{n}$ and $\sum\limits_{n=1}^{\infty} \dfrac{1}{n^2}$ both have the limit of the ratio of consecutive terms equal to 1, but we know that the first one diverges whereas the second one converges.

---

## EXERCISES

**7.3.1** Determine if the following series converge or diverge. If possible, determine what they converge to.

(a) $\sum\limits_{n=1}^{\infty} \dfrac{n+1}{n^2 + 3n + 1}$

(b) $\sum\limits_{n=1}^{\infty} \dfrac{2}{n^2 - n + 1}$

(c) $\sum\limits_{n=1}^{\infty} \dfrac{2^n + 3^n}{5^n}$    **Hints:** 84

(d) $\sum\limits_{n=1}^{\infty} \dfrac{(n!)^2}{(2n)!}$    **Hints:** 201

(e) $\sum\limits_{n=1}^{\infty} \sin\left(\dfrac{1}{n}\right)$    **Hints:** 120

**7.3.2** Modify Problem 7.12 to compare series whose terms are all nonpositive.

**7.3.3**

(a) Prove the convergence part of the Integral Test: suppose an infinite sequence $\{a_n\}_{n=1}^{\infty}$ is given by $a_n = f(n)$ for some continuous decreasing positive function $f$. If $\int_1^{\infty} f(x)\,dx$ converges, then $\sum_{k=1}^{\infty} a_k$ converges.

(b) Prove, in the case of part (a), that

$$\sum_{k=2}^{\infty} a_k < \int_1^{\infty} f(x)\,dx < \sum_{k=1}^{\infty} a_k.$$

**Hints:** 95

**7.3.4**

(a) Prove the Limit Comparison Test. **Hints:** 188, 37

(b) Prove that if $\{a_n\}$, $\{b_n\}$ are sequences with nonnegative terms such that $\lim\limits_{n \to \infty} \dfrac{a_n}{b_n} = 0$, and $\sum b_n$ converges, then $\sum a_n$ converges. **Hints:** 242

(c)   State and prove a result similar to part (b), but where $\lim\limits_{n\to\infty} \dfrac{a_n}{b_n} = \infty$. **Hints:** 203

**7.3.5★**   Determine if $\displaystyle\sum_{n=1}^{\infty} \dfrac{1}{n^{(n+1)/n}}$ converges or diverges. **Hints:** 41, 289

**7.3.6★**   Prove the **Root Test** for series: Suppose $\sum a_n$ is a series with positive terms. Let $r = \lim\limits_{n\to\infty} \sqrt[n]{a_n}$. Then:

- If $r < 1$, then the series converges.

- If $r > 1$ (including $r = \infty$), then the series diverges.

- If $r = 1$, then this test doesn't give us any information.

**Hints:** 48, 146, 257

## 7.4   ALTERNATING SERIES

All of the convergence tests that we've developed so far are for series all of whose terms are nonnegative. The tests can be easily modified for series all of whose terms are nonpositive: just multiply all the terms by −1. But trickier are series that have both positive and negative terms.

One easy way to tell if a general series converges is when the same series converges if we take the absolute value of the terms:

> **Definition:**   We say that $\sum a_n$ is **absolutely convergent** if $\sum |a_n|$ converges.

Absolute convergence is a stronger condition than convergence:

> **Problem 7.19:** Prove that if $\sum a_n$ is absolutely convergent, then $\sum a_n$ converges.

*Solution for Problem 7.19:*   Since all of our convergence tests from Section 7.3 deal with series with nonnegative terms, we write the terms in our given series as the difference of two nonnegative terms:

$$a_n = (a_n + |a_n|) - |a_n|$$

for all $n$. We know that $\sum |a_n|$ converges by definition, and furthermore we have

$$0 \le a_n + |a_n| \le 2|a_n|,$$

so by the Series Comparison Test, $\sum(a_n + |a_n|)$ also converges. Thus, since a sum of convergent series is also a convergent series, we have

$$\sum_{n=1}^{\infty} a_n = \sum_{n=1}^{\infty}(a_n + |a_n|) - \sum_{n=1}^{\infty} |a_n|,$$

and hence $\sum a_n$ converges. $\square$

For example, we now know that

$$1 - \frac{1}{4} + \frac{1}{9} - \frac{1}{16} + \frac{1}{25} - \cdots$$

converges, because it absolutely converges—that is,

$$1 + \frac{1}{4} + \frac{1}{9} + \frac{1}{16} + \frac{1}{25} + \cdots$$

converges. Thus, $\displaystyle\sum_{n=1}^{\infty} \frac{(-1)^{n+1}}{n^2}$ is absolutely convergent.

However, there are series that converge but that do not converge absolutely:

**Problem 7.20:** Show that the **alternating harmonic series**

$$1 - \frac{1}{2} + \frac{1}{3} - \frac{1}{4} + \frac{1}{5} - \cdots$$

converges.

*Solution for Problem 7.20:* We can explore this by looking at the partial sums:

$$s_1 = a_1 = 1$$
$$s_2 = s_1 + a_2 = 1 - \frac{1}{2} = \frac{1}{2}$$
$$s_3 = s_2 + a_3 = \frac{1}{2} + \frac{1}{3} = \frac{5}{6}$$
$$s_4 = s_3 + a_4 = \frac{5}{6} - \frac{1}{4} = \frac{7}{12}$$
$$s_5 = s_4 + a_5 = \frac{7}{12} + \frac{1}{5} = \frac{47}{60}$$
$$s_6 = s_5 + a_6 = \frac{47}{60} - \frac{1}{6} = \frac{37}{60}$$

We can represent this graphically on the number line, as in the diagram below. Each arrow is the result of adding the next term.

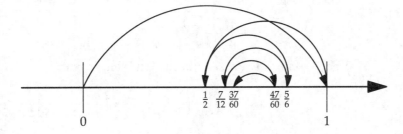

We notice that the sums of an odd number of terms $\left(1, \frac{5}{6}, \frac{47}{60}, \ldots\right)$ are all greater than the sums of an even number of terms $\left(0, \frac{1}{2}, \frac{7}{12}, \frac{37}{60}, \ldots\right)$. Furthermore, the odd sums are decreasing whereas the even sums are increasing, so since both sequences (the odd sums and the even sums) are bounded and monotonic, they each converge. Finally, because $\lim_{n \to \infty}(s_{2n+1} - s_{2n}) = 0$, the odd sums and the even sums must converge to the same value, which is the value to which the entire series converges. $\square$

The alternating harmonic series actually converges to $\log 2$, but we won't be able to prove this until Section 7.6.

The argument that we used in Problem 7.20 to prove that the alternating harmonic series converges can be generalized:

> **Important:** **The Alternating Series Test:** Let $\sum a_n$ be a series in which:
>
> (a) the terms are *alternating*: $a_n$ is positive for odd $n$ and negative for even $n$ (or vice versa),
>
> (b) $|a_{n+1}| < |a_n|$ for all $n$, and
>
> (c) $\lim\limits_{n \to \infty} a_n = 0$.
>
> Then $\displaystyle\sum_{n=1}^{\infty} a_n$ converges.

We can sketch a proof; it's essentially the same as our argument in Problem 7.20 of the convergence of the alternating harmonic series. Suppose $a_1 > 0$ and $a_2 < 0$ (the proof is essentially the same if they are reversed). We let $s_n = a_1 + a_2 + \cdots + a_n$ be the sum of the first $n$ terms.

Note that $s_1, s_3, s_5, \ldots$ is a strictly decreasing sequence: for example, note that $s_3 = s_1 + a_2 + a_3$, and the conditions imply that $a_2 + a_3 < 0$. Similarly, $s_2, s_4, s_6, \ldots$ is a strictly increasing sequence. Further, each $s_i$ (with $i$ odd) is strictly greater than each $s_j$ (with $j$ even), and $\lim(s_i - s_j) = 0$.

Thus, the odd $s$'s converge downwards and the even $s$'s converge upwards, and where they meet is the limit of the original sequence. They must converge to the same value, since $\lim(s_i - s_j) = 0$.

The alternating harmonic series from Problem 7.20 is an example of a series that is convergent but that is not absolutely convergent. Such a series is called **conditionally convergent**. One thing we have to be very careful about is that if we have a sequence that is convergent but not absolutely convergent, then the order in which we sum the terms of the series is very important! For example, if we make the faulty assumption that we can "rearrange" the terms of the series, then we can arrive at the following bogus conclusion:

> **Bogus Solution:**  We start with
> $$S = 1 - \frac{1}{2} + \frac{1}{3} - \frac{1}{4} + \frac{1}{5} - \frac{1}{6} + \cdots.$$
> We rearrange the terms so that every third term is positive.
> $$S = 1 - \frac{1}{2} - \frac{1}{4} + \frac{1}{3} - \frac{1}{6} - \frac{1}{8} + \frac{1}{5} - \frac{1}{10} - \frac{1}{12} + \cdots.$$
> We add some parentheses and combine some terms:
> $$S = \left(1 - \frac{1}{2}\right) - \frac{1}{4} + \left(\frac{1}{3} - \frac{1}{6}\right) - \frac{1}{8} + \left(\frac{1}{5} - \frac{1}{10}\right) - \frac{1}{12} + \cdots$$
> $$= \frac{1}{2} - \frac{1}{4} + \frac{1}{6} - \frac{1}{8} + \frac{1}{10} - \frac{1}{12} + \cdots.$$
> But now we have
> $$S = \frac{1}{2}\left(1 - \frac{1}{2} + \frac{1}{3} - \frac{1}{4} + \frac{1}{5} - \frac{1}{6} + \cdots\right) = \frac{1}{2}S,$$
> so $S = 0$.

Clearly the sum is not 0: indeed, we saw in Problem 7.20 that it is between $\frac{1}{2}$ and 1 (in fact, it is $\log 2$). So what we did must be illegal.

> **WARNING!!** ☢ We can't arbitrarily rearrange terms in an infinite series. This is why series are formally defined as sequences of partial sums: the order in which we sum the terms of a sequence to get the sum of a series is important!

A remarkable fact is that we can rearrange the terms of a conditionally convergent series to get it to sum to *any* real number! So we have to be really careful when working with them. We don't have such a problem with absolutely convergent series: any rearrangement of the terms will still converge to the same sum, although this is somewhat difficult to prove.

## EXERCISES

**7.4.1** For each of the following series, determine whether it converges or diverges. If it converges, determine whether it is absolutely convergent, and if possible compute the value to which it converges.

(a) $\displaystyle\sum_{k=1}^{\infty} \frac{(-1)^k}{3^k}$

(b) $\displaystyle\sum_{k=1}^{\infty} \frac{(-1)^k}{k^2}$

(c) $\displaystyle\sum_{k=1}^{\infty} \frac{(-1)^k}{\sqrt{k}}$

(d) $\displaystyle\sum_{k=1}^{\infty} \frac{(-1)^k \log k}{k}$

(e) $\displaystyle\sum_{k=1}^{\infty} \frac{(-1)^{2k}}{k^{\frac{3}{2}}}$

(f) $\displaystyle\sum_{k=1}^{\infty} \frac{(-1)^{k^2} k^2}{k^3 + 1}$

**7.4.2** Show that if $\displaystyle\sum_{n=1}^{\infty} a_n$ is absolutely convergent, then $\displaystyle\sum_{n=1}^{\infty} a_n^2$ converges.

## 7.5 TAYLOR POLYNOMIALS

Back when we first started studying derivatives, we saw that one important application is the tangent line approximation of the graph of $f$ near $x = a$. The tangent line to the graph of $f$ at the point $(a, f(a))$ has slope $f'(a)$, so the formula for the linear function $p(x)$ that approximates $f(x)$ near $a$ is

$$p(x) = f(a) + f'(a)(x - a).$$

This is called a **first-order** approximation of $f$ at $x = a$, since $p(a) = f(a)$ and $p'(a) = f'(a)$. In other words, $p$ matches $f$ in both value and first derivative at $x = a$.

A better and yet still relatively simple approximation would be with a quadratic polynomial. Of course, we will demand that our approximation be slightly better than the linear approximation—specifically, it should also match the second derivative at $x = a$.

Let's look at the special case where $a = 0$, since that's simpler, and it will guide us to the general case.

> **Problem 7.21:** Let $f$ be a twice-differentiable function at $x = 0$. Find the quadratic polynomial $p$ such that $p(0) = f(0)$, $p'(0) = f'(0)$, and $p''(0) = f''(0)$.

*Solution for Problem 7.21:* We want a quadratic polynomial, so we know that $p$ is of the form

$$p(x) = c_2 x^2 + c_1 x + c_0.$$

We want to determine the coefficients so that $p(0) = f(0)$, $p'(0) = f'(0)$, and $p''(0) = f''(0)$.

We can just plug in $x = 0$ to get:

$$c_0 = p(0) = f(0).$$

So $c_0 = f(0)$.

When we take the derivative, we have

$$p'(x) = 2c_2 x + c_1,$$

and hence $c_1 = p'(0) = f'(0)$.

When we take the second derivative, we have

$$p''(x) = 2c_2,$$

so we have $2c_2 = p''(0) = f''(0)$, hence $c_2 = \frac{1}{2} f''(0)$.

Therefore, our quadratic approximation is

$$p(x) = f(0) + f'(0)x + \frac{f''(0)}{2} x^2.$$

$\square$

Quadratic approximations are typically more accurate than linear approximations, and are especially useful in situations when a linear approximation is no good, like the following example:

**Problem 7.22:** Estimate $\cos 0.1$ using a quadratic approximation at $x = 0$.

*Solution for Problem 7.22:* We let $f(x) = \cos x$. We could try a linear approximation: we have $f'(x) = -\sin x$, so $f'(0) = -\sin 0 = 0$, and our linear approximation is

$$p(x) = f(0) + f'(0)x = 1 + 0x = 1.$$

That is, our linear approximation tells us that $\cos x \approx 1$ near $x = 0$. This is interesting, but it doesn't help us to approximate $\cos 0.1$ unless we are willing to settle for $\cos 0.1 \approx 1$.

Instead, noting that $f''(x) = -\cos x$ so that $f''(0) = -\cos 0 = -1$, we try a quadratic approximation:

$$p(x) = f(0) + f'(0)x + \frac{f''(0)}{2} x^2 = 1 - \frac{1}{2} x^2.$$

This approximation gives us $\cos 0.1 \approx 1 - \frac{1}{2}(0.1)^2 = .995$. $\square$

If you do this on your calculator, you'll get $\cos 0.1 = 0.995004\ldots$, so our approximation is pretty good. We can also sketch the graphs $y = \cos x$ and $y = 1 - \frac{1}{2} x^2$, at right, to see how they compare. The graph of $\cos x$ is the dashed black curve and the graph of $1 - \frac{1}{2} x^2$ is the solid gray curve. Near $x = 0$, they are very close—in our sketch they are virtually indistinguishable—so this is a pretty good approximation (and much better than the linear approximation $y = 1$).

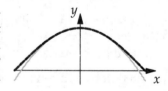

How do we generalize this to an approximation near $x = a$?

**Problem 7.23:** Let $f$ be a twice-differentiable function at $x = a$. Find a quadratic polynomial $p$ such that $p(a) = f(a)$, $p'(a) = f'(a)$, and $p''(a) = f''(a)$.

*Solution for Problem 7.23:* Recall the formula for the linear approximation at $x = a$:

$$p(x) = f(a) + f'(a)(x - a)$$

The trick was writing the polynomial in terms of $x - a$ rather than $x$.

So, using this same trick to get a quadratic approximation at $x = a$, we let

$$p(x) = c_2(x - a)^2 + c_1(x - a) + c_0,$$

and solve so that $p(a) = f(a)$, $p'(a) = f'(a)$, and $p''(a) = f''(a)$.

We can do essentially the same calculations that we did in Problem 7.21. Plugging in $x = a$ and solving $p(a) = f(a)$ gives us

$$c_0 = p(a) = f(a),$$

so $c_0 = f(a)$.

Next, differentiating and plugging in $x = a$ gives us

$$c_1 = p'(a) = f'(a),$$

so $c_1 = f'(a)$.

Lastly, differentiating again and plugging in $x = a$ gives us

$$2c_2 = p''(a) = f''(a),$$

so $c_2 = \frac{1}{2}f''(a)$.

Therefore, the quadratic approximation is

$$p(x) = f(a) + f'(a)(x - a) + \frac{f''(a)}{2}(x - a)^2.$$

Note that when $a = 0$ this gives us our approximation near $x = 0$ from Problem 7.21. □

> **Important:** The quadratic approximation of a twice-differentiable function $f$ at $x = a$ is
>
>
>
> $$p(x) = f(a) + f'(a)(x - a) + \frac{f''(a)}{2}(x - a)^2.$$
>
> Note that $p$ agrees with $f$ in value, first derivative, and second derivative at $x = a$. We say that $p$ is a **second-order** approximation of $f$.

The more general form of the quadratic approximation is useful when we want to approximate values far from $x = 0$.

**Problem 7.24:** Estimate $\log 0.9$ using quadratic estimation.

*Solution for Problem 7.24:* We set up a quadratic approximation at $a = 1$. Let $f(x) = \log x$. Then $f'(x) = \frac{1}{x}$ and $f''(x) = -\frac{1}{x^2}$. Thus $f'(1) = 1$ and $f''(1) = -1$, and the approximating quadratic polynomial is

$$p(x) = f(1) + f'(1)(x - 1) + \frac{f''(1)}{2}(x - 1)^2 = (x - 1) - \frac{1}{2}(x - 1)^2.$$

Plugging in $x = 0.9$ gives

$$p(0.9) = (-0.1) - (0.5)(-0.1)^2 = -0.005 - 0.1 = -0.105.$$

Hence, $\log 0.9 \approx -0.105$. Your calculator will say $\log 0.9 = -0.10536\ldots$, so again this is a pretty good approximation, much better than the linear $\log 0.9 \approx -0.1$. □

It should seem reasonable that we can make a polynomial approximation even better by adding more terms. Again, to keep things simple, we'll start by examining approximations near 0.

---

**Problem 7.25:** We want to construct a degree $n$ polynomial

$$p(x) = c_n x^n + c_{n-1} x^{n-1} + \cdots + c_1 x + c_0$$

such that $p^{(k)}(0) = f^{(k)}(0)$ for all $0 \leq k \leq n$. (Note that $f^{(0)}(x) = f(x)$ by convention.)

(a) For all $0 \leq k \leq n$, compute $p^{(k)}(0)$ in terms of the coefficients $\{c_i\}$.

(b) Solve for the coefficients so that $p^{(k)}(0) = f^{(k)}(0)$ for all $0 \leq k \leq n$.

---

*Solution for Problem 7.25:*

(a) We can certainly compute the $k^{\text{th}}$ derivative $p^{(k)}(x)$ as a polynomial in $x$, but it's a bit messy, and we only need to compute $p^{(k)}(0)$. This means that we only need to determine the constant term of $p^{(k)}(x)$.

We know that taking the derivative of a monomial reduces the degree by 1. Therefore, the $k^{\text{th}}$ derivative of a monomial will be a nonzero constant only if the monomial is $c_k x^k$. Thus, only the $c_k x^k$ term of $p(x)$ will matter in $p^{(k)}(0)$. The smaller-degree terms will vanish when we take the $k^{\text{th}}$ derivative, and the larger degree terms will still have a factor of $x$, so they will vanish when we plug in $x = 0$.

So we just need to compute the $k^{\text{th}}$ derivative of $c_k x^k$. The first derivative is $k c_k x^{k-1}$, the second derivative is $k(k-1) c_k x^{k-2}$, and so on, as each exponent from $k$ down to 1 gets multiplied as a constant. So the $k^{\text{th}}$ derivative of $c_k x^k$ is $k! c_k$. Hence $p^{(k)}(0) = k! c_k$ for all $0 \leq k \leq n$.

(b) We need $c_k k! = p^{(k)}(0) = f^{(k)}(0)$, hence

$$c_k = \frac{f^{(k)}(0)}{k!}$$

for all $0 \leq k \leq n$. (Note that $0! = 1! = 1$, so this matches our earlier formulas.) Hence, the degree $n$ polynomial approximating $f(x)$ at 0 is

$$p(x) = f(0) + f'(0)x + \frac{f''(0)}{2!}x^2 + \frac{f'''(0)}{3!}x^3 + \cdots + \frac{f^{(n)}(0)}{n!}x^n$$

$$= \sum_{k=0}^{n} \frac{f^{(k)}(0)}{k!} x^k.$$

$\square$

We have thus seen that we can approximate $f$ by a degree $n$ polynomial at $x = 0$, provided that $f$ is differentiable at least $n$ times. We have a special name for these polynomials:

---

**Definition:** Let $f$ be an $n$-times-differentiable function. The degree $n$ **Taylor polynomial of $f$ at** 0 is the polynomial

$$p(x) = f(0) + f'(0)x + \frac{f''(0)}{2!}x^2 + \frac{f'''(0)}{3!}x^3 + \cdots + \frac{f^{(n)}(0)}{n!}x^n$$

$$= \sum_{k=0}^{n} \frac{f^{(k)}(0)}{k!} x^k.$$

It is the unique degree $n$ polynomial with the property that $p^{(k)}(0) = f^{(k)}(0)$ for all $0 \leq k \leq n$; that is, $p$ is the unique degree $n$ polynomial whose value at 0 and first $k$ derivatives at 0 agree with those of $f$.

---

We can easily do the same calculation at $x = a$ (we will omit it here for brevity, but it is exactly the same calculation as in Problem 7.25, except we replace $x$ with $x - a$ throughout):

---

**Definition:** Let $f$ be an $n$-times-differentiable function. The degree $n$ **Taylor polynomial of $f$ at** $a$ (for any real number $a$ in the domain of $f$) is the polynomial

$$p(x) = f(a) + f'(a)(x - a) + \frac{f''(a)}{2!}(x - a)^2 + \frac{f'''(a)}{3!}(x - a)^3 + \cdots + \frac{f^{(n)}(a)}{n!}(x - a)^n$$

$$= \sum_{k=0}^{n} \frac{f^{(k)}(a)}{k!}(x - a)^k.$$

It is the unique degree $n$ polynomial with the property that $p^{(k)}(a) = f^{(k)}(a)$ for all $0 \leq k \leq n$; that is, $p$ is the unique degree $n$ polynomial whose value at $a$ and first $k$ derivatives at $a$ agree with those of $f$.

---

**Concept:** Think of Taylor polynomials as a natural extension of our earlier concept of tangent line approximation. Indeed, the graph of the degree 1 Taylor polynomial of $f$ at $a$ is the tangent line to $f$ at $(a, f(a))$.

---

You will also sometimes see the term **Maclaurin polynomial** to mean the Taylor polynomial at 0, but this term is less commonly used.

Of course, we can only have a Taylor polynomial of $f$ at $a$ if all the derivatives that we need are defined.

Let's try a quick example:

---

**Problem 7.26:** Estimate $\sin 0.2$ using a cubic Taylor polynomial.

---

*Solution for Problem 7.26:* Of course, we choose to construct the polynomial at 0. (Always try for 0 unless there's a good reason not to.)

We list the function and its derivatives at 0:

$$\begin{array}{ll} f(x) = \sin x & f(0) = 0 \\ f'(x) = \cos x & f'(0) = 1 \\ f''(x) = -\sin x & f''(0) = 0 \\ f'''(x) = -\cos x & f'''(0) = -1 \end{array}$$

At this point, don't make the following silly, but regrettably common, error:

---

**Bogus Solution:** The polynomial is

$$p(x) = f(0) + f'(0)x + f''(0)x^2 + f'''(0)x^3 = x - x^3.$$

---

Each of the coefficients has to be divided by the corresponding factorial. So the polynomial is

$$p(x) = f(0) + f'(0)x + \frac{f''(0)}{2}x^2 + \frac{f'''(0)}{6}x^3 = x - \frac{1}{6}x^3.$$

To finish, we plug in $x = 0.2$:

$$\sin 0.2 \approx (0.2) - \frac{1}{6}(.008) = \frac{1}{5} - \frac{1}{750} = \frac{149}{750} = 0.198667\ldots.$$

---

The calculator says $\sin 0.2 = 0.19866933\ldots$, so this approximation is pretty close. $\square$

It is reasonable to ask the question: how good are the approximations given by Taylor polynomials? Given a function $f$, we can estimate the error of a degree $n$ Taylor polynomial $p$ of $f$ at $a$. We define error in the most obvious manner: as the amount that the approximation differs from the actual value.

---

**Definition:** The **error** in the degree $n$ Taylor polynomial approximation $p$ of $f$ at $a$ is

$$E(x) = f(x) - p(x),$$

where $f(x)$ is the actual value of $f$, and $p(x)$ is the degree $n$ Taylor polynomial at $a$.

---

For example, in Problem 7.26, the error in our approximation is

$$E(x) = \sin x - x + \frac{1}{6}x^3,$$

and in particular,

$$E(0.2) = \sin 0.2 - \frac{149}{750}.$$

We would like to be able to estimate the error. Fortunately, we have tools available for this, since the error function has a particularly nice property. Recall that we've rigged our Taylor polynomial $p$ so that its first $n$ derivatives agree with those of $f$ at $a$. But what does that mean for $E(x)$? Since

$$E^{(k)}(x) = f^{(k)}(x) - p^{(k)}(x),$$

we know that $E(a) = 0$ and that the first $n$ derivatives of $E$ vanish at $a$; that is,

$$E(a) = E'(a) = E''(a) = \cdots = E^{(n)}(a) = 0.$$

And since $p$ is a degree $n$ polynomial, its higher derivatives are all 0. So in particular, we have

$$E^{(n+1)}(x) = f^{(n+1)}(x).$$

Suppose we are are using $p$ to estimate $f(c)$ for some $c > a$. We know that if $f^{(n+1)}$ is continuous, then $|f^{(n+1)}(x)|$ has some maximum value $M$ on $[a, c]$. So

$$|E^{(n+1)}(x)| \le M.$$

What happens if we integrate this $n + 1$ times? We get

$$|E(x)| \le \frac{M}{(n+1)!}(x-a)^{n+1} \le \frac{M}{(n+1)!}(c-a)^{n+1}.$$

Note that all of the constants of integration disappear while we do this, since all of the lower derivatives of $E$ vanish at $a$.

So our conclusion is:

---

**Important:** The absolute value of the error in estimating $f(c)$ by a Taylor polynomial of degree $n$ about $a$ is at most

$$\left| \frac{M}{(n+1)!}(c-a)^{n+1} \right|,$$

where $M$ is the maximum value of $|f^{(n+1)}(x)|$ for $x$ between $a$ and $c$.

---

Here's an example:

---

**Problem 7.27:** Determine the absolute value of the maximum error in the quadratic estimation of $\log 0.9$.

---

*Solution for Problem 7.27:* We have the quadratic approximation

$$p(x) = (x - 1) - \frac{1}{2}(x - 1)^2,$$

which gave us

$$p(0.9) = (-0.1) - (0.5)(-0.1)^2 = -0.005 - 0.1 = -0.105.$$

So $\log 0.9 \approx -0.105$.

To determine the error bound, we need to look at $f'''(x) = \frac{2}{x^3}$ on the interval $[0.9, 1]$. This is maximized at $x = 0.9$, giving $f'''(0.9) = \frac{2}{(0.9)^3} = \frac{2000}{729} = 2.7435\ldots$. Thus, our error bound is

$$\left| \frac{\frac{2}{(0.9)^3}}{3!}(-0.1)^3 \right| = \frac{1}{2187} \approx 0.000457\ldots.$$

Note that this is the absolute value of the maximum possible error, not the actual error. Indeed, a calculator will show that the actual error is about $0.000361$. $\square$

## EXERCISES

**7.5.1** Approximate $\sqrt{0.9}$ using a cubic Taylor polynomial. Determine the bound on the error.

**7.5.2** What is the estimate of $(1 + \epsilon)^{\frac{1}{n}}$ by a cubic Taylor polynomial, where $n$ is a positive integer?

**7.5.3** Estimate $e^{0.1}$ to 6 decimal places using a Taylor polynomial about 0.

**7.5.4** Let $p(x) = ax^2 + bx + c$ be a quadratic polynomial. Find the degree 2 Taylor polynomial of $p$ at:

(a) $x = 0$      (b) $x = 1$      (c) $x = r$ where $r$ is a root of $p$    **Hints:** 171, 164

---

## 7.6 TAYLOR SERIES

If $f$ is an infinitely-differentiable function, we can now approximate $f$ by polynomials with arbitrarily high degree. We can "take the limit" of these polynomials to get an "infinite-degree polynomial," called a **power series**.

In general, a **power series** is an infinite series of the form $\displaystyle\sum_{k=0}^{\infty} c_k(x - a)^k$ for some sequence of coefficients $\{c_k\}$.

Most often, we have $a = 0$, giving a power series of the form $\displaystyle\sum_{k=0}^{\infty} c_k x^k$. If we let the coefficients be the coefficients of a Taylor polynomial, then we get:

---

**Definition:** The **Taylor series** at $a$ of an infinitely-differentiable function $f$ is

$$\sum_{k=0}^{\infty} \frac{f^{(k)}(a)}{k!}(x - a)^k,$$

for the values of $x$ for which the infinite series converges. This is also called the **Maclaurin series** of $f$ if $a = 0$.

---

> **Concept:** Note that the first $n + 1$ terms of the power series representation of $f$ at $a$ give us exactly the degree $n$ Taylor polynomial of $f$ at $a$. So we can think of the Taylor series as the limit as $n \to \infty$ of the degree $n$ Taylor polynomials at $a$ (even though we have not defined what a "limit of polynomials" means).

We'll start with what arguably is the most important example:

**Problem 7.28:** Find the Taylor series of $f(x) = e^x$ at $x = 0$, and determine for what values of $x$ it converges.

*Solution for Problem 7.28:* We know that all derivatives of $e^x$ are themselves $e^x$. So for all $k > 0$, we have $f^{(k)}(0) = e^0 = 1$. Hence the Taylor series is

$$1 + x + \frac{x^2}{2!} + \frac{x^3}{3!} + \cdots = \sum_{k=0}^{\infty} \frac{x^k}{k!}.$$

To determine the values of $x$ for which this converges, we can use the Ratio Test, which is usually the most useful test for power series. The ratio of successive terms of the series is

$$\frac{\left|\frac{x^{n+1}}{(n+1)!}\right|}{\left|\frac{x^n}{n!}\right|} = \left|\frac{x}{n+1}\right|.$$

For any value of $x$, we have $\lim_{n \to \infty} \frac{x}{n+1} = 0$. Thus, by the Ratio Test, the Taylor series converges for all $x \in \mathbb{R}$. $\square$

In Problem 7.28, we showed that $\sum_{k=0}^{\infty} \frac{x^k}{k!}$ converges, but we don't know what it converges to. We'd like to say that

$$e^x = 1 + x + \frac{x^2}{2!} + \frac{x^3}{3!} + \cdots,$$

but how do we know that this is true, and that the power series doesn't converge to some other value?

What we do know is that

$$e^x \approx 1 + x + \frac{x^2}{2!} + \cdots + \frac{x^n}{n!}$$

is the degree $n$ Taylor polynomial approximation, and moreover we know that the error in this approximation is given by

$$|E_n(x)| = \left|e^x - \left(1 + x + \frac{x^2}{2!} + \cdots + \frac{x^n}{n!}\right)\right| \leq \left|\frac{M}{(n+1)!}x^{n+1}\right|,$$

where $M$ is the maximum value of the $(n+1)^{st}$ derivative of exp between $0$ and $x$. This derivative is itself the exponential function, so $M$ is $e^x$ (if $x > 0$) or $e^0 = 1$ (if $x \leq 0$), but the important fact is that $M$ does not depend on $n$. Also, we just showed in Problem 7.28 that the series $\sum_{k=0}^{\infty} \frac{x^k}{k!}$ converges for all $x$, and thus by the Divergence Test, the terms of the sequence that we are summing must converge to $0$. Thus

$$\lim_{n \to \infty} |E_n(x)| \leq \lim_{n \to \infty} \left|\frac{M}{(n+1)!}x^{n+1}\right| = M \lim_{n \to \infty} \left|\frac{x^{n+1}}{(n+1)!}\right| = 0.$$

That is, the error terms $E_n(x)$ converge to $0$ as $n \to \infty$, and thus we can say that $e^x$ equals the sum of its power series:

$$e^x = 1 + x + \frac{x^2}{2!} + \frac{x^3}{3!} + \cdots.$$

In particular, we have a proof of a fact that we have seen in the past:

$$1 + 1 + \frac{1}{2!} + \frac{1}{3!} + \frac{1}{4!} + \cdots = e^1 = e.$$

> **Concept:** A function equals the sum of its Taylor series, where the series converges, if and only if the error terms converge to 0. Thus, if we can prove that the bounds of the error terms of the Taylor polynomials of a function $f(x)$ converge to 0 as $n \to \infty$, then we have proved that the sum of the Taylor series is equal to $f(x)$.

The converse of the last sentence above is not true: a function could have the bounds of the error terms of its Taylor polynomials not converge to 0, yet the error itself converges to 0, and thus the function is equal to the sum of its Taylor series. However, examples of this are very difficult to produce. The main idea to keep in mind is that a Taylor series of $f(x)$ does not automatically converge to $f(x)$: it may converge to something else (see Problem 7.50 for an example), or it may not converge. We have to do additional work to show that a Taylor series of $f(x)$ actually sums to $f(x)$.

Naturally, the question of convergence of power series is central to using them effectively, so next we examine when power series converge. For simplicity, we'll initially consider power series at 0.

> **Problem 7.29:** Let $\sum_{n=0}^{\infty} c_n x^n$ be a power series, for some sequence $\{c_n\}_{n=0}^{\infty}$ of coefficients, and let $r, s$ be real numbers with $|r| < |s|$. Show that if the power series converges at $x = s$, then it converges absolutely at $x = r$.

*Solution for Problem 7.29:* Since $|c_n r^n| \leq |c_n s^n|$ for all $n$, it would be easy if we could use the Series Comparison Test. Unfortunately, we don't know that $\sum |c_n s^n|$ converges, since we only know that $\sum c_n s^n$ converges, not that it converges absolutely. So we must use a little trick to get around this.

If $\sum c_n s^n$ converges, then the sequence $\{|c_n s^n|\}$ must be bounded, so let $B = \sup\{|c_n s^n|\}$. Then (noting that $s \neq 0$ since $0 \leq |r| < |s|$), we have $|c_n| \leq \frac{B}{|s|^n}$ for all $n$. This lets us bound $|c_n r^n|$ using $\left|\frac{r}{s}\right|$, as follows:

$$|c_n r^n| \leq \frac{B}{|s|^n} \cdot |r|^n = B\left(\left|\frac{r}{s}\right|\right)^n.$$

But we know that a geometric series with ratio $\left|\frac{r}{s}\right| < 1$ converges. Therefore, by the Series Comparison Test, the series $\sum |c_n r^n|$ also converges, and thus the power series $\sum c_n x^n$ converges absolutely at $x = r$. $\square$

> **Problem 7.30:** Let $\sum_{n=0}^{\infty} c_n x^n$ be a power series. Show that either the power series converges absolutely for all $x \in \mathbb{R}$, or there exists some positive $R \in \mathbb{R}$ such that the power series converges absolutely for all $x \in (-R, R)$ and diverges for all $x \in (-\infty, -R) \cup (R, \infty)$.

Before proceeding with the proof, notice that the statement says nothing about what happens at $x = R$ or $x = -R$. At either of these values, the power series might converge absolutely, converge conditionally, or diverge.

*Solution for Problem 7.30:* Let

$$\mathcal{S} = \left\{ |x| \;\middle|\; \sum_{n=0}^{\infty} c_n x^n \text{ converges at } x \right\}.$$

If $S$ is unbounded, then for any $r \in \mathbb{R}$, there exists $s \in \mathbb{R}$ such that $|s| \in S$ with $|r| < |s|$. By the definition of $S$, the power series converges at $x = s$. Hence, by Problem 7.29, the power series converges absolutely at $x = r$. Since $r \in \mathbb{R}$ was arbitrary, we conclude that the power series converges for all $x \in \mathbb{R}$.

Otherwise, $S$ is bounded, and is nonempty since $0 \in S$ (because every power series at 0 converges at $x = 0$.) Thus $S$ has an upper bound; let $R = \sup S$. For any $r \in \mathbb{R}$ such that $|r| < R$, there exists $s \in \mathbb{R}$ with $|s| \in S$ such that $|r| < |s| \leq R$ (because otherwise, $|r|$ would be an upper bound for $S$, contradicting the fact that $|r| < R$). By the definition of $S$, the power series converges at $x = s$. Thus, by Problem 7.29, the power series converges absolutely for $x = r$. Since this is true for any $r \in \mathbb{R}$ such that $|r| < R$, we conclude that the power series converges for all $x \in (-R, R)$.

Finally, if $r \in \mathbb{R}$ is such that $|r| > R$, then $|r| \notin S$, so the power series does not converge at $x = r$. $\square$

We also note that every power series of the form $\sum c_n x^n$ converges at $x = 0$. This is the case where $R = 0$ in Problem 7.30, for which the set $S = \{0\}$. Summarizing the result of Problem 7.30 gives us:

---

**Definition:** The **radius of convergence** of the power series $\displaystyle\sum_{n=0}^{\infty} c_n x^n$ is:

- $\infty$ if the series converges for all $x \in \mathbb{R}$,

- $0$ if the series converges for $x = 0$ and diverges for all $x \neq 0$, or

- $R$ if the series converges (absolutely) for $x \in (-R, R)$ and diverges for $x \in (-\infty, -R) \cup (R, \infty)$.

---

Happily, there is a straightforward way to determine the radius of convergence of a power series in terms of its coefficients:

---

**Problem 7.31:** Let $\displaystyle\sum_{n=0}^{\infty} c_n x^n$ be a power series, for some sequence $\{c_n\}_{n=0}^{\infty}$ of coefficients. Let

$$R = \lim_{n \to \infty} \left| \frac{c_n}{c_{n+1}} \right|,$$

provided this limit exists. Show that $R$ is the radius of convergence of $\sum c_n x^n$. (In particular, if $R = \infty$, show that the power series converges absolutely for all $x \in \mathbb{R}$.)

---

*Solution for Problem 7.31:* As in Problem 7.28, we use the Ratio Test to examine the convergence of the power series $\sum |c_n x^n|$. We compute the limit of the ratio of two consecutive terms of the series:

$$\lim_{n \to \infty} \frac{|c_{n+1} x^{n+1}|}{|c_n x^n|} = \lim_{n \to \infty} \left| \frac{c_{n+1}}{c_n} \right| |x|.$$

If $R = \infty$, then the above limit is 0 for all $x \in \mathbb{R}$, and thus by the Ratio Test, the series converges for all $x \in \mathbb{R}$. If $R = 0$, then the above limit is $\infty$ for all nonzero $x$, and thus by the Ratio Test, the series converges only for $x = 0$. Otherwise, the limit is

$$\lim_{n \to \infty} \left| \frac{c_{n+1}}{c_n} \right| |x| = \frac{|x|}{R}.$$

If $|x| < R$, then this limit is less than 1, so by the Ratio Test, the series converges. On the other hand, if $|x| > R$, then this limit is greater than 1, so by the Ratio Test, the series diverges. $\square$

Note again that we get no information about what happens at $x = R$ and $x = -R$. The Ratio Test is inconclusive and we need to check convergence directly at those two points.

The above results all hold for general power series of the form $\sum_{n=0}^{\infty} c_n(x-a)^n$, except then we replace the conditions $|x| < R$ (or $|x| > R$) with $|x-a| < R$ (or $|x-a| > R$). The results are:

---

**Definition:** The **radius of convergence** of the power series $\sum_{n=0}^{\infty} c_n(x-a)^n$ is:

- $\infty$ if the series converges for all $x \in \mathbb{R}$,

- $0$ if the series converges for $x = a$ and diverges for all $x \neq a$, or

- $R$ if the series converges (absolutely) for $x \in (a-R, a+R)$ and diverges for $x \in (-\infty, a-R) \cup (a+R, \infty)$.

---

**Important:** The radius of convergence of the power series $\sum_{n=0}^{\infty} c_n(x-a)^n$ is

$$R = \lim_{n \to \infty} \left| \frac{c_n}{c_{n+1}} \right|,$$

provided this limit exists. In particular, if $R = \infty$, then the power series converges absolutely for all $x \in \mathbb{R}$.

---

Our next task is to develop a catalog of Taylor series of some common functions. The first class of functions that we mention is trivial: the Taylor series of a polynomial function is just the polynomial itself, since the higher-order derivatives of a polynomial function are all 0. This "series" clearly always converges to the original function.

The next class of functions is the basic trig functions:

**Problem 7.32:** Find the Taylor series (about $x = 0$) of $\sin x$ and $\cos x$, determine their radii of convergence, and show that the series converge to their corresponding functions (where the series converge).

*Solution for Problem 7.32:* We do sine first. The derivatives are

$$\sin x, \cos x, -\sin x, -\cos x, \sin x, \ldots,$$

which cycle every 4 terms. So the values of these derivatives at $x = 0$ are:

$$0, 1, 0, -1, 0, 1, 0, -1, 0, \ldots,$$

repeating every four terms. Thus, we have the Taylor series

$$x - \frac{x^3}{3!} + \frac{x^5}{5!} - \frac{x^7}{7!} + \cdots.$$

This can be written in summation notation as:

$$\sum_{n=0}^{\infty} (-1)^n \frac{x^{2n+1}}{(2n+1)!}.$$

To determine the radius of convergence, we can't directly use the Ratio Test, since every other term is 0. But we can still take the ratio of two consecutive non-zero terms:

$$\left| \frac{(-1)^{n+1} \frac{x^{2n+3}}{(2n+3)!}}{(-1)^n \frac{x^{2n+1}}{(2n+1)!}} \right| = \frac{x^2}{(2n+3)(2n+2)}.$$

---

For any fixed $x$, the limit of this as $n \to \infty$ is 0. Thus, the Taylor series converges for all $x \in \mathbb{R}$.

Also, we compute the error term for the degree $n$ Taylor polynomial approximation. Note that $\left| \frac{d^{n+1}}{dx^{n+1}} \sin x \right| \le 1$ for all $x$, hence

$$|E_n(x)| \le \left| \frac{x^{n+1}}{(n+1)!} \right|,$$

which approaches 0 as $n \to \infty$. Therefore, the Taylor series converges to $\sin x$ for all $x \in \mathbb{R}$, and we are justified in writing

$$\sin x = x - \frac{x^3}{3!} + \frac{x^5}{5!} - \frac{x^7}{7!} + \cdots = \sum_{n=0}^{\infty} (-1)^n \frac{x^{2n+1}}{(2n+1)!}$$

for all $x \in \mathbb{R}$.

There's a similar pattern for cosine:

$$\cos x = 1 - \frac{x^2}{2!} + \frac{x^4}{4!} - \frac{x^6}{6!} + \cdots = \sum_{n=0}^{\infty} (-1)^n \frac{x^{2n}}{(2n)!},$$

and this series also converges for all $x \in \mathbb{R}$. (The reasoning is essentially the same as that for sine, so we will omit the details.) $\square$

**Sidenote:** One really clever thing to note is that, if we extend our use of power series to complex numbers (which we can do, although we have not proved this), then the power series of exp, sin, and cos give us a proof of Euler's Formula! We write

$$e^{ix} = 1 + ix + \frac{(ix)^2}{2!} + \frac{(ix)^3}{3!} + \frac{(ix)^4}{4!} + \cdots .$$

We know that the powers of $i$ cycle as $1, i, -1, -i, 1, i, -1, -i, 1, \ldots$, so we can simplify:

$$e^{ix} = 1 + ix - \frac{x^2}{2!} - i\frac{x^3}{3!} + \frac{x^4}{4!} - \cdots .$$

Separate the real and imaginary parts, and we're done:

$$e^{ix} = \left(1 - \frac{x^2}{2!} + \frac{x^4}{4!} + \cdots\right) + i\left(x - \frac{x^3}{3!} + \frac{x^5}{5!} + \cdots\right)$$
$$= \cos x + i \sin x.$$

So we have "proved" Euler's Formula:

$$e^{ix} = \cos x + i \sin x.$$

We continue building our catalog of power series:

**Problem 7.33:** Find the Taylor series for $\log x$ about $x = 1$, and determine where it converges.

*Solution for Problem 7.33:* Note that we can't construct a power series of $\log x$ about $x = 0$ since the function is not defined there! Instead, $x = 1$ seems like the best location, since $\log x$ and its derivatives are easy to evaluate at $x = 1$.

We start by listing the derivatives of $\log x$:

$$f'(x) = 1/x,$$
$$f''(x) = -1/x^2,$$
$$f'''(x) = 2/x^3,$$
$$f^{(4)}(x) = -6/x^4.$$

We can see the pattern in the derivatives of log:

$$f^{(n)}(x) = (-1)^{n+1} \frac{(n-1)!}{x^n},$$

hence $f^{(n)}(1) = (-1)^{n+1}(n-1)!$ and $\dfrac{f^{(n)}(1)}{n!} = \dfrac{(-1)^{n+1}}{n}$. Thus, the Taylor series of log at $x = 1$ is

$$(x-1) - \frac{1}{2}(x-1)^2 + \frac{1}{3}(x-1)^3 - \frac{1}{4}(x-1)^4 + \frac{1}{5}(x-1)^5 - \cdots = \sum_{k=1}^{\infty} \frac{(-1)^{k+1}}{k}(x-1)^k.$$

To determine the radius of convergence, we take the ratio of successive coefficients:

$$\frac{\frac{1}{n-1}}{\frac{1}{n}} = \frac{n}{n-1}.$$

This ratio has limit 1 as $n \to \infty$. So the radius of convergence is 1, and we can conclude that the series converges absolutely for $x \in (0,2)$ and diverges for $x \in (-\infty, 0) \cup (2, \infty)$. The test doesn't tell us anything about $x = 0$ or $x = 2$. However, for $x = 0$, the series is the harmonic series, which diverges, and for $x = 2$, the series is the alternating harmonic series, which converges. Thus, the Taylor series converges for $x \in (0, 2]$.

Next, we check if the Taylor series converges to $\log x$ for $x \in (0, 2]$. The error term of the degree $n$ Taylor polynomial is bounded as

$$|E_n(x)| \le \left| \frac{f^{(n+1)}(z)}{(n+1)!}(x-1)^{n+1} \right|$$

for some $z$ between 1 and $x$. Note that $f^{(n+1)}(z) = (-1)^{n+2} \frac{n!}{z^{n+1}}$. If $x > 1$, then $z > 1$ and we have $|f^{(n+1)}(z)| \le n!$. Thus

$$|E_n(x)| \le \left| \frac{(x-1)^{n+1}}{n+1} \right|,$$

and since $0 < x - 1 \le 1$, we have that $E_n(x)$ approaches 0 as $n \to \infty$. Therefore, the Taylor series converges to $\log x$ for $x \in [1, 2]$.

On the other hand, if $x < z < 1$, then $|f^{(n+1)}(z)| = \frac{n!}{z^{n+1}} \le \frac{n!}{x^{n+1}}$, and

$$|E_n(x)| \le \left| \frac{\frac{n!}{x^{n+1}}}{(n+1)!}(x-1)^{n+1} \right| = \frac{1}{(n+1)} \left( \frac{1-x}{x} \right)^{n+1} = \frac{1}{(n+1)} \left( \frac{1}{x} - 1 \right)^{n+1}.$$

If $\frac{1}{2} \le x < 1$, then $\left( \frac{1}{x} - 1 \right) \le 1$, which means that $E_n(x)$ approaches 0 as $n \to \infty$. Hence, we can conclude that the Taylor series converges to $\log x$ for $x \in \left[ \frac{1}{2}, 1 \right)$. Unfortunately, if $0 < x < \frac{1}{2}$, then $\left( \frac{1}{x} - 1 \right) > 1$, and thus the bound for $|E_n(x)|$ grows arbitrarily large as $n \to \infty$. So we cannot conclude that the Taylor series converges to $\log x$ for $x \in \left( 0, \frac{1}{2} \right)$. However, this argument also does not prove that the series *doesn't* converge to $\log x$, because we are only computing a *bound* for $|E_n(x)|$, and not $E_n(x)$ itself. The fact is that $E_n(x)$ does approach 0 as $n \to \infty$ for all

$x \in (0, 2]$, and thus the Taylor series does converge to $\log x$, although this is quite difficult to prove for $x \in \left(0, \frac{1}{2}\right)$ (in particular it requires a different method of error bounding for the degree $n$ Taylor polynomial).

In summary,

$$\log x = (x - 1) - \frac{1}{2}(x-1)^2 + \frac{1}{3}(x-1)^3 - \frac{1}{4}(x-1)^4 + \frac{1}{5}(x-1)^5 - \cdots = \sum_{k=1}^{\infty} \frac{(-1)^{k+1}}{k}(x-1)^k$$

for all $x \in (0, 2]$. $\square$

To make it look a little nicer, the above equation is more customarily written by shifting the variable by 1:

$$\log(1 + x) = \sum_{k=1}^{\infty} \frac{(-1)^{k+1}}{k}x^k = x - \frac{x^2}{2} + \frac{x^3}{3} - \frac{x^4}{4} + \cdots.$$

The interval of convergence for this power series is $(-1, 1]$. If we plug in $x = 1$, we get the alternating harmonic series, proving that

$$\log 2 = 1 - \frac{1}{2} + \frac{1}{3} - \frac{1}{4} + \cdots.$$

One really useful fact about power series is that we can differentiate and integrate them term-by-term.

---

**Problem 7.34:** Differentiate the Taylor series of $\sin x$ term-by-term. What do we get?

---

*Solution for Problem 7.34:* We start with

$$\sin x = x - \frac{x^3}{3!} + \frac{x^5}{5!} - \frac{x^7}{7!} + \cdots.$$

When we take the derivative term-by-term, we get:

$$1 - \frac{x^2}{2!} + \frac{x^4}{4!} - \frac{x^6}{6!} + \cdots,$$

which indeed is the Taylor series for $\cos x$. $\square$

It is hardly a coincidence that $\frac{d}{dx}(\sin x) = \cos x$, and that the term-by-term differentiation of the Taylor series of $\sin x$ gives the Taylor series of $\cos x$. You can also verify that taking the term-by-term derivative of the Taylor series of $e^x$ (which we know converges to $e^x$) gives back the Taylor series of $e^x$; this is consistent with $\frac{d}{dx}e^x = e^x$.

However, it is quite difficult to prove that this behavior generalizes, so we will have to state the relevant result without proof:

---

**Important:** Suppose $f(x)$ is a function whose Taylor series $\displaystyle\sum_{n=0}^{\infty} c_n(x - a)^n$ converges to $f(x)$ within its radius of convergence. Then the power series

$$\sum_{n=1}^{\infty} nc_n(x - a)^{n-1}$$

obtained by taking the term-by-term derivative $\frac{d}{dx}c_n(x - a)^n = nc_n(x - a)^{n-1}$ is the Taylor series of $f'(x)$, and converges to $f'(x)$ with the same radius of convergence.

---

The above result helps us construct new power series easily.

**Problem 7.35:** Find the Taylor series (at $x = 0$) of $\tan^{-1} x$.

*Solution for Problem 7.35:* Rather than computing derivatives of $\tan^{-1}$, there is an easier solution. We know that $\dfrac{d}{dx} \tan^{-1} x = \dfrac{1}{1 + x^2}$, so we can find the Taylor series of $\dfrac{1}{1 + x^2}$ and antidifferentiate it.

Happily, the power series of $\dfrac{1}{1 + x^2}$ is just a geometric series with common ratio $-x^2$. Specifically:

$$\frac{1}{1 + x^2} = 1 - x^2 + x^4 - x^6 + x^8 - \cdots .$$

So we take antiderivatives term-by-term, and we get

$$\tan^{-1} x = C + x - \frac{x^3}{3} + \frac{x^5}{5} - \frac{x^7}{7} + \cdots .$$

Don't forget about the $C$! We have to be careful about the constant. When we plug in $x = 0$, we see that $C = \tan^{-1} 0 = 0$, so the constant is 0. Therefore,

$$\tan^{-1} x = x - \frac{x^3}{3} + \frac{x^5}{5} - \frac{x^7}{7} + \cdots .$$

To finish, we should determine the values of $x$ for which this power series converges. The geometric series converges for $-1 < x < 1$, so the Taylor series for $\tan^{-1}$ also converges in this region. But, the series for $\tan^{-1}$ also converges at $x = 1$ and $x = -1$, since in either case it is an alternating series with decreasing terms that go to 0. So the interval of convergence is $[-1, 1]$. $\square$

**WARNING!!** Differentiating or integrating a Taylor series may alter convergence or divergence at the endpoints of the convergence interval.

Note that the convergence of the arctan series at $x = 1$ gives us a neat formula:

$$\frac{\pi}{4} = \tan^{-1} 1 = 1 - \frac{1}{3} + \frac{1}{5} - \frac{1}{7} + \cdots .$$

There is another formula for $\pi$ that is presented in Section 7.A.

## EXERCISES

**7.6.1** Find the Taylor series, and their radii of convergence, for the following functions:

(a) $e^{-x}$ about $x = 0$. **Hints:** 80

(b) $\sin x^2$ about $x = 0$. **Hints:** 24

(c) $xe^{-x^2}$ about $x = 0$. **Hints:** 245

(d) $\sqrt{x + 1}$ about $x = 2$. **Hints:** 30

(e) $\frac{1}{1-x^2}$ about $x = 0$. **Hints:** 217

**7.6.2** Verify that the term-by-term differentiation of the Taylor series of $\cos x$ yields the Taylor series for $-\sin x$.

**7.6.3** Compute the first 4 nonzero terms of the Taylor series of $e^x \sin x$ at $x = 0$ in two ways:

(a) directly by computing the first five derivatives of $f(x) = e^x \sin x$; and

(b) by multiplying together the Taylor series of $e^x$ and $\sin x$.

**7.6.4★** Find a function whose Taylor series is

$$\frac{x^2}{2} - \frac{x^3}{3 \cdot 2} + \frac{x^4}{4 \cdot 3} - \frac{x^5}{5 \cdot 4} + \cdots$$

for $|x| < 1$. **Hints:** 284, 221

## REVIEW PROBLEMS

**7.36** Define a sequence $\{a_n\}_{n=1}^\infty$ by $a_1 = \sqrt{2}$ and $a_n = \sqrt{2a_{n-1}}$ for all $n > 1$. Determine $\lim_{n \to \infty} a_n$. **Hints:** 91

**7.37** For each of the following series, prove that it converges, and if possible, determine what it converges to:

(a) $\displaystyle\sum_{k=1}^\infty \frac{2k-1}{3k^3+1}$  (b) $\displaystyle\sum_{k=1}^\infty \frac{3^k + 4^k}{7^k}$  (c) $\displaystyle\sum_{k=1}^\infty \frac{(-2)^k}{3^k - 1}$  (d) $\displaystyle\sum_{k=1}^\infty \frac{k^2 3^k}{k!}$  (e) $\displaystyle\sum_{k=1}^\infty \frac{1}{k^e}$

**7.38** Find the first four terms of the Taylor series about $x = 0$ of the following functions:

(a) $e^{-x^2}$  (b) $\cos x^3$  (c) $e^{x^2 + \sin x}$  (d) $\dfrac{1}{\sqrt{1 - 4x^2}}$

**7.39** Compute $\displaystyle\sum_{n=0}^\infty \frac{2^{n-1}}{n!}$. **Hints:** 240

**7.40** Estimate $\displaystyle\int_0^1 \sin x^2 \, dx$ to 3 decimal places using power series. **Hints:** 124

**7.41** Let $p$ and $q$ be positive real numbers. Compute $\lim_{n \to \infty} \sqrt[n]{p^n + q^n}$. **Hints:** 252

**7.42** Let $c > 0$ be a real number. Prove that $\displaystyle\sum_{n=1}^\infty \frac{n!}{(cn)^n}$ converges if $c > \frac{1}{e}$ and diverges if $c < \frac{1}{e}$. *(Source: HMMT)*

**7.43** Define a function $f$ via the power series

$$f(x) = 1 + \frac{x}{2} + \frac{x^2}{4} + \frac{x^3}{8} + \cdots = \sum_{n=0}^\infty \frac{x^n}{2^n},$$

for $-1 \le x \le 1$. Compute $\sqrt{e^{\int_0^1 f(x) \, dx}}$. *(Source: HMMT)* **Hints:** 59

## CHALLENGE PROBLEMS

**7.44** Suppose that the sequence $\{a_n\}_{n=1}^\infty$ satisfies $0 < a_n \le a_{2n} + a_{2n+1}$ for all $n \ge 1$. Prove that $\displaystyle\sum_{n=1}^\infty a_n$ diverges. *(Source: Putnam)* **Hints:** 58, 21

**7.45** Define $a_n = \left(\displaystyle\sum_{i=1}^n \frac{1}{i}\right) - \log n$.

(a) Use appropriate definite integral(s) to prove that $0 < a_{n+1} < a_n$ for all $n > 1$. **Hints:** 2, 159

(b) Use (a) to prove that $\lim_{n\to\infty} a_n$ exists.

Note: $\lim_{n\to\infty} a_n$ is called **Euler's Constant** and is usually denoted $\gamma$. It is an important number in analysis, but not much is known about it: indeed it is not known whether $\gamma$ is rational or irrational, although it has been computed to 2 billion decimal places.

**7.46** Define a sequence $\{a_n\}$ by

$$a_n = \left( \frac{1}{\sqrt{n^2 - 0^2}} + \frac{1}{\sqrt{n^2 - 1^2}} + \frac{1}{\sqrt{n^2 - 2^2}} + \cdots + \frac{1}{\sqrt{n^2 - (n-1)^2}} \right).$$

Compute $\lim_{n\to\infty} a_n$. *(Source: HMMT)* **Hints:** 27, 15, 235

**7.47** The **Fibonacci numbers** are defined as $a_0 = a_1 = 1$ and $a_n = a_{n-1} + a_{n-2}$ for all $n \geq 2$. Let

$$f(x) = \sum_{n=0}^{\infty} a_n x^n = 1 + x + 2x^2 + 3x^3 + 5x^4 + 8x^5 + \cdots .$$

(a) Prove that the radius of convergence of $f$ is at least $\frac{1}{2}$. **Hints:** 222

(b) Prove that if $|x| < \frac{1}{2}$, then $f(x) = \frac{1}{1-x-x^2}$. **Hints:** 264

**7.48** The **Binomial Theorem** works for non-integer exponents too! Specifically, we can write

$$(1 + x)^p = 1 + \binom{p}{1}x + \binom{p}{2}x^2 + \binom{p}{3}x^3 + \cdots ,$$

even when $p$ is not a positive integer. Explain this equation and prove it. What are the necessary conditions (if any) on $x$ and $p$? **Hints:** 299

**7.49★** Let $n \geq 2$ be an integer, and for any real number $\alpha$, let $C(\alpha)$ be the coefficient of $x^n$ in the power series expansion of $(1 + x)^\alpha$. Prove that

$$\int_0^1 \left( C(-t - 1) \left( \sum_{k=1}^{n} \frac{1}{t + k} \right) \right) dt = (-1)^n n.$$

*(Source: Putnam)* **Hints:** 17, 270

**7.50★** Consider the function

$$f(x) = \begin{cases} e^{-\frac{1}{x^2}} & \text{if } x \neq 0, \\ 0 & \text{if } x = 0. \end{cases}$$

(a) Show that, for all positive integers $n$, there exists a polynomial $p_n$ such that

$$f^{(n)}(x) = \begin{cases} p_n\left(\frac{1}{x}\right) e^{-\frac{1}{x^2}} & \text{if } x \neq 0, \\ 0 & \text{if } x = 0. \end{cases}$$

**Hints:** 66, 56

(b) Using part (a), compute the Taylor series of $f$ at 0, and show that for all nonzero $x \in \mathbb{R}$, the Taylor series converges to something other than $f(x)$.

## 7.A  A STRANGE FORMULA FOR $\pi$

> **WARNING!!**   This section will use a lot of "magic" results that we have not proved, or even really rigorously defined.

> **Problem 7.51:**  Show that
> $$\frac{\pi^2}{6} = 1 + \frac{1}{4} + \frac{1}{9} + \frac{1}{16} + \cdots .$$

> **Sidenote:**  The argument below was first shown by the mathematician Leonhard Euler in the 18$^{\text{th}}$ century.

*Solution for Problem 7.51:*  We start with the power series for sine:

$$\sin x = x - \frac{x^3}{3!} + \frac{x^5}{5!} - \cdots ,$$

and we divide by $x$:

$$f(x) = \frac{\sin x}{x} = 1 - \frac{x^2}{3!} + \frac{x^4}{5!} - \cdots .$$

As we know, this converges for all $x \in \mathbb{R}$.

We can make the substitution $y = x^2$ to define

$$g(y) = 1 - \frac{y}{3!} + \frac{y^2}{5!} - \cdots .$$

This still converges for all $y \in \mathbb{R}$.

We now examine the zeroes of this power series; that is, we find the values of $y$ such that $g(y) = 0$. The zeroes of $f(x)$ are the integer multiples of $\pi$, so the zeroes of $g(y)$ are the squares of integer multiples of $\pi$. That is, the zeroes of $g(y)$ are exactly the elements of the set $\{\pi^2, 4\pi^2, 9\pi^2, \ldots\}$.

This means—and here we are taking a lot of liberty and using some manipulations that we have not proved—that we can write

$$1 - \frac{y}{3!} + \frac{y^2}{5!} - \cdots = g(y) = \left(1 - \frac{y}{\pi^2}\right)\left(1 - \frac{y}{4\pi^2}\right)\left(1 - \frac{y}{9\pi^2}\right)\cdots .$$

We now examine the linear (or $y$) terms on both sides of this equation. On the left side, it is clearly $-\frac{1}{6}$, but on the right side, it is the sum of the $y$-coefficients of the individual factors, giving

$$-\left(\frac{1}{\pi^2} + \frac{1}{4\pi^2} + \frac{1}{9\pi^2} + \cdots\right).$$

These must be equal, so we have

$$-\frac{1}{6} = -\left(\frac{1}{\pi^2} + \frac{1}{4\pi^2} + \frac{1}{9\pi^2} + \cdots\right).$$

Finally, we multiply by $-\pi^2$, and we get

$$\frac{\pi^2}{6} = 1 + \frac{1}{4} + \frac{1}{9} + \frac{1}{16} + \cdots .$$

$\square$

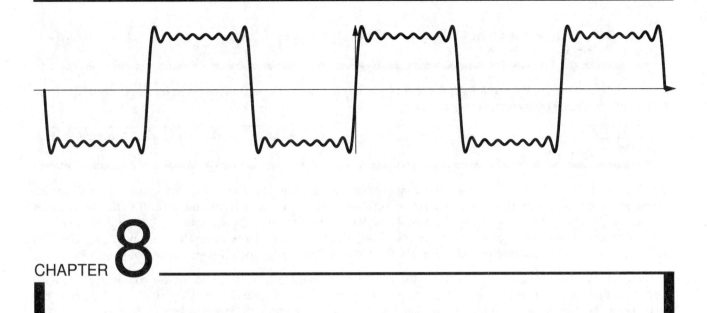

# CHAPTER 8

PLANE CURVES

## 8.1 Parametric curves

Let's go back to our example of the circle of radius 1 centered at the origin of the coordinate plane. We can think of the circle as the set of all points $(x, y)$ such that

$$x = \cos \theta, \ y = \sin \theta,$$

where $\theta \in \mathbb{R}$. If we further restrict $\theta \in [0, 2\pi)$, then each value of $\theta$ gives a unique point on the circle.

This concept—of describing the $x$- and $y$-coordinates of the points of a curve in terms of a new third variable ($\theta$ in our example)—can be made more general:

> **Definition:** A **parametric curve** $C$ is a set of points in the coordinate plane satisfying the following: there exists an interval $I \subseteq \mathbb{R}$ and real-valued functions $u$ and $v$, each with domain $I$, such that
>
> $$C = \{(u(t), v(t)) \mid t \in I\}.$$
>
> The functions $u$ and $v$ are called **parametric functions**, and the pair $(u, v)$ is called a **parameterization** of $C$.

Usually $I$ is a closed interval, so that the points of the curve $C$ corresponding to the endpoints of $I$ are the **endpoints** of the parameterization of $C$. Note that in the above definition, it is perfectly valid to have $I = \mathbb{R}$.

In our circle example above, we have $u(t) = \cos t$ and $v(t) = \sin t$, where $t$ ranges over the interval $[0, 2\pi]$. We could have used a different interval for the domain of the parametric functions, such as $[0, 2\pi)$, or $[\pi, 3\pi]$, or even all of $\mathbb{R}$: these are different parameterizations (since the functions have different domains), but they all result in the same parametric curve, since they all produce the set of points consisting of the unit circle.

First, let's quickly observe that parametric curves really aren't totally new:

**Problem 8.1:** Suppose $f$ is a function such that Dom($f$) is an interval. Explain how the graph $y = f(x)$ of a function $f$ is a parametric curve.

*Solution for Problem 8.1:* We just let $u(t) = t$ and $v(t) = f(t)$ for all $t \in$ Dom($f$). This gives us all points of the form $(t, f(t))$, which is exactly the graph of $y = f(x)$. □

**Problem 8.2:** Are parameterizations unique? For example, are there other parameterizations of the circle with center $(0, 0)$ and radius 1?

*Solution for Problem 8.2:* There are infinitely many parameterizations of a given parametric curve. For example, the parametric functions $u(t) = \cos ct$ and $v(t) = \sin ct$ give the same circle (centered at $(0, 0)$ with radius 1) for any nonzero real number $c$ (assuming we adjust the domain interval of $t$ appropriately). A slightly more exotic parameterization is something like $u(t) = \cos t^2$ and $v(t) = \sin t^2$. In fact, more generally, we have $u(t) = \cos(f(t))$ and $v(t) = \sin(f(t))$ as a parameterization for any function $f$ whose range includes an interval of length $2\pi$. □

So what exactly is the difference between these different parameterizations? The answer comes from how we think about parametric curves. We can visualize a parametric curve as a particle moving along a path, where the variable $t$ represents time. Thinking of this visualization, we can see how the parameterizations

$$u(t) = \cos t, \ v(t) = \sin t$$

and

$$u(t) = \cos 2t, \ v(t) = \sin 2t$$

differ: they give the same curve, but in the second parameterization, the particle is moving twice as fast. It only takes $\pi$ units of time for the particle to make a complete revolution in the second parameterization, versus $2\pi$ units of time in the first parameterization. Since, as we have seen, many uses of calculus deal with how quantities are changing over time, it is very useful to have this temporal quality to parameterizations.

**Problem 8.3:** How does the parameterization

$$u(t) = \cos(-t), \ v(t) = \sin(-t)?$$

describe the motion of a particle on the unit circle?

*Solution for Problem 8.3:* Note that if $x = \cos(-t)$ and $y = \sin(-t)$, then for any $t$ we have $x^2 + y^2 = 1$, so this curve is the same circle with center $(0, 0)$ and radius 1 that we have been considering so far. However, with this new parameterization, we think of the particle moving around the circle in the clockwise direction. For example, at $t = 0$, the particle "starts" at $(\cos 0, \sin 0) = (1, 0)$, and at $t = \frac{\pi}{2}$, the particle is at the point $\left(\cos(-\frac{\pi}{2}), \sin(-\frac{\pi}{2})\right) = (0, -1)$, so the particle has moved one-quarter of the way around the circle in the clockwise direction. □

**Concept:** For simplicity of writing, we often would write the parameterization of the circle from Problem 8.3 as

$$(\cos(-t), \sin(-t)).$$

It is understood that the "coordinates" are actually parametric equations describing the path of the curve.

**Problem 8.4:** What are parametric equations of the line passing through $(x_0, y_0)$ with slope $m$?

*Solution for Problem 8.4:* We can think of the line "starting" at $(x_0, y_0)$, with the particle moving $m$ units in the $y$-direction for every unit of motion in the $x$-direction. Thus, possible parametric equations are:

$$u(t) = x_0 + t, \; v(t) = y_0 + mt,$$

for $t \in \mathbb{R}$. □

One common use of parametric equations is to describe the motion of an object that is a "sum" of two (or more) separate motions. A classic example of this is the following:

**Problem 8.5:** A wheel of radius 2 feet is moving along a straight path at 1 revolution per second. At time $t = 0$ sec, the point at which the wheel touches the ground is painted yellow. Determine parametric equations for the path of the yellow point.

To show more clearly what's going on, we can sketch a picture of the motion:

The wheel starts at the position on the left and rotates clockwise. The later positions of the wheel (in 1/8-second increments) are shown. The yellow point that we are tracking is the dark dot (a portion of the wheel containing the dot is shown in darker shading to add a little contrast). The dashed arc is the path.

*Solution for Problem 8.5:* We impose a coordinate system, where we set $(0, 0)$ to be where the point starts. The idea is to combine the two separate motions that are present: the wheel moving down the path and the point rotating around the center of the wheel.

We can start by writing parametric equations for the center of the wheel. The center moves, in 1 second, a distance equal to the circumference of the circle; thus, the center moves $4\pi$ feet per second. Hence, a parametric representation for the center of the wheel is $(4\pi t, 2)$. (Again, this is really the parametric equations $u(t) = 4\pi t$ and $v(t) = 2$, and the curve traced by the center of the wheel is given by $(u(t), v(t))$.)

Now we determine the position of the dot relative to the center of the circle. The dot is rotating in the clockwise direction, one revolution per second, starting at the point $(0, -2)$. Many answers are possible, but perhaps the simplest is

$$(-2 \sin 2\pi t, -2 \cos 2\pi t).$$

Pay close attention to how we combined all the data about the rotation to come up with these functions. The $2\pi t$ term gives the proper speed: the dot makes one complete revolution of the circle every second, since $\sin 2\pi t$ and $\cos 2\pi t$ each have period 1. Also, the factor of 2 gives the correct radius, and swapping the sine and cosine terms and multiplying by $-1$ gives the correct starting point at $t = 0$ and direction of movement. As a check, plugging in $t = \frac{1}{4}$ gives the point $(-2, 0)$, which is where the point should be relative to the center after a quarter-circle clockwise rotation from the starting point $(0, -2)$.

To get the overall position of the yellow dot, we add together the parameterizations of the motion of the center of the wheel along the road and the motion of the dot around the wheel, giving:

$$(4\pi t - 2 \sin 2\pi t, 2 - 2 \cos 2\pi t).$$

We can sketch the graph of this as $t$ runs from 0 to 3, giving 3 revolutions of the circle:

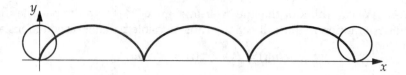

□

The curve from Problem 8.5 is called a **cycloid**. We also get an interesting picture if the point is in the interior of the circle:

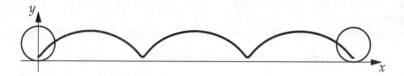

Notice the "corners" are not as sharp. We leave it as an exercise to determine the parametric equations for this curve.

Our next goal is to compute the slope of a tangent line to a parametric curve. Specifically, we want to determine the slope of the tangent line to the parametric curve $C$, given by parameterization $(u(t), v(t))$, at the **point** $(u(a), v(a))$ for some $a$.

There are a couple of ways to approach this. One is to think about what we mean by slope: the slope of the tangent line measures

$$\frac{\text{the rate of change of } y}{\text{the rate of change of } x}.$$

But what is the rate of change of $y$ at $(u(a), v(a))$? It's the rate by which the $y$ part of the parameterization is changing, and that's just $v'(a)$. (Note that when we write this derivative, we think of $v$ as a function of $t$, so we are computing $v'(t)$ and plugging in the value $t = a$.) Similarly, the rate of change of $x$ is $u'(a)$. Thus, the slope of the tangent line at $(u(a), v(a))$ is $\dfrac{v'(a)}{u'(a)}$, assuming $u'(a) \neq 0$.

Another way to determine the slope of the tangent line to a parametric curve is to recall how we determined the slope of the tangent line to the graph $y = f(x)$ of a function $f$. We start with a secant line of our parametric curve between $t = a$ and $t = a + h$, as shown at right. We can write an expression for the slope of this secant:

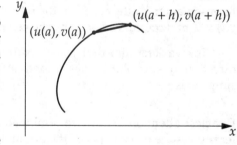

$$\text{Slope} = \frac{\text{Change in } y}{\text{Change in } x} = \frac{v(a + h) - v(a)}{u(a + h) - u(a)}.$$

To get the slope of the tangent line, we let the secant line approach the tangent line; that is, we let $h$ approach 0:

$$\lim_{h \to 0} \frac{v(a + h) - v(a)}{u(a + h) - u(a)}.$$

This does not exactly look like a derivative. But we can make it look more recognizable by multiplying and dividing by $h$:

$$\lim_{h \to 0} \left( \frac{v(a + h) - v(a)}{h} \cdot \frac{h}{u(a + h) - u(a)} \right).$$

This is clearly $\dfrac{v'(a)}{u'(a)}$, as expected.

What happens if $u'(a) = 0$? Then the $x$-coordinate is not changing, so if the vertical coordinate is changing—that is, if $v'(a)$ is nonzero—then we should get a vertical tangent line. This means that the particle is moving vertically (parallel to the $y$-axis) along the curve.

Points where $u'(a) = v'(a) = 0$ may not have well-defined tangent lines. On the other hand, we expect that the slope of the tangent line to a parametric curve is a continuous function of the parameter—that is, the tangent line should vary "smoothly" if possible. Thus, at points where $u'(a) = v'(a) = 0$, we can try to use

$$\lim_{t \to a} \frac{v'(t)}{u'(t)}$$

as the slope of our tangent line. For example, the curve given by the parameterization $(u(t), v(t)) = (t^3, t^3)$ is clearly the line $y = x$, so the tangent line at $(0, 0)$ should have slope 1. We have $u'(0) = v'(0) = 0$, but

$$\lim_{t \to 0} \frac{v'(t)}{u'(t)} = \lim_{t \to 0} \frac{3t^2}{3t^2} = \lim_{t \to 0} 1 = 1,$$

as expected.

To summarize:

> **Definition:** Let $C$ be a parametric curve given by parameterization $(u(t), v(t))$, and let $a$ be a value in the domain of $u$ and $v$. The **tangent line** to $C$ at $(u(a), v(a))$ is the line passing through $(u(a), v(a))$ with slope $\dfrac{v'(a)}{u'(a)}$, provided $u'(a) \neq 0$. If $u'(a) = 0$ and $v'(a) \neq 0$, then the tangent line is the vertical line through $(u(a), v(a))$. If $u'(a) = v'(a) = 0$, then the tangent line through $(u(a), v(a))$ has slope $\displaystyle\lim_{t \to a} \frac{v'(t)}{u'(t)}$ if defined.

We can also write the slope of a tangent line to a parametric curve as:

$$\frac{dy}{dx} = \frac{\frac{dy}{dt}}{\frac{dx}{dt}}.$$

In other words, the slope $\frac{dy}{dx}$ is the ratio of the derivatives $\frac{dy}{dt}, \frac{dx}{dt}$ of the parametric equations (in terms of $t$). We can remember this formula as "canceling the $dt$s," even though this is only a notational device.

Let's go back to our cycloid:

> **Problem 8.6:** Recall the cycloid from Problem 8.5 was given parametrically by
>
> $$(4\pi t - 2\sin 2\pi t, 2 - 2\cos 2\pi t).$$
>
> At any time $t$, what is the slope of the tangent line to the cycloid?

*Solution for Problem 8.6:* Taking the derivatives of the parametric equations gives us

$$\frac{dx}{dt} = 4\pi - 4\pi \cos 2\pi t, \quad \frac{dy}{dt} = 4\pi \sin 2\pi t.$$

So the slope of a tangent line is

$$\frac{dy}{dx} = \frac{\frac{dy}{dt}}{\frac{dx}{dt}} = \frac{4\pi \sin 2\pi t}{4\pi - 4\pi \cos 2\pi t} = \frac{\sin 2\pi t}{1 - \cos 2\pi t}.$$

Note that if $t$ is an integer, this quantity is $\frac{0}{0}$. These are the "sharp corners" of the cycloid. At these points, we can consider the limit of this quantity, and attempt to use l'Hôpital's Rule. Specifically, for any integer $n$,

$$\lim_{t \to n} \frac{\sin 2\pi t}{1 - \cos 2\pi t} = \lim_{t \to n} \frac{2\pi \cos 2\pi t}{2\pi \sin 2\pi t} = \lim_{t \to n} \cot 2\pi t,$$

which is undefined, so l'Hôpital's Rule does not apply. In fact, the limit is undefined. $\square$

> **Sidenote:** At the sharp corner points of the cycloid, we notice that
>
> $$\lim_{t \to n^+} \frac{\sin 2\pi t}{1 - \cos 2\pi t} = +\infty \quad \text{and} \quad \lim_{t \to n^-} \frac{\sin 2\pi t}{1 - \cos 2\pi t} = -\infty.$$
>
> Since both $+\infty$ and $-\infty$ each could be the "slope" of a vertical line, it is OK for us to say that the cycloid has vertical tangent lines at these points. This is very similar to our definition of vertical asymptote, in which we only required a limit of $\pm\infty$ from either direction, and not the same limit from both directions at once.

The slope of the tangent line gives us the direction of movement along the curve. Related to the direction of movement is the speed of movement:

**Problem 8.7:** Suppose a particle is at $(u(t), v(t))$ at time $t$. What is the speed of the particle at $t = a$?

*Solution for Problem 8.7:* If the particle were moving horizontally as a function $x(t)$ of $t$, then its speed would just be $|dx/dt|$, the absolute value of the derivative $x'(t)$. (Note that speed is always nonnegative, so we take the absolute value.) Similarly, if the particle were moving vertically as a function $y(t)$ of $t$, its speed would be $|dy/dt|$.

But our particle is moving in an arbitrary direction. So to calculate its speed, we break up the particle into its $x$- and $y$-components, and apply the Pythagorean Theorem. That is, the particle is moving at a speed of $|dx/dt| = |u'(t)|$ in the $x$-direction, and a speed of $|dy/dt| = |v'(t)|$ in the $y$-direction. Thus, to compute the speed of the particular in the direction of the curve, we form a right triangle with sides of length $|u'(t)|$ and $|v'(t)|$, and compute the length of the hypotenuse of this triangle.

Therefore, the speed of the particle at $t = a$ on the curve parameterized by $(u(t), v(t))$ is

$$\sqrt{(u'(a))^2 + (v'(a))^2}.$$

$\square$

Note that at points where $u'(a) = v'(a) = 0$, the particle comes to a stop (that is, has speed 0).

**Problem 8.8:** Once again, recall that the cycloid from Problem 8.5 was given parametrically by

$$(4\pi t - 2\sin 2\pi t, 2 - 2\cos 2\pi t).$$

At any time $t$, what is the speed of the point whose path forms the cycloid?

*Solution for Problem 8.8:* The derivatives of the parametric equations are:

$$\frac{dx}{dt} = 4\pi - 4\pi \cos 2\pi t, \quad \frac{dy}{dt} = 4\pi \sin 2\pi t.$$

So the speed is

$$\sqrt{(4\pi - 4\pi \cos 2\pi t)^2 + (4\pi \sin 2\pi t)^2}$$

This simplifies to

$$4\pi \sqrt{(1 - \cos 2\pi t)^2 + \sin^2 2\pi t}$$

This equals

$$4\pi \sqrt{1 - 2\cos 2\pi t + \cos^2 2\pi t + \sin^2 2\pi t} = 4\pi \sqrt{2 - 2\cos 2\pi t}.$$

Finally, we can rewrite this as

$$8\pi \sqrt{\frac{1 - \cos 2\pi t}{2}} = 8\pi |\sin \pi t|.$$

Again, when $t$ is an integer, the speed is 0, and the point comes to a complete (instantaneous) stop. □

We can use speed to get the length of a parametric curve in the same way that we do for motion in 1 dimension: we integrate speed to get distance.

---

**Definition:** The **length** of the parametric curve $(u(t), v(t))$ from $t = a$ to $t = b$ is

$$\int_a^b \sqrt{(u'(t))^2 + (v'(t))^2}\, dt.$$

---

One interesting thing to note is that while the speed depends on the choice of parameterization, the length does not, provided that the new parameterization "moves in the same direction" as the original parameterization. (You can explore the details of this statement and try to prove it as a Challenge Problem.) This should not be a surprise, as the length of a curve should not depend on how fast a particle is moving along the curve—the length should be an inherent property of the curve.

We can check that our new definition of length matches our prior intuitive notion of length for a particularly important example:

**Problem 8.9:** Verify the formula for the circumference of a circle.

*Solution for Problem 8.9:* For simplicity, we can assume that the circle has radius $r > 0$ and center $(0, 0)$. So a simple parameterization is $(r \cos t, r \sin t)$ for $t \in [0, 2\pi]$. Thus, to compute the circumference, we integrate

$$\int_0^{2\pi} \sqrt{r^2 \sin^2 t + r^2 \cos^2 t}\, dt.$$

This is just $\int_0^{2\pi} r\, dt = 2\pi r$. □

To finish this section, we'll look at a more open-ended problem, where we're given a parametric curve and we want to find out as much as we can about it.

**Problem 8.10:** Explore the **astroid** given by the parameterization $(\cos^3 t, \sin^3 t)$. Sketch its graph, determine the slopes of its tangent lines, and compute its length.

*Solution for Problem 8.10:* The first thing we notice is that the parameterizing functions are periodic with period $2\pi$. So taking $t \in [0, 2\pi]$ will give us the entire curve. When $t$ is a multiple of $\frac{\pi}{2}$, we get the same points as the circle of radius 1 centered at $(0, 0)$, so the astroid passes through $(1, 0)$, $(0, 1)$, $(-1, 0)$, and $(0, -1)$.

We can compute the slopes of the tangent lines by first computing the derivatives of the parameterizing equations:

$$\frac{dx}{dt} = -3\cos^2 t \sin t, \qquad \frac{dy}{dt} = 3\sin^2 t \cos t.$$

So the slope of a tangent line is

$$\frac{dy}{dx} = \frac{3\sin^2 t \cos t}{-3\cos^2 t \sin t} = -\frac{\sin t}{\cos t} = -\tan t.$$

However, we have to be a little bit careful: since we canceled out $\sin t \cos t$ in our above calculation, we actually have points where $\frac{dx}{dt} = \frac{dy}{dt} = 0$ whenever $\sin t = 0$ or $\cos t = 0$. These are the four points of the astroid that lie on the $x$-axis or $y$-axis, and they may appear as "sharp corners" of our curve.

Also, since the slopes of the tangent lines to the circle given parametrically by $(\cos t, \sin t)$ are

$$\frac{\cos t}{-\sin t} = -\cot t,$$

we see that the astroid at time $t$ has the inverse slope of the circle at time $t$. Thus, the astroid should like something look an "inverted circle," as shown at right.

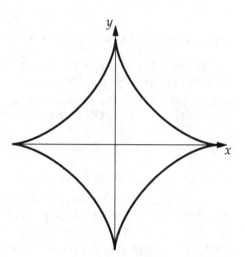

We can also compute its length:

$$\int_0^{2\pi} \sqrt{\left(\frac{dx}{dt}\right)^2 + \left(\frac{dy}{dt}\right)^2} \, dt = \int_0^{2\pi} \sqrt{9\cos^4 t \sin^2 t + 9\sin^4 t \cos^2 t} \, dt.$$

We can pull out the common factors, but we're careful not to forget the absolute value when doing so!

$$\int_0^{2\pi} 3|\cos t \sin t| \sqrt{\cos^2 t + \sin^2 t} \, dt.$$

We know that $\cos^2 t + \sin^2 t = 1$, so we are left with:

$$\int_0^{2\pi} 3|\cos t \sin t| \, dt.$$

The absolute value sign makes things slightly delicate. We're perhaps safest using the trig identity $\cos t \sin t = \frac{1}{2}\sin 2t$, giving:

$$\frac{3}{2} \int_0^{2\pi} |\sin 2t| \, dt.$$

The easiest way to finish is to note that this is 4 times the value of the same integral from $t = 0$ to $t = \frac{\pi}{2}$. On $\left[0, \frac{\pi}{2}\right]$, we have $\sin 2t \geq 0$, so we can remove the absolute value and we have:

$$6 \int_0^{\pi/2} \sin 2t \, dt = -3\cos 2t \Big|_0^{\pi/2} = 6.$$

Thus the length of the astroid is 6. It is perhaps a surprise that the length is rational. $\square$

What's amazing (but not too hard to prove) is that the astroid is an example of a **hypocycloid**, which is like our earlier example of a cycloid, but instead traces the path of a point on a circle rotating inside another larger circle. As an exercise, you will prove that a particular hypocycloid is the astroid that we just explored.

## EXERCISES

**8.1.1** Write parametric equations for the following curves:

(a)   A circle of radius 2 centered at $(1, 1)$.

(b)   A spiral centered at $(0, 0)$ where the radius increases at a constant rate of 4 units per revolution, so that the spiral passes through (in order): $(0, 0)$, $(0, 1)$, $(-2, 0)$, $(0, -3)$, $(4, 0)$, $(0, 5)$, $(-6, 0)$, ....

(c)★   An ellipse with major axis of length 4 parallel to the $x$-axis, minor axis of length 2 parallel to the $y$-axis, and centered at $(2, -3)$. **Hints:** 16

**8.1.2**   Find parametric equations for the cycloid traced by a point inside of a wheel of radius 2, where the point starts (at $t = 0$) halfway between the center of the wheel and the ground, and the wheel moves to the right at 1 revolution per second. Also determine the speed (in terms of $t$) that the point is traveling as it traces the path of the cycloid.

**8.1.3**   Consider the curve given by the parameterization $(\cos t, t + \sin t)$ for $t \in [0, \pi]$.

(a)   Find the the slope of the tangent line to the curve at $t = \frac{\pi}{2}$.

(b)   Find the length of the curve.

**8.1.4★**   Find parametric equations for the hypocycloid that is produced when we track a point on a circle of radius $\frac{1}{4}$ that rotates inside circle of radius 1. Show that this curve is the astroid from Problem 8.10. **Hints:** 3, 131, 248

**8.1.5★**   Sketch the curve given by the parameterization $(\cos 3t, \sin 5t)$. This curve is known as a **Lissajous curve**. **Hints:** 183, 75

---

**Sidenote:** One more interesting formula, that we won't prove in this text, is a version of what is known as **Green's Theorem** in vector calculus.

Suppose that $(u(t), v(t))$ parameterizes a closed simple smooth curve from $t = a$ to $t = b$ in the counterclockwise direction. ("Closed simple smooth" essentially means that the curve starts and ends at the same point, doesn't intersect itself except at its endpoints, and doesn't have any sharp corners.) Then the area it encloses is

$$\frac{1}{2} \int_a^b (u(t)v'(t) - u'(t)v(t)) \, dt.$$

We can see an example of Green's Theorem with the circle of radius $r$: it has parameterization $(r \cos t, r \sin t)$, so Green's Theorem tells us the area is

$$\frac{1}{2} \int_0^{2\pi} ((r \cos t)(r \cos t) - (-r \sin t)(r \sin t)) \, dt.$$

The integrand simplifies to just $r^2$, so the area is $\pi r^2$, as expected.

---

# 8.2   POLAR COORDINATES

You have likely seen polar coordinates before. Polar coordinates provide an alternative system for describing points in the plane, in terms of their positions relative to the origin.

> **Definition:** A point $P$ in the coordinate plane is represented in **polar coordinates** as $(r, \theta)$, where $r$ is the distance from $P$ to the origin, and $\theta$ is the angle between the positive $x$-axis and the ray $\overrightarrow{OP}$, where $O$ is the origin, measured in the usual counterclockwise direction. The number $r$ is called the **magnitude** of $P$ and the angle $\theta$ is called the **argument** of $P$.

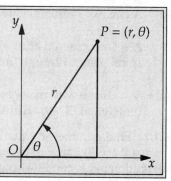

The first task is converting between our usual "rectangular" coordinates and polar coordinates.

> **Problem 8.11:**
> (a) If $P$ is given in rectangular coordinates by $(x, y)$, what are the polar coordinates $(r, \theta)$ in terms of $x$ and $y$?
> (b) If $P$ is given in polar coordinates by $(r, \theta)$, what are the rectangular coordinates $(x, y)$ in terms of $r$ and $\theta$?

*Solution for Problem 8.11:*

(a) The picture accompanying the definition of polar coordinates makes it pretty clear what we need to do. We just use basic facts about right triangles. We have $r^2 = x^2 + y^2$, so $r = \sqrt{x^2 + y^2}$. We also have $\tan \theta = \dfrac{y}{x}$, so $\theta = \tan^{-1}\left(\dfrac{y}{x}\right)$. However, this only works for points in the first quadrant, as in the diagram to the right. What happens if we have a point in the second quadrant, creating an obtuse angle? In this case, we still have $r = \sqrt{x^2 + y^2}$, but we don't have $\theta = \tan^{-1}\left(\dfrac{y}{x}\right)$, since the range of $\tan^{-1}$ is $\left(-\frac{\pi}{2}, \frac{\pi}{2}\right)$ and we have $\theta \in \left(\frac{\pi}{2}, \pi\right)$ in the second quadrant.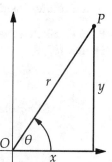

The formula $\theta = \tan^{-1}\left(\dfrac{y}{x}\right)$ only gives $\theta$ up to a constant $\pm \pi$, since $\tan^{-1}$ only has the range $\left(-\frac{\pi}{2}, \frac{\pi}{2}\right)$. For example, the point $(-1, -1)$ in polar coordinates is given by $r = \sqrt{2}$ and $\theta = \frac{5\pi}{4}$, but $\frac{5\pi}{4} \neq \tan^{-1}(1)$. We need to use our geometric knowledge of where the point lies to determine whether we need to add or subtract a factor of $\pi$. Another problem is if $x = 0$. Then $\frac{y}{x}$ is undefined, so we cannot compute $\tan^{-1}\left(\dfrac{y}{x}\right)$. However, we know that we must have $\theta = \frac{\pi}{2}$ or $\frac{3\pi}{2}$, depending on whether $y$ is positive or negative.

(b) The other direction—going from polar to rectangular—is much easier:

$$x = r \cos \theta,$$
$$y = r \sin \theta,$$

and there are no exceptions to this rule.

$\square$

It will be convenient for us to allow for polar coordinates with negative $r$. We think of this as a distance "in the negative direction" of the ray that forms angle $\theta$ with the positive $x$-axis. This also means that, in polar coordinates, $(r, \theta) = (-r, \theta + \pi)$ for any $r$ and $\theta$.

One perhaps unfortunate feature of polar coordinates is that any point has infinitely many different representations. For example, the point $(x, y) = (1, 0)$ in rectangular coordinates can be represented in polar coordinates as any of the following:

$$(1, 0), (1, 2\pi), (1, 4\pi), (1, -2\pi), (1, -4\pi), (-1, \pi), (-1, 3\pi), (-1, -\pi), (-1, -3\pi), \ldots.$$

Our main use of polar coordinates will be to describe the graph of curves of the form $r = f(\theta)$, as in the following example:

**Problem 8.12:** Describe the graph of $r = a \sin \theta$, where $a$ is a positive real number.

*Solution for Problem 8.12:* We can initially try to study this graph by plugging in a few common values of $\theta$ and determining what the corresponding points are on the graph.

For example:

- Setting $\theta = 0$ gives $r = a \sin 0 = 0$, so the (rectangular) point $(0, 0)$ lies on the graph;

- Setting $\theta = \frac{\pi}{2}$ gives $r = a \sin \frac{\pi}{2} = a$, so the (rectangular) point $(0, a)$ lies on the graph;

- Setting $\theta = \pi$ gives $r = a \sin \pi = 0$, so the (rectangular) point $(0, 0)$ lies on the graph (again);

- Setting $\theta = \frac{3\pi}{2}$ gives $r = a \sin \frac{3\pi}{2} = -a$, so the (rectangular) point $(0, a)$ lies on the graph (again).

This is not much information.

Let's look a little more closely at the shape of this graph by considering what happens as $\theta$ varies from 0 to $2\pi$. At $\theta$ increases from 0 to $\frac{\pi}{2}$, the radius $r$ increases from 0 to $a$. Then as $\theta$ increases from $\frac{\pi}{2}$ to $\pi$, the radius decreases from $a$ back to 0. We may also note as $\theta$ ranges from $\pi$ to $2\pi$, we get exactly the same graph, since $a \sin(\theta + \pi) = -a \sin(\theta)$.

To determine exactly what the graph looks like, we can convert to rectangular coordinates. Noting that $y = r \sin \theta$, we have $\frac{y}{r} = \sin \theta$, so our equation is $r = a \sin \theta = a \frac{y}{r}$, or $r^2 = ay$. (We need to be a little careful, as this doesn't work when $r = 0$, but that point is just the origin, which we know is on the graph.) But we also have $r^2 = x^2 + y^2$, so we get the equation

$$x^2 + y^2 = ay.$$

To examine the graph of this, we complete the square:

$$x^2 + \left(y - \frac{a}{2}\right)^2 = \frac{a^2}{4}.$$

Therefore, the graph is a circle centered at $\left(0, \frac{a}{2}\right)$ with radius $\frac{a}{2}$. Here is a picture:

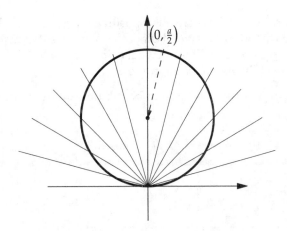

The rays in the picture above indicate different values of $\theta$, and are there to illustrate how $r$ increases as $\theta$ increases from 0 to $\frac{\pi}{2}$, and then decreases as $\theta$ increases from $\frac{\pi}{2}$ to $\pi$. $\square$

**Problem 8.13:** Sketch the graph of $r = 2\sin 3\theta$, and write it as rectangular equation in $x$ and $y$.

*Solution for Problem 8.13:* As in the previous problem, we can analyze what happens to $r$ as we vary $\theta$:

- As $\theta$ ranges from 0 to $\frac{\pi}{3}$, the radius increases from 0 to 2 and then decreases back to 0.

- As $\theta$ ranges from $\frac{\pi}{3}$ to $\frac{2\pi}{3}$, the radius goes from 0 to $-2$ and then back to 0.

- As $\theta$ ranges from $\frac{2\pi}{3}$ to $\pi$, the radius goes from 0 to 2 and then back to 0.

- And so on. . . .

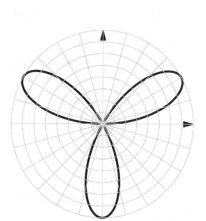

Sketching this gives us a 3-leafed **rose**, as shown to the right. Note that each range of $\theta$ between multiples of $\frac{\pi}{3}$ gives a leaf of the rose, but that the leaves overlap in pairs: for example, the leaf for $\theta \in [0, \frac{\pi}{3}]$ overlaps with the leaf for $\theta \in [\pi, \frac{4\pi}{3}]$.

To get a rectangular equation, we can use the triple-angle formula:

$$\sin 3\theta = 3\sin\theta - 4\sin^3\theta.$$

So we have

$$r = 2\left(3\frac{y}{r} - 4\frac{y^3}{r^3}\right)$$

We multiply by $r$ and substitute $r^2 = x^2 + y^2$ to get:

$$x^2 + y^2 = 6y - 8\frac{y^3}{x^2 + y^2}.$$

To clean this up, we can clear the denominator:

$$(x^2 + y^2)^2 + 2y^3 - 6x^2y = 0.$$

$\square$

More generally, the graph of $r = a\sin n\theta$, where $n$ is a positive integer, is called a **rose**. As we saw in Problem 8.12, a circle is a special case of a rose. Roses are good examples of curves that are ideal for polar coordinates: the rectangular equation for these curves are usually somewhat complicated, but the polar equations are simple and, more importantly, give us an idea of the nature of the curves.

When exploring these sorts of graphs, you have to be a little careful about missing "hidden" points. For example:

**Problem 8.14:** Is the polar point $\left(1, \frac{\pi}{2}\right)$ on the graph of $r = \cos 2\theta$?

*Solution for Problem 8.14:* You might quickly say "no":

> **Bogus Solution:** Plugging in $\theta = \frac{\pi}{2}$ gives $r = \cos\pi = -1$, so the point $\left(-1, \frac{\pi}{2}\right)$ is on the graph, not $\left(1, \frac{\pi}{2}\right)$.

However, $\left(1, \frac{\pi}{2}\right)$ is on the graph! Remember that any point has infinitely many different polar representations. Since $\theta = \frac{3\pi}{2}$ gives $r = -1$, the point $\left(-1, \frac{3\pi}{2}\right)$ is on the graph. But this is the same point as $\left(1, \frac{\pi}{2}\right)$, so $\left(1, \frac{\pi}{2}\right)$ *is* on the graph. $\square$

> **WARNING!!**   Points can be represented in polar coordinates in infinitely many ways.
> ☢

The polar curve $r = f(\theta)$ can be viewed as a special case of a parametric curve. Since $x = r \cos \theta$ and $y = r \sin \theta$, our curve is parameterized by

$$(r \cos \theta, r \sin \theta) = (f(\theta) \cos \theta, f(\theta) \sin \theta),$$

for the parameter $\theta$. This allows us to use apply our parametric curve tools from Section 8.1 to study polar curves. For instance:

**Problem 8.15:** Let $r = f(\theta)$ be the equation of a curve in polar coordinates. What is the slope of the tangent line to this curve at any given value of $\theta$?

*Solution for Problem 8.15:* Treating our polar curve as a parametric curve, we can use the usual idea of

$$\frac{dy}{dx} = \frac{dy/d\theta}{dx/d\theta}.$$

Thus, we evaluate $dx/d\theta$ and $dy/d\theta$ in terms of $r$ and $\theta$.

We start with

$$y = r \sin \theta = f(\theta) \sin \theta.$$

Then we use the product rule:

$$\frac{dy}{d\theta} = f(\theta)(\cos \theta) + f'(\theta)(\sin \theta).$$

Since $r = f(\theta)$, we will write $r' = f'(\theta)$, and thus

$$\frac{dy}{d\theta} = r \cos \theta + r' \sin \theta.$$

Similarly,

$$x = r \cos \theta = f(\theta) \cos \theta,$$

so upon differentiating, we get

$$\frac{dx}{d\theta} = f(\theta)(-\sin \theta) + f'(\theta)(\cos \theta).$$

Thus

$$\frac{dx}{d\theta} = -r \sin \theta + r' \cos \theta.$$

Putting this all together, we have

$$\text{Slope of tangent at } \theta = \frac{r \cos \theta + r' \sin \theta}{-r \sin \theta + r' \cos \theta}.$$

$\square$

There's really no point of memorizing this formula. It doesn't come up that often, and it's easy to rederive when you need it. The key thing to remember is:

$$\frac{dy}{dx} = \frac{dy/d\theta}{dx/d\theta}.$$

**Problem 8.16:** Find the slope of the tangent line to $r = 3\cos 2\theta$ at $\theta = \frac{\pi}{3}$.

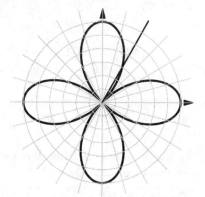

*Solution for Problem 8.16:* First, we should get a rough idea of what the graph looks like. The $\cos 2\theta$ term has an interval of $\frac{\pi}{2}$ between zeroes, so the graph is a 4-leaf rose (the leaves do not overlap), as shown to the right. We have also drawn the ray corresponding to $\theta = \pi/3$. At this point, you might jump to the wrong conclusion:

> **Bogus Solution:** We want the slope of the tangent at the point where the ray hits the curve.

However, it's not that point at all! We plug in $\theta = \frac{\pi}{3}$ and we get $r = 3\cos\frac{2\pi}{3} = -\frac{3}{2}$. The resulting point is in the 3rd quadrant, as shown below:

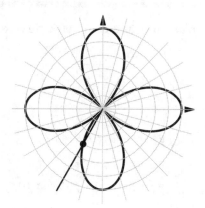

In rectangular coordinates, it's the point $\left(-\dfrac{3}{4}, -\dfrac{3\sqrt{3}}{4}\right)$.

Now, to compute the slope of the tangent line, we just use the formula from Problem 8.15:

$$\frac{dy}{dx} = \frac{3\cos 2\theta \cos\theta - 6\sin 2\theta \sin\theta}{-3\cos 2\theta \sin\theta - 6\sin 2\theta \cos\theta}.$$

We then plug in $\theta = \frac{\pi}{3}$:

$$\frac{3\cos\frac{2\pi}{3}\cos\frac{\pi}{3} - 6\sin\frac{2\pi}{3}\sin\frac{\pi}{3}}{-3\cos\frac{2\pi}{3}\sin\frac{\pi}{3} - 6\sin\frac{2\pi}{3}\cos\frac{\pi}{3}}.$$

To finish, we substitute $\sin\frac{\pi}{3} = \sin\frac{2\pi}{3} = \frac{\sqrt{3}}{2}$ and $\cos\frac{\pi}{3} = \frac{1}{2}$, $\cos\frac{2\pi}{3} = -\frac{1}{2}$ to get:

$$\frac{3\left(-\frac{1}{2}\right)\left(\frac{1}{2}\right) - 6\left(\frac{\sqrt{3}}{2}\right)\left(\frac{\sqrt{3}}{2}\right)}{-3\left(-\frac{1}{2}\right)\left(\frac{\sqrt{3}}{2}\right) - 6\left(\frac{\sqrt{3}}{2}\right)\left(\frac{1}{2}\right)} = \frac{-\frac{3}{4} - \frac{18}{4}}{\frac{3\sqrt{3}}{4} - \frac{6\sqrt{3}}{4}} = \frac{-21}{-3\sqrt{3}} = \frac{7\sqrt{3}}{3}.$$

So the slope is $\dfrac{7\sqrt{3}}{3}$, and the tangent line is shown in the picture below:

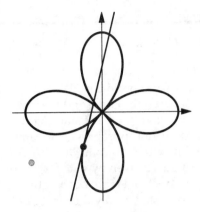

□

As we've seen, finding tangent lines to polar curves is a bit messy. This is not a big surprise, since lines themselves are not all that nice in polar coordinates, as we will see in the next problem.

**Problem 8.17:** Find the equation, in polar coordinates, of the line through the rectangular point $(x_0, y_0)$ with slope $m$.

*Solution for Problem 8.17:* There's really no easy way to do this except to do it first in rectangular coordinates and then convert to polar coordinates. The rectangular equation for the line is

$$y - y_0 = m(x - x_0).$$

We convert this to polar coordinates:

$$r \sin \theta - y_0 = m(r \cos \theta - x_0).$$

To write this in the usual form of a polar curve, we solve for $r$:

$$r(\sin \theta - m \cos \theta) = y_0 - mx_0,$$

giving

$$r = \frac{y_0 - mx_0}{\sin \theta - m \cos \theta}.$$

□

There are other ways to describe lines in polar coordinates; some of them will be explored further in the exercises.

## EXERCISES

**8.2.1** For each of the following equations in polar coordinates, describe the graph, and find the slope of the tangent line at the given point.

(a) $r = a \cos \theta + b \sin \theta$, where $a$ and $b$ are positive real numbers, with the slope of the tangent line at the point where $\theta = 0$. **Hints:** 128

(b) $r = a + b \sin \theta$, where $a$ and $b$ are positive real numbers, with the slope of the tangent line at the point where $\theta = \frac{\pi}{2}$. (These curves are called **limaçons**.) **Hints:** 285

(c)★ $r = 1 - \sin 2\theta$, with the slope of the tangent line at the origin. **Hints:** 28, 19

**8.2.2** Find the equation in polar coordinates of the line with slope $m$ that passes through the polar point $(r_0, \theta_0)$. **Hints:** 246

## 8.3 AREAS IN POLAR COORDINATES

Suppose $r = f(\theta)$ is a curve given in polar coordinates. We would like to compute the area of the "sector" between the curve and the rays given by the starting and ending angles $\theta = a$ and $\theta = b$, as in the picture to the right. To compute this area, we can set up an appropriate Riemann sum of smaller regions whose areas we know how to compute. When we compute the area under a rectangular curve given by $y = f(x)$, we divide the region into rectangles. However, rectangles are not a natural object to work with in polar coordinates, so instead we divide our region into a number of small circular sectors:

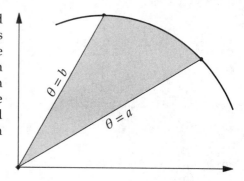

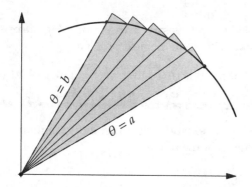

Those regions may look like triangles, but they actually have circular arcs at the far end, so that they are sectors of a circle. Fortunately, areas of sectors are easy to compute:

**Problem 8.18:** If a sector has radius $r$ and angle $\Delta\theta$, then what is its area?

*Solution for Problem 8.18:* A circle of radius $r$ has area $\pi r^2$, and a sector of angle $\Delta\theta$ covers a proportion of $\dfrac{\Delta\theta}{2\pi}$ of the entire circle. So the area of the sector is $\frac{1}{2}r^2(\Delta\theta)$. (Note that if $\Delta\theta = 2\pi$, then we get the whole circle of area $\pi r^2$.) $\square$

Given that we can compute the areas of the sectors, we can sum up the sectors to get an approximation of the area of the region:

$$\sum_i \frac{1}{2}(r_i)^2(\Delta\theta_i),$$

where $r_i$ is the radius of the $i^{\text{th}}$ sector, and $\Delta\theta_i$ is the measure of the angle of that sector. This is a Riemann sum, so when we take the limit of this as the number of sectors grows, we get a definite integral.

Summing up, we see the following:

**Important:** The area of the region between $r = f(\theta)$ and the rays $\theta = a$ and $\theta = b$ is

$$\frac{1}{2}\int_a^b r^2\,d\theta = \frac{1}{2}\int_a^b (f(\theta))^2\,d\theta.$$

> **WARNING!!** ☢ The most common mistake is to use simply $\int_a^b f(\theta)\, d\theta$ for the area. To avoid this error, remember that the area of a circle of radius $r$ is $\pi r^2$. This circle is given by the polar curve $r = 1$, and we can compute its area via the integral
>
> $$\frac{1}{2}\int_0^{2\pi} r^2\, d\theta = \frac{1}{2}(2\pi r^2) = \pi r^2.$$

A typical example is the following:

**Problem 8.19:** Find the area of one leaf of the rose given by $r = 3\sin 2\theta$.

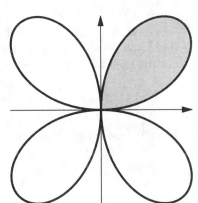

*Solution for Problem 8.19:* As we've seen before, this is a 4-leaf rose. One leaf of the rose ranges from $\theta = 0$ to $\theta = \frac{\pi}{2}$. Thus the definite integral for the area is

$$\frac{1}{2}\int_0^{\pi/2} 9\sin^2 2\theta\, d\theta = \frac{9}{2}\int_0^{\pi/2}\sin^2 2\theta\, d\theta.$$

Now use the substitution $u = 2\theta$ to get

$$\frac{9}{4}\int_0^{\pi}\sin^2 u\, du.$$

There are lots of ways to finish from here. For instance, we can now use the trig identity $\sin^2 u = \frac{1}{2}(1 - \cos 2u)$ to get

$$\frac{9}{8}\int_0^{\pi}(1 - \cos 2u)\, du.$$

Note that the latter term integrates to 0 since the integral covers an entire period of $\cos 2u$. Therefore, the area is just $\frac{9}{8}\pi$. $\square$

A slightly more complicated example is the following:

**Problem 8.20:** Find the area of the region that is the intersection of the interiors of the graphs of $r = 2(1 + \cos\theta)$ and $r = 2(1 - \cos\theta)$.

These curves are called **cardioids**.

*Solution for Problem 8.20:* We can sketch a picture, shown at right. The curve on the right is $r = 2(1 + \cos\theta)$ and the curve on the left is $r = 2(1 - \cos\theta)$. These curves intersect when

$$2(1 + \cos\theta) = 2(1 - \cos\theta),$$

so $\cos\theta = 0$, which corresponds to points on the $y$-axis.

One way to compute the area is to note that the graphs are reflections of each other across the $y$-axis, so the total area is just twice the area inside $r = 2(1 + \cos\theta)$ between $\theta = \frac{\pi}{2}$ and $\theta = \frac{3\pi}{2}$, as shown below:

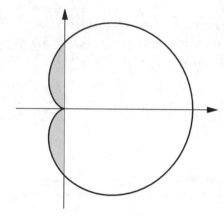

Even easier than that, because of the symmetry of the graph across the $x$-axis, the original area is 4 times the area inside $r = 2(1 + \cos \theta)$ between $\theta = \frac{\pi}{2}$ and $\theta = \pi$ (which is the top half of the shaded region in the diagram above). Thus, the original area is given by the definite integral

$$4 \cdot \frac{1}{2} \int_{\pi/2}^{\pi} r^2 \, d\theta = 2 \int_{\pi/2}^{\pi} (2(1 + \cos \theta))^2 \, d\theta.$$

Expanding the square in the integrand gives

$$8 \int_{\pi/2}^{\pi} (1 + 2 \cos \theta + \cos^2 \theta) \, d\theta.$$

Now we use the fact that $\cos^2 \theta = \frac{1}{2}(1 + \cos 2\theta)$. So our integral becomes

$$8 \int_{\pi/2}^{\pi} \left( \frac{3}{2} + 2 \cos \theta + \frac{1}{2} \cos 2\theta \right) d\theta.$$

This gives

$$8 \left( \frac{3}{2}\theta + 2 \sin \theta + \frac{1}{4} \sin 2\theta \right) \Big|_{\pi/2}^{\pi}.$$

Hence, the area is $8\left(\frac{3\pi}{4} - 2\right) = 6\pi - 16$. As a check, note that this is about 2.85, which is plausible for a region that fills much of a rectangle with an approximate "height" of 4 and an approximate "width" of about 1. □

## Exercises

**8.3.1**  Find the area between the curves $r = \theta$ and $r = 2\theta$ for $0 \leq \theta \leq \pi$.

**8.3.2**  Find the area of region that is outside the curve $r = 1 - \cos \theta$ but inside the curve $r = 1$.

**8.3.3★**  Find the shaded area, shown at right, inside the limaçon given by the graph of $r = 1 + 2 \sin \theta$. **Hints:** 269, 206, 272

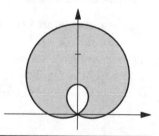

## Review Problems

**8.21**  Write parametric equations to describe the curves traced by the following motions:

(a)  A particle tracing a circle with center $(0, 0)$ and radius 2, starting at $(2, 0)$ at time $t = 0$, moving counterclockwise with constant speed of 1 radian/sec.

(b)  A cannonball fired from $(0,0)$ with initial velocity 100m/sec, shot at an angle $\frac{\pi}{3}$ above the ground, with gravity $g = -9.8\text{m/sec}^2$.

(c)  A point starting at the bottom edge of a bicycle wheel (with radius 30 cm) that is rotating at 1 revolution per second, where the bicycle is moving forward at the rate implied by the rotation of the wheel. (For example, using meters as units, $(0,0)$ is the starting point, and after 0.5 seconds the point is at $(0.3\pi, 0.6)$.)

(d)★  A particle tracing a circle with center $(0,0)$ and radius 2, starting at $(2,0)$ at time $t = 0$, moving clockwise with speed $\sqrt{t}$. **Hints:** 106

**8.22**  Imagine a string (of negligible thickness) unwinding from a fixed circular bobbin of radius 10, so that the string that is unwound is always tangent to the bobbin, as in the picture to the right. (Three positions of the string are shown in gray.) Assume that the string unwinds at the constant rate of one full loop of string per second. Determine parametric equations for the curve traced out by the end of the string, as shown by the dark curve at right. **Hints:** 115

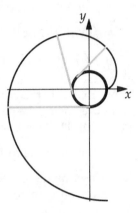

**8.23**  Let $C$ be a circle of radius 3 centered at $(0,0)$. Let $\mathcal{D}$ be a circle of radius 1 centered at $(4,0)$, and let $P = (3,0)$ be the point on $\mathcal{D}$ that is tangent to $C$. Find parametric equations for the **epicycloid** that is produced when we trace the path of $P$ as $\mathcal{D}$ rolls around $C$, so that the center of $\mathcal{D}$ moves counterclockwise around $C$ at a rate of 1 revolution per second. **Hints:** 255, 268

**8.24**  The **Archimedes spiral** is the graph of $r = \theta$ for $\theta \geq 0$.

(a)  Sketch the spiral.

(b)  Find the slope of the tangent line to the spiral at $\theta$.

(c)  Find the area of region bounded by the spiral and to the left of the $y$-axis when $0 \leq \theta \leq 2\pi$.

**8.25**  Find the area of the region that is in the interior of the two cardioids $r = 1 + \sin\theta$ and $r = 1 + \cos\theta$. (The region is shown at right.) **Hints:** 253

**8.26**  Prove that the graph of the polar equation

$$A\cos\theta + B\sin\theta + \frac{C}{r} = 0,$$

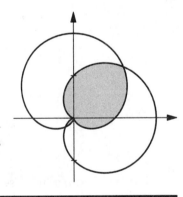

where $A, B, C$ are nonzero real numbers, is a line. What is the geometric interpretation of the constants $A$, $B$, and $C$? And what happens if one or more of them is zero? **Hints:** 199

## CHALLENGE PROBLEMS

**8.27**  Suppose a planet revolves around a star at distance $R$ and the planet has a moon that revolves around the planet at distance $r$, with $0 < r < R$. (Assume that all motion is in the same plane and that all orbits are circular.) At time $t = 0$, the planet is at $(R, 0)$ and the moon is at $(R + r, 0)$. The planet takes 1 year to revolve around the star and the moon takes $\frac{1}{4}$ year to revolve around the planet.

(a)  Write parametric equations for the position of the moon at time $t$ (in years). (Assume all movement is counterclockwise.) As a check, at time $t = \frac{1}{2}$, the position of the moon should be $(r - R, 0)$ and at $t = 1$ it should be back to $(R + r, 0)$.

(b)  Sketch some graphs of the moon's path. Do this for different values of $\frac{r}{R}$, and try to determine the conditions on $\frac{r}{R}$ that affect the shape of the graph. **Hints:** 70

(c)  Does the moon ever come to a "full stop" relative to the star? **Hints:** 209

**8.28** Describe the graph of $r = \dfrac{\ell}{1 + \epsilon \cos \theta}$ where $\epsilon > 1$ and $\ell$ is a positive constant. **Hints:** 88, 5

**8.29** Show that the length of a parametric curve is independent of the choice of parameterization in the following sense:

Suppose that $(u(t), v(t))$ is a parameterization of a curve $C$ for $t \in [a, b]$. Let $f$ be a differentiable function whose domain includes $[c, d]$ such that:

- $f(c) = a$ and $f(d) = b$,
- $f([c, d]) = [a, b]$, and
- $f'(t) \geq 0$ for all $t \in [c, d]$.

Show that $C$ is the curve given by the parameterization $(u(f(t)), v(f(t)))$ for $t \in [c, d]$, and that the length of $C$ computed using the parameterization $(u(f(t)), v(f(t)))$ equals the length of $C$ computed using the parameterization $(u(t), v(t))$. **Hints:** 68, 96

**8.30** Consider the rose $r = \cos n\theta$ where $n$ is a positive integer.

(a) Describe the graph of the rose (in terms of $n$). (You will have to distinguish between the cases where $n$ is even and where $n$ is odd.)

(b) Compute the area of one petal of the rose.

(c)★ The **width** of the rose is the length of the longest segment, parallel to the $y$-axis, that can be inscribed in the first petal of the rose (that is, the petal that contains part of the positive $x$-axis). The example for $n = 2$ is shown below (the width is the length of the dark black segment):

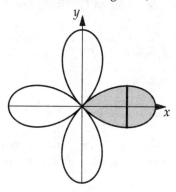

Find the width of the rose $r = \cos 2\theta$. **Hints:** 52

(d)★ Determine what you can about the width of the rose $r = \cos n\theta$. (You will not be able to find an explicit formula for $n > 2$, but see if you can find a relatively simple equation for the value of $\theta$ such that $(\cos n\theta, \theta)$ and $(\cos n\theta, -\theta)$ are the endpoints, in polar coordinates, of the required line segment.) **Hints:** 74

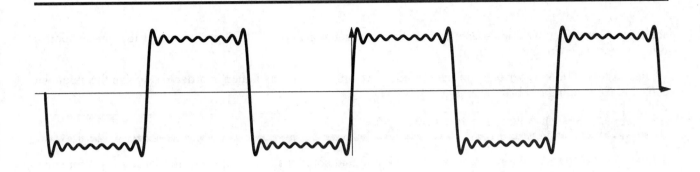

# DIFFERENTIAL EQUATIONS

## 9.1 DEFINITIONS AND BASIC EXAMPLES

A **differential equation** is an equation that relates a function, the function's derivative(s), and an independent variable. This is not a totally new idea—we've already seen some simple types of differential equations. For example,

$$y' = 2x$$

is a differential equation that relates two variables $x$ and $y$. Usually, in differential equations, we have a dependent variable (often $y$) that is understood to be a function of $x$ or $t$ or whatever our independent variable is. The context will usually make clear which variable represents the function and which represents the independent variable.

As we know, to solve the differential equation $y' = 2x$, we just compute the antiderivative of $f$:

$$y = \int 2x\, dx = x^2 + C.$$

Of course, this only determines $y$ up to a constant $C$.

Most differential equations involve both $y$ and $y'$ terms. For example:

**Problem 9.1:** Find a solution to the differential equation $y' = y$.

*Solution for Problem 9.1:* In words, this equation asks: what function is equal to its derivative? One function that you probably immediately think of is $y = e^x$, but that's not the only answer. The complete answer is $y = ce^x$, where $c$ is a constant (possibly 0). A bit later, we will see how to show that there are no other solutions. $\square$

Often, a differential equation will come with an **initial condition**. This is a condition of the form $x = x_0$, $y = y_0$ for some constants $x_0$ and $y_0$. This means that we are forcing the point $(x_0, y_0)$ to be on the graph of our solution—we sometimes think of this as the "initial" point of our solution. Assuming that we are thinking of $y$ as a function of $x$, we may write the initial condition as $y(x_0) = y_0$. This is a shorthand for $y = f(x)$ and $f(x_0) = y_0$, where $f$ is some function. When writing differential equations, we generally are a little sloppy and use $y$ to represent both a function and a dependent variable.

Regardless of how we write the initial condition, we plug it into our solution in order to solve for the unknown constant. Continuing our basic example:

**Problem 9.2:** Find the solution to $y' = y$ where $y(0) = 2$.

*Solution for Problem 9.2:* From Problem 9.1, we know that solutions to $y' = y$ are of the form $y = ce^x$ for some constant $c$. We plug in $x = 0$ and $y = 2$ to get $2 = ce^0 = c$, so $c = 2$. Thus, the solution is $y = 2e^x$. $\square$

A **first-order** differential equation involves $y'$ but no higher derivatives of $y$. The most basic form of a first-order differential equation is

$$y' = f(x, y)$$

where $f(x, y)$ is some function involving $x$ and $y$.

Many differential equations cannot be solved explicitly. However, we have other tools that we can use to analyze them. One geometric tool that we use to study first-order differential equations is called a **slope field**. Using a slope field involves thinking geometrically about what $y' = f(x, y)$ really means. Since one interpretation of $y'$ is as the slope of the tangent line to the graph of $y$, the equation $y' = f(x, y)$ means that the slope of a tangent line to the graph of $y$ at the point $(x, y)$ is $f(x, y)$.

A slope field is what results when we represent these slopes as small line segments on the plane. For instance, shown to the right is the slope field for the differential equation $y' = -\frac{x}{y}$. At each point $(x, y)$, we draw a small line segment with slope $-\frac{x}{y}$. For example, at $(3, 2)$, we have a segment with slope $-\frac{3}{2}$. If $y = 0$ (that is, along the $x$-axis), then $-\frac{x}{y}$ is undefined, so we have segments with "infinite" slope; that is, vertical segments.

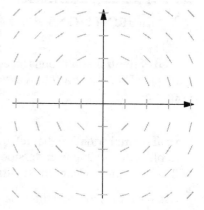

The key fact is: any curve that is the graph of a solution to $y' = f(x, y)$ must match these segments in slope. This allows us to sketch likely solution curves by tracing curves that "match" the slope field. For instance, in the differential equation $y' = -\frac{x}{y}$ whose slope field is shown at right, the slope field suggests that the solution curves might be circles, as in the diagram below:

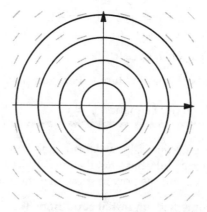

Specifically, it looks like the solutions are given implicitly by the equation $x^2 + y^2 = c$ for any positive constant $c$. However, this is only a guess based on our slope field. To be sure, we must check that these solutions are correct:

**Problem 9.3:** Show that the functions given implicitly by the equation $x^2 + y^2 = c$, where $c$ is some positive constant, are solutions to the differential equation $y' = -\dfrac{x}{y}$.

*Solution for Problem 9.3:* We can implicitly differentiate our candidate solution:

$$2x + 2yy' = 0,$$

and solving for $y'$ we see that indeed $y' = -\frac{x}{y}$ (where this is defined). $\square$

An important hard theorem of analysis states that if $f$ is continuous (although we haven't really defined what "continuous" means for a multivariable function), then the first-order differential equation $y' = f(x, y)$ with initial condition $y(x_0) = y_0$ has a solution, and if $f$ satisfies a slightly stronger condition called *Lipschitz continuous* (which again, we won't define), then the solution is unique. This is not too surprising when we think about it in terms of a slope field: if we are given the starting point $(x_0, y_0)$, then the slope field tells us what the solution curve through $(x_0, y_0)$ must look like. We simply trace our curve so that, at each point, the direction of the curve is given by the slope field.

Thus, in Problem 9.3, since there is exactly one curve of the form $x^2 + y^2 = c$ passing through any point of the plane, this theorem about uniqueness of solutions tells us that these indeed are the only solutions of this differential equation.

Using slope fields is a fancy game of connect-the-dots. Here's another example:

**Problem 9.4:** Use slope fields to guess at the solutions to $y' = \dfrac{x}{y}$. Then, confirm that your guess satisfies the differential equation.

*Solution for Problem 9.4:* Note that this is almost the same function as we had in Problem 9.3, except without the minus sign. We sketch our slope field: at each point $(x, y)$, we draw a little line segment with slope $\frac{x}{y}$. We've drawn it somewhat "finer" than in Problem 9.3—meaning we've drawn more little slopes—so that we can better see the behavior. Notice the qualitative features of this slope field. Near the $x$-axis and away from the $y$-axis are places where $|x|$ is relatively large and $|y|$ is relatively small, so $\left|\frac{x}{y}\right|$ is large, and the slopes are near vertical. On the other hand, near the $y$-axis and away from the $x$-axis are places where $|x|$ is relatively small and $|y|$ is relatively large, so $\left|\frac{x}{y}\right|$ is small, and the slopes are near horizontal.

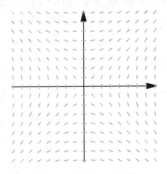

We "connect the dots"—that is, we try to draw curves along the directions given by the slope field—and we get something like the picture to the right. These curves look a lot like hyperbolas. How can we check?

We suspect the solutions are $y^2 - x^2 = c$ for some constant $c$. To check that these satisfy our differential equation, we implicitly differentiate:

$$2yy' - 2x = 0.$$

Solving for $y'$ gives $y' = \frac{x}{y}$, as we want.

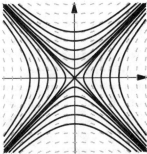

Our diagram appears to have a problem at $(0, 0)$, in that there are two lines crossing: the solution $y = x$ and the solution $y = -x$. This is an apparent violation of the uniqueness of solutions through a given point. However, the function $\frac{x}{y}$ is not continuous at $(0, 0)$, so this result does not violate the theorem about uniqueness of solutions. $\square$

Let's do one more slope field example that looks slightly different than the previous two:

**Problem 9.5:** Using a slope field, analyze the solutions to $y' = 2 - y$.

*Solution for Problem 9.5:* This may look like a "trivial" differential equation that we can just antidifferentiate:

> **Bogus Solution:** We antidifferentiate $y' = 2 - y$ to get
>
> $$y = \int (2 - y)\, dy = 2y - \frac{1}{2}y^2 + C,$$
>
> so solving gives $\frac{1}{2}y^2 - y = C$.

This is incorrect: indeed, we can plug the above "solution" into the original differential equation and see that it doesn't work. What we should have written is

$$y = \int (2 - y)\, dx.$$

However, the last term is a function of $y$ integrated as a function of $x$, so we cannot integrate it (with respect to $x$) unless we know beforehand how to express $y$ in terms of $x$.

We draw the slope field at right: at each point $(x, y)$ we draw a little line with slope $2 - y$. Note that the slopes only depend on $y$ and not on $x$. We notice that the slopes seem to "funnel" the graph towards $y = 2$. We can thus sketch some solution curves, and we can guess that the graphs of the solutions look like the picture at right below. Intuitively, this makes sense: if $y$ is far from 2, then $y' = 2 - y$ draws $y$ rapidly closer to 2. Then, as $y$ gets closer to 2, the rate of change $y'$ gets small, so the $y$-coordinate of the curve moves very slowly towards 2.

You might have a guess as to what equations have these curves as their graphs. The "decaying" behavior of $y$ towards 2 as $x \to \infty$ is our clue. The correct answer is that these curves are the graphs of $y = 2 + ce^{-x}$ for some constant $c$. Note in particular that $c = 0$ gives the constant solution $y = 2$.

To check that our guess is correct, we compute $y' = -ce^{-x}$, and indeed we see that

$$y' = -ce^{-x} = 2 - (2 + ce^{-x}) = 2 - y.$$

$\square$

One important fact to note about drawing solutions curves on a slope field of $y' = f(x, y)$ is that the solution curves can never intersect. This is due to the theorem about the uniqueness of the solution of a first-order differential equation with an initial condition. Drawing a curve through a point of a slope field is the geometric equivalent of drawing the graph of the *unique* solution through that point, so by the uniqueness of such a solution, there can only be one curve through any given point, and hence the curves cannot intersect. Except (and there is often an "except" in calculus!), there may be multiple solutions at points where the function $f(x, y)$ is not continuous. Such points (for example, the point $(0, 0)$ in Problem 9.3) may have multiple solution curves passing through them.

Besides slope fields, another way that we can study differential equations without actually explicitly solving them is by numerically estimating solutions. This is a very rich subject, one that is largely beyond the scope of this book. The simplest method of estimating solutions is to calculate repeated tangent line approximations: this is called **Euler's Method** and is covered in more detail in Section 9.A.

Generally, the easiest method of solving differential equations is called **separation of variables**. Let's illustrate it with our basic example from Problem 9.3.

---

**Problem 9.6:** Our goal is to solve $y' = -\dfrac{x}{y}$.

(a) Write the equation as $\dfrac{dy}{dx} = -\dfrac{x}{y}$. Pretend that the "$dx$" and "$dy$" are variables, and rearrange so that all the $x$ terms are on one side and all the $y$ terms are on the other side.

(b) Compute the antiderivatives of both sides.

(c) Write the solution. Why do we need only one constant and not two (since we took two antiderivatives)?

---

*Solution for Problem 9.6:*

(a) We write the differential equation as

$$\frac{dy}{dx} = -\frac{x}{y}.$$

We move all the $x$ terms to one side and all the $y$ terms to the other side. This includes "multiplying by $dx$":

$$y\,dy = -x\,dx.$$

(b) We can antidifferentiate both sides:

$$\int y\,dy = -\int x\,dx$$

This gives

$$\frac{y^2}{2} = -\frac{x^2}{2} + C.$$

(c) Cleaning it up a little gives $x^2 + y^2 = 2C = c$ as expected. Notice that we don't need a constant on both sides: each antiderivative is determined up to an arbitrary constant, so their difference is also determined up to an arbitrary constant.

□

This general method is called **separation of variables**. It requires that our differential equation be **separable**, meaning that we can split all the $x$ terms on one side and all the $y$ terms on the other side, with "$dx$" on the side with the $x$ terms and "$dy$" on the side with the $y$ terms. To be more specific:

---

**Definition:** A two-variable function $f(x, y)$ is called **separable** if we can write

$$f(x, y) = g(x)h(y)$$

where $g(x)$ is a function that depends solely on $x$, and $h(y)$ is a function that depends solely on $y$.

---

**Important:** We can use **separation of variables** to solve the differential equation $y' = f(x, y)$ if $f$ is separable. We write $\dfrac{dy}{dx} = f(x, y) = g(x)h(y)$ and rearrange the equation as

$$\frac{dy}{h(y)} = g(x)\,dx.$$

We then antidifferentiate both sides: the left side in terms of $y$ and the right side in terms of $x$.

Note that we will always get a constant from our antidifferentiation. If we have an initial condition, we can plug it in and solve for the constant to get the unique solution.

> **WARNING!!** ☢ Even though we are treating $dx$ and $dy$ as variable terms, they are really just notational conveniences. What we really have when we write
>
> $$\frac{dy}{h(y)} = g(x)\,dx$$
>
> is instead the equation
>
> $$\frac{1}{h(y)}\frac{dy}{dx} = g(x).$$
>
> Then when we integrate this equation with respect to $x$, the left side becomes
>
> $$\int \frac{1}{h(y)}\frac{dy}{dx}\,dx = \int \frac{1}{h(y)}\,dy,$$
>
> where the last equality is an application of the Chain Rule. In other words, when we "multiply by $dx$," we are really just setting up our equation to properly apply the Chain Rule when antidifferentiating.

We can go back and revisit our basic example of a differential equation from Problem 9.1:

**Problem 9.7:** Solve the differential equation $y' = y$.

*Solution for Problem 9.7:* We write this equation as $\dfrac{dy}{dx} = y$, and use separation of variables to write as

$$\frac{dy}{y} = dx.$$

Integrating both sides gives

$$\int \frac{dy}{y} = \int dx,$$

giving $\log|y| = x + C$. Exponentiating then gives $|y| = e^{x+C} = ce^x$, where $c = e^C$. Note that $c > 0$ in this expression.

The absolute value sign is a bit annoying. We can get rid of it by absorbing any factor of $-1$ into the constant $c$. So we are OK with writing $y = ce^x$. In our previous expression $|y| = ce^x$, the constant $c$ had to be positive. When we take away the absolute value sign, we allow $c$ to be negative (or zero).

Thus, any solution of $y' = y$ is of the form $y = ce^x$ for some constant $c \in \mathbb{R}$. □

Here's another example:

**Problem 9.8:** Solve the differential equation $y' = y - 2xy$ with $y(1) = 2$.

*Solution for Problem 9.8:* We write the equation as

$$\frac{dy}{dx} = y(1 - 2x).$$

Then separate the variables:

$$\frac{dy}{y} = (1 - 2x)\,dx.$$

We can now integrate both sides:

$$\int \frac{dy}{y} = \int (1 - 2x)\, dx.$$

This gives us

$$\log |y| = x - x^2 + C,$$

so we can exponentiate both sides to get

$$|y| = e^{x-x^2+C} = ce^{x-x^2}.$$

(Note that we've adjusted the constant by letting $c = e^C$.)

Again, we can get rid of the absolute value sign by absorbing any factor of $-1$ into the constant $c$, giving $y = ce^{x-x^2}$. (Recall in our previous expression $|y| = ce^{x-x^2}$, the constant $c$ had to be positive. When we we take away the absolute value sign, we allow $c$ to be negative or zero.)

Finally, since we are given an initial condition, we can solve for $c$. We plug in $x = 1$ and $y = 2$:

$$2 = ce^{1-1} = ce^0 = c.$$

So $c = 2$, and our solution is $y = 2e^{x-x^2}$. $\square$

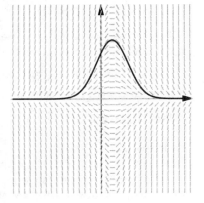

We can graph this over a slope field to double-check that our answer looks correct. The slope field and the graph of $y = 2e^{x-x^2}$ are shown at right. We see the expected behavior of the graph. As $x$ gets large, the function tends to 0. It has its peak at the value of $x$ that maximizes $x - x^2$, which is $x = \frac{1}{2}$. (The slope field is deceptive near the $x$-axis, since as $y$ gets close to 0, the slopes get close to horizontal, but the slope field drawn is not fine-grained enough to show this.)

One of the most important examples of a differential equation is $y' = ky$, where $k$ is some constant. In English, this means that the quantity changes at a rate proportional to the quantity itself. Another way to write it is $\frac{y'}{y} = k$. This interpretation means that $y$ is growing at a constant **relative rate**.

There are many "real-world" phenomena that we can model with the differential equation $y' = ky$. Some examples are:

- population growth

- spread of disease

- radioactive decay

- temperature change

- continuously compounded interest

. . . or indeed any situation which is properly modeled with a constant relative growth rate. We'll look at some of these examples a bit more closely in a moment.

First, let's solve the equation!

**Problem 9.9:** Find the solutions to $y' = ky$, where $k$ is a constant.

*Solution for Problem 9.9:* We can solve this by separation of variables. Arrange the equation as

$$\frac{dy}{y} = k\,dx,$$

and integrate to get $\log|y| = kx + C$. Exponentiating gives

$$|y| = e^{kx+C} = ce^{kx},$$

where $c = e^C > 0$. Allowing $y$ to be 0 or negative lets us remove the absolute value sign and have any $c \in \mathbb{R}$, so the solutions are $y = ce^{kx}$ for any constant $c$.

As a check, we compute

$$y' = \frac{d}{dx}(ce^{kx}) = k(ce^{kx}) = ky,$$

which is valid for any $c \in \mathbb{R}$. $\square$

Not surprisingly, this is called the **exponential growth** differential equation:

---

**Important:** The solutions to $y' = ky$, where $k$ is a constant, are $y = ce^{kx}$ for any constant $c$.

---

Before we look at specific examples, let's examine how the solutions behave. If $k > 0$, then the quantity $y$ grows without bound since $\lim\limits_{x\to\infty} e^x = \infty$. On the other hand, if $k < 0$, then the quantity $y$ tends towards 0, since $\lim\limits_{x\to\infty} e^{-x} = 0$. Finally, if $k = 0$, then the quantity is a constant: the differential equation is just $y' = 0$, and our solutions are $y = c$ for a constant $c$.

We can see this differential equation in action in some problems.

**Problem 9.10:** A radioactive substance decays at a rate proportional to the amount of the substance present. Suppose we start with 100 g of Alpinium, a highly fictitious and toxic radioactive material. After 1 hour, we have 75 g of Alpinium remaining. How long will it take until we have only 10 g remaining?

*Solution for Problem 9.10:* The first sentence of the problem describes our differential equation: it tells us that we have the equation $y' = ky$ for some $k < 0$. We know that $k$ is negative because the quantity is *decreasing* over time. The solution to this equation is $y = ce^{kt}$ where $c$ is some other constant. (Note that we use $t$ instead of $x$, since the independent variable is time.)

We don't know $k$ or $c$, so we might be in a little bit of trouble. However, fear not, for we are given *two* conditions: at $t = 0$, we know $y = 100$, and at $t = 1$, we know $y = 75$. Plugging in the first condition gives $100 = ce^0 = c$, so $c = 100$. Now we have $y = 100e^{kt}$, and we can plug in the second condition, giving $75 = 100e^k$. Thus $k = \log(3/4)$.

Hence our solution is that the amount of material at time $t$ is $y = 100e^{(\log 3/4)t}$. We could leave it like this, or we could write it as

$$y = 100(e^{\log 3/4})^t = 100(3/4)^t.$$

But the first form is preferred to finish the problem. We want to know when the amount of material will be 10 g. So, we plug in $y = 10$, and we need to solve for $t$:

$$10 = 100e^{(\log 3/4)t}.$$

This gives

$$\log(1/10) = (\log(3/4))t,$$

and thus

$$t = \frac{\log(1/10)}{\log(3/4)} \approx \frac{-2.3026}{-0.2877} \approx 8.0039.$$

Thus, it will take slightly over 8 hours for our sample to decay to 10g. □

Another basic example is temperature change: heating and cooling. **Newton's Law of Heating** states that the temperature of a body changes at a rate proportional to the difference between the body's temperature and the ambient temperature. Here's an example:

**Problem 9.11:** Eric's office is kept at a temperature of 70°. Eric heats up his coffee in the microwave to a temperature of 200°. After 1 minute, the coffee has cooled to 170°. Eric is picky and will only drink his coffee if it is at least 120°. How long does Eric have (after removing the coffee from the microwave) to drink it before he will need to reheat it?

*Solution for Problem 9.11:* You may notice that the units of the temperature measurements are conspicuously absent (although the context seems to imply that the temperatures are in Fahrenheit.) But do these units matter? Not really—all that matters is the difference between the coffee and the ambient (room) temperature. So, we let the variable $y$ at any time $t$ be the difference between the temperature of the coffee and the temperature of the room.

Hence the differential equation is our usual $y' = ky$, with the two conditions $y(0) = 130$ and $y(1) = 100$. As we know, the solution is $y = ce^{kt}$ for some constants $c$ and $k$ (with $k < 0$, since $y$ tends to 0).

Plugging in $y = 130$ and $t = 0$ gives $130 = ce^0 = c$, so we have $c = 130$ and thus our solution is now $y = 130e^{kt}$. Then, plugging in $y = 100$ and $t = 1$ gives $100 = 130e^k$, so $k = \log(10/13)$. Thus the solution is

$$y = 130e^{\log(10/13)t}.$$

We want to know when $y = 50$, so we plug it in and solve for $t$. This gives

$$50 = 130e^{\log(10/13)t},$$

from which we get $t = \log(5/13)/\log(10/13) \approx 3.64$. Thus, Eric has only about 3.64 minutes to drink up. (He should be less picky.) □

These are just some of the real-world problems that can be simply modeled by the exponential growth equation $y' = ky$. You will see others in the exercises.

However, in many cases, the $y' = ky$ model for population growth is not quite accurate. For instance, most populations have external pressures (such as predators, scarcity of resources, etc.) that tend to slow down the growth rate as the population grows larger. For these populations, we can modify our differential equation slightly:

$$y' = ky - ay^2.$$

This is called the **logistic growth equation**. Note that $y = 0$ is a solution, but if $y \neq 0$, then we can write the logistic equation as

$$\frac{y'}{y} = k - ay.$$

Written in this form, we note that $\frac{y'}{y}$ is the relative growth rate; that is, the growth rate as a fraction of the total population. In the regular exponential growth model, $\frac{y'}{y}$ is constant. The new $-ay$ term in the logistic growth equation is the "limiting" factor that slows down the growth as the population gets larger.

Before solving the logistic equation, we might inquire about an **equilibrium**. This is a value $c$ such that $y = c$ is a solution.

**Problem 9.12:** Does the logistic equation $y' = ky - ay^2$ have any equilibrium solutions? If so, what?

*Solution for Problem 9.12:* An equilibrium solution $y = c$ has $y' = 0$. We plug these in to the equation and get $0 = kc - ac^2 = c(k - ac)$. Thus $c = 0$ and $c = \frac{k}{a}$ are the equilibrium solutions. $\square$

When studying the logistic equation, we often let $L = \frac{k}{a}$ equal the equilibrium, and rewrite the equation in terms of $L$. The equation then becomes:

$$\frac{y'}{y} = k\left(1 - \frac{y}{L}\right).$$

**Problem 9.13:** Solve the logistic differential equation $y' = ky - ay^2$, where $k$ and $a$ are positive constants and $y$ is a function of $t$. (Write your answer in terms of $L = k/a$.) Assuming that $y > 0$ at $t = 0$, what happens to $y$ as $t \to \infty$?

*Solution for Problem 9.13:* We'll write the equation in terms of $L$ as

$$\frac{y'}{y} = k\left(1 - \frac{y}{L}\right).$$

Note that $y = L$ is a solution: the right side of the above equation is 0, and the left side is also 0 since $y' = 0$. If $y \neq L$, then we can separate the variables:

$$\frac{dy}{y(1 - \frac{y}{L})} = k\,dt.$$

We want to integrate both sides of this, but first we can divide both sides by $L$ to make it slightly nicer:

$$\int \frac{dy}{y(L - y)} = \int \frac{k}{L}\,dt.$$

The left side is now the reciprocal of a factorable quadratic, so we use partial fractions on the left side. Note that

$$\frac{1}{y(L - y)} = \frac{1}{L}\left(\frac{1}{y} + \frac{1}{L - y}\right).$$

Our equation becomes

$$\int \frac{1}{L}\left(\frac{1}{y} + \frac{1}{L - y}\right) dy = \int \frac{k}{L}\,dt.$$

Now the $(1/L)$ terms cancel, and after integrating we have:

$$\log|y| - \log|L - y| = kt + C.$$

We consolidate the logs, and this becomes

$$\log\left|\frac{y}{L - y}\right| = kt + C.$$

Next, we exponentiate, giving

$$\left|\frac{y}{L - y}\right| = e^{kt+C} = ce^{kt},$$

where $c = e^C > 0$. Allowing $c$ to be 0 or negative allows us to eliminate the absolute value, leaving

$$\frac{y}{L - y} = ce^{kt}.$$

If $c = 0$, then we get the solution $y = 0$ (we consider this a solution because it is a solution to the original equation $y' = ky - ay^2$). If $c \neq 0$, then solving for $y$, we conclude that

$$y = \frac{L}{1 + \alpha e^{-kt}},$$

where $\alpha = c^{-1}$ is a nonzero constant. Finally, note that letting $\alpha = 0$ recovers our equilibrium solution $y = L$.

As $t \to \infty$, the exponential term in the denominator approaches 0. Therefore, $y$ approaches $L$, the limiting population, as we expect. $\square$

We'll finish this section with a harder differential equation modeling problem.

**Problem 9.14:** Sometime Monday morning, it starts snowing in Los Angeles (!) at a constant rate. At noon, a snowplow starts to plow Hollywood Boulevard in L.A., and plows in a straight line at a rate inversely proportional to the amount of snow on the ground. The plow covers exactly twice as much ground between noon and 1 p.m. as it does between 1 p.m. and 2 p.m. (and it is snowing at the same constant rate throughout). What time did it start snowing?

*Solution for Problem 9.14:* It's not clear immediately how to approach this problem, so we begin by trying to model the problem and listing all of the data that we know.

We can model this situation by letting $t$ be our time variable (in hours), so that $t = 0$ corresponds to noon. Suppose that $T$ is the time that it starts snowing; note that $T < 0$. The amount of snow on the ground at time $t$ is then $r(t - T)$, where $r$ is the hourly snowfall rate.

Let the position of the snowplow along Hollywood Boulevard be given by $s(t)$, with $s(0) = 0$. The fact that the distance covered in the second hour is one-half the distance covered in the first hour is represented by the equation

$$s(2) - s(1) = \frac{1}{2}(s(1) - s(0)) = \frac{1}{2}s(1),$$

which simplifies to $s(2) = \frac{3}{2}s(1)$. We also have the stated fact that the plow moves at a rate inversely proportional to the amount of snow on the ground, so this gives the differential equation

$$\frac{ds}{dt} = \frac{k}{r(t - T)},$$

where $k > 0$ is some constant. Integrating this gives

$$s(t) = \frac{k}{r} \log |t - T| + C,$$

where $C$ is some constant. Since we are only concerned with $t \geq 0$, we always have $t - T > 0$, and we can eliminate the absolute value signs. Next, plugging in $t = 0$ and using $s(0) = 0$ yields

$$0 = \frac{k}{r} \log(-T) + C,$$

so $C = -\frac{k}{r} \log(-T)$, and our equation becomes

$$s(t) = \frac{k}{r}(\log(t - T) - \log(-T)) = \frac{k}{r} \log\left(\frac{T - t}{T}\right).$$

Our last bit of data that we haven't used yet is $s(2) = \frac{3}{2}s(1)$, so we plug that in:

$$\frac{k}{r} \log\left(\frac{T - 2}{T}\right) = s(2) = \frac{3}{2}s(1) = \frac{3}{2} \cdot \frac{k}{r} \log\left(\frac{T - 1}{T}\right).$$

The constant terms $\frac{k}{r}$ cancel, and clearing the denominators we have

$$2\log\left(\frac{T-2}{T}\right) = 3\log\left(\frac{T-1}{T}\right).$$

The constants outside the logarithms can be brought inside as exponents, so after exponentiating both sides we have

$$\left(\frac{T-2}{T}\right)^2 = \left(\frac{T-1}{T}\right)^3.$$

This simplifies to $T(T-2)^2 = (T-1)^3$, or $T^2 - T - 1 = 0$. The roots of this, by the quadratic formula, are

$$T = \frac{1 \pm \sqrt{5}}{2}.$$

Since $T < 0$, we choose the negative root, giving $T = \dfrac{1-\sqrt{5}}{2} \approx -0.618$, and we conclude that it started snowing approximately 0.618 hours before noon, or at about 11:23 a.m. $\square$

## EXERCISES

**9.1.1** Sketch the slope field and some solutions curves for the following equations. Find the explicit solutions if you can.

(a) $y' = x(y-1)$   (b) $y' = x + y$   **Hints:** 111   (c) $y' = \dfrac{x+y}{x-y}$   **Hints:** 112   (d) $y' = 1 + y^2$

**9.1.2** Solve the following differential equations:

(a) $y' = xy$   (b) $y' = xe^y$ with $y(0) = 0$   (c) $y' = y^2 \sin x$

**9.1.3** Solve $y'' = 2$ where $y(0) = 1$ and $y'(0) = 0$.

**9.1.4** Solve $y' = 2y - y^2$ where $y(0) = 1$.

**9.1.5** Some milk is removed from the refrigerator at a temperature of 2 degrees Celsius and placed in a glass in a room that's kept at a constant temperature of 20 degrees. After 1 minute, the milk has warmed to 5 degrees. When will the milk warm to 10 degrees?

**9.1.6★** A **homogeneous** differential equation is an equation of the form $y' = f\left(\dfrac{y}{x}\right)$ for some function $f$. For example $y' = \dfrac{y^2 + x^2}{2xy}$ is homogeneous, since the right side can be written as $\frac{1}{2}\left(\frac{y}{x} + \frac{1}{\frac{y}{x}}\right)$. Show that we can solve any homogeneous equation by making the substitution $y = vx$.

## 9.2 SECOND-ORDER LINEAR DIFFERENTIAL EQUATIONS

A type of differential equation that comes up very frequently (especially in physics) is a **2nd order linear homogeneous equation with constant coefficients**. That's a mouthful—what that means is an equation of the form

$$y'' + ay' + by = 0,$$

where $a$ and $b$ are real numbers. We can decode some of the adjectives:

- *2nd order* means $y''$ appears in the equation, but not $y'''$ or any other higher derivatives of $y$.

- *linear* means $y''$, $y'$, and $y$ appear only by themselves as linear terms: nothing like $y^2$ is allowed.

- *homogeneous* means there are no terms that involve only the independent variable.

- *constant coefficients* means that $a$ and $b$ are real numbers and not functions of the independent variable (such as $x$ or $t$).

To begin to study this type of differential equation, let's first take the middle term out:

---

**Problem 9.15:** Consider the differential equation $y'' + by = 0$, where $y$ is a function of $x$.

(a)  If $b = 0$, what are the solutions?

(b)  If $b < 0$, what are the solutions? (Try $b = -1$ at first if you're stuck.)

(c)  If $b > 0$, what are the solutions? (Try $b = 1$ at first if you're stuck.)

---

*Solution for Problem 9.15:* The nature of the solutions depends on whether $b$ is positive, negative or 0. However, we expect that in all cases, solutions to second-order differential equations will depend on two arbitrary constants, as opposed to a single constant that we saw in solutions to first-order equations. One reason to expect this is that we may have to antidifferentiate twice to solve a second-order equation, and each antidifferentiation will introduce an arbitrary constant. We will also see why we get two constants as we work through each case below.

(a)  Naturally, $b = 0$ is the easiest. In this case, the equation is simply $y'' = 0$. We integrate this once to get $y' = c$ for some constant $c$, and then we integrate this again to get $y = cx + d$ for some new constant $d$. More typically, we call the constants $c_1$ and $c_2$, so that the solutions of $y'' = 0$ are all of the form

$$y = c_1 x + c_2,$$

where $c_1$ and $c_2$ are constants. Once again, note that our solution contains two constants, since we are solving a second-order equation.

(b)  Next is the case where $b < 0$. It may be easier to determine the solutions if we write it as $y'' = -by$. This looks very similar to the exponential growth equation $y' = ky$, except that we now have $y''$ on the left side instead of $y'$. In a similar manner, we can search for an exponential solution of the form $y = e^{\lambda x}$ for some constant $\lambda$. Then we have $y' = \lambda e^{\lambda x}$ and $y'' = \lambda^2 e^{\lambda x}$, so to satisfy $y'' = -by$ we must have $\lambda^2 = -b$, or $\lambda = \pm \sqrt{-b}$. (Now we see why we must have $b < 0$; otherwise, the square root does not exist. We treat the case of $b > 0$ in part (c) below.) For simplicity, let $k = \sqrt{-b}$, so that the original differential equation is $y'' - k^2 y = 0$, and thus we have found solutions $y = e^{\pm kx}$.

  Because differentiation is linear, any linear combination of our two solutions $e^{kx}$ and $e^{-kx}$ will be a solution to the differential equation $y'' - k^2 y = 0$. To verify this, we simply compute, where $c_1$ and $c_2$ are arbitrary constants:

$$y = c_1 e^{kx} + c_2 e^{-kx}$$
$$y' = k c_1 e^{kx} - k c_2 e^{-kx}$$
$$y'' = k^2 c_1 e^{kx} + k^2 c_2 e^{-kx} = k^2 y.$$

(c)  The method from part (b) doesn't work if $b > 0$, because $\sqrt{-b}$ is not a real number. Instead, for this case, we can look first at $b = 1$ to get an idea. If $b = 1$, then we are looking for solutions to $y'' + y = 0$. Happily, we already know two functions that are solutions to this equation: $y = \sin x$ and $y = \cos x$. Moreover, we can prove that any solution is of the form $y = c_1 \sin x + c_2 \cos x$ for constants $c_1$ and $c_2$, although we will leave the details of this as a Challenge Problem.

  To extend this argument to other values of $b$, we use essentially the same logic as in part (b). Each differentiation of $y$ must introduce a factor of $\omega = \pm \sqrt{b}$, so that differentiating twice will introduce a factor of

$\omega^2 = b$. Thus, the solutions of $y'' + \omega^2 y = 0$ are of the form

$$y = c_1 \sin \omega x + c_2 \cos \omega x,$$

where $c_1$ and $c_2$ are constants.

$\square$

Let's summarize the solutions to Problem 9.15.

> **Important:** In all of the following, $k$ and $\omega$ are positive constants, and $c_1$ and $c_2$ are arbitrary constants.
>
> - Solutions to $y'' = 0$ are of the form $y = c_1 x + c_2$.
> - Solutions to $y'' - k^2 y = 0$ are of the form $y = c_1 e^{kx} + c_2 e^{-kx}$.
> - Solutions to $y'' + \omega^2 y = 0$ are of the form $y = c_1 \sin \omega x + c_2 \cos \omega x$.

Now let's turn our attention to the more general form of the equation:

$$y'' + ay' + by = 0,$$

where $a$ and $b$ are constants. Since exponentials figure prominently in solutions to many of the differential equations that we have already seen, let's start our investigation there.

**Problem 9.16:** Suppose that $y = e^{rx}$ is a solution to $y'' + ay' + by = 0$, where $r$ is a constant. What equation does $r$ satisfy?

*Solution for Problem 9.16:* We can immediately compute $y' = re^{rx}$ and $y'' = r^2 e^{rx}$. We plug these in to the differential equation and get

$$r^2 e^{rx} + are^{rx} + be^{rx} = 0.$$

Dividing by $e^{rx}$ (which is never 0) leaves $r^2 + ar + b = 0$. $\square$

Thus, we get an exponential solution of $y'' + ay' + by = 0$ of the form $y = e^{rx}$ if and only if $r$ is a root of the **characteristic polynomial** $\lambda^2 + a\lambda + b$. More generally, if this quadratic has two distinct real roots $r_1$ and $r_2$, then every solution to the differential equation is of the form

$$y = c_1 e^{r_1 x} + c_2 e^{r_2 x}$$

for some constants $c_1$ and $c_2$.

> **WARNING!!** We have not actually proved that *every* solution to the above differential equation is of the form $y = c_1 e^{r_1 x} + c_2 e^{r_2 x}$. We have shown that these are solutions, but we haven't proved that there are no other solutions. In fact, those *are* all of the solutions, although this is difficult to prove with the tools we currently have.

If the characteristic polynomial $\lambda^2 + a\lambda + b$ has a double root $r$, then every solution to the differential equation is of the form

$$y = (c_1 x + c_2)e^{rx},$$

although we will leave it as an exercise to check that these are in fact solutions.

The remaining case is if the roots of the characteristic polynomial are not real. Not surprisingly, in light of part (c) of Problem 9.15, we get trigonometric terms:

**Problem 9.17:** Consider the differential equation $y'' + ay' + by = 0$, and suppose that the roots of the characteristic polynomial $\lambda^2 + a\lambda + b$ are $r \pm si$, where $s \neq 0$. Show that $y = e^{rx} \sin sx$ is a solution to the differential equation.

*Solution for Problem 9.17:* Let $y = e^{rx} \sin sx$. We first compute $y'$ and $y''$:

$$y' = se^{rx} \cos sx + re^{rx} \sin sx = e^{rx}(r \sin sx + s \cos sx),$$
$$y'' = e^{rx}(rs \cos sx - s^2 \sin sx) + re^{rx}(r \sin sx + s \cos sx) = e^{rx}((r^2 - s^2) \sin sx + 2rs \cos sx).$$

This gives

$$y'' + ay' + by = e^{rx}(((r^2 - s^2) + ar + b) \sin sx + (2rs + as) \cos sx).$$

But we also know that the sum of the roots of $\lambda^2 + a\lambda + b = 0$ is $-a$, and the product of the roots is $b$. Therefore, $2r = -a$ and $r^2 + s^2 = b$, which gives

$$y'' + ay' + by = e^{rx}(((2r^2 - b) + ar + b) \sin sx + (-as + as) \cos sx) = e^{rx}((-ar + ar) \sin sx) = 0,$$

as desired. $\square$

A similar computation shows that $y = e^{rx} \cos sx$ is also a solution to the differential equation (we will leave the details of this computation as an exercise). Further, any linear combination of solutions is also a solution. Thus, we see that solutions to $y'' + ay' + by$, where the characteristic polynomial has complex roots $r \pm si$, are

$$y = e^{rx}(c_1 \sin sx + c_2 \cos sx)$$

for constants $c_1$ and $c_2$.

We can now summarize the solutions to second-order linear differential equations with constant coefficients:

**Important:**  Consider the differential equation

$$y'' + ay' + by = 0,$$

with characteristic equation $\lambda^2 + a\lambda + b = 0$. In all cases, $c_1$ and $c_2$ are constants.

- If the characteristic equation has distinct real roots $r_1$ and $r_2$, then every solution is of the form
$$y = c_1 e^{r_1 x} + c_2 e^{r_2 x}.$$

- If the characteristic equation has a double root $r$, then every solution is of the form
$$y = e^{rx}(c_1 x + c_2).$$

- If the characteristic equation has complex roots $r \pm si$, then every solution is of the form
$$y = e^{rx}(c_1 \sin sx + c_2 \cos sx).$$

A common example of this sort of differential equation is the motion of a spring.

> **Problem 9.18:** A spring obeys **Hooke's Law**, which states that the force exerted by the spring is proportional to the amount of displacement from the equilibrium position, and in the opposite direction (that is, towards equilibrium). Newton's Second Law of Motion states that $F = ma$, where $F$ is force, $m$ is mass, and $a$ is acceleration. Show that the motion of a spring, with no resistance or other force present, is given by
>
> $$s = A\sin(\theta + \omega t)$$
>
> for suitable constants $A$, $\theta$, and $\omega$.

*Solution for Problem 9.18:* We can write Hooke's Law as $F = -ks$, where $F$ is force, $s$ is displacement, and $k > 0$ is the constant of proportionality. We are also given Newton's Second Law $F = ma$, and we know that acceleration is the second derivative of displacement.

Putting this all together, we have the equation

$$s'' = a = \frac{F}{M} = -\frac{k}{m}s.$$

If we relabel the constant factor by letting $\omega = \sqrt{\frac{k}{m}}$, then we can rewrite this more conveniently as

$$s'' = -\omega^2 s.$$

As we have just seen, the solutions to this differential equation are of the form

$$s = c_1 \cos \omega t + c_2 \sin \omega t.$$

This does not quite look like what we want, which is $A\sin(\theta + \omega t)$. But we can expand our desired answer using the sine angle-addition formula:

$$A\sin(\theta + \omega t) = A(\sin\theta \cos\omega t + \cos\theta \sin\omega t).$$

This does look like the solution to our differential equation, provided that we can solve $c_1 = A\sin\theta$ and $c_2 = A\cos\theta$ for some $\theta$. We must have $A = \sqrt{c_1^2 + c_2^2}$, so we divide both sides of our solution by $A$:

$$\frac{s}{A} = \frac{c_1}{A}\cos\omega t + \frac{c_2}{A}\sin\omega t.$$

Now we can choose $\theta$ so that $\sin\theta = \frac{c_1}{A}$ and $\cos\theta = \frac{c_2}{A}$, noting that $\sin^2\theta + \cos^2\theta = 1$. Then we have

$$\frac{s}{A} = \sin\theta \cos\omega t + \cos\theta \sin\omega t.$$

The right side is exactly the sine angle-sum formula, and we can finish:

$$s = A\sin(\theta + \omega t),$$

as desired. $\square$

---

## EXERCISES

**9.2.1** Solve the following differential equations:

(a) $y'' - 4y' + 3y = 0$ where $y(0) = 1$ and $y'(0) = 2$.

(b) $y'' + 6y' + 9y = 0$ where $y(0) = 0$ and $y'(0) = 1$.

(c) $y'' - 4y' + 13y = 0$ where $y(0) = 2$ and $y'(0) = -1$.

**9.2.2** Show that, if $\lambda^2 + a\lambda + b = 0$ has complex roots $\lambda = r \pm si$, then $e^{rx} \cos sx$ is a solution to the differential equation $y'' + ay' + by = 0$.

**9.2.3** Show that, if $\lambda^2 + a\lambda + b = 0$ has a double root $r$, then $e^{rx}(c_1 x + c_2)$ is a solution to the differential equation $y'' + ay' + by = 0$. **Hints:** 35

**9.2.4★** Solve the differential equation $y'' + 2y' + 2y = e^{-3x}$. **Hints:** 85, 200

# REVIEW PROBLEMS

**9.19** Solve the differential equation $y' = 1 + y^2$ with initial condition $y(0) = 0$.

**9.20** Solve the differential equation $(x^2 + 1)y' = (xy)^2$ with initial condition $y(1) = 2$.

**9.21** Solve the equation $y' = 3y - y^2$ with initial condition $y(0) = 5$, and determine $\lim\limits_{t \to \infty} y(t)$.

**9.22** Solve the equation $2y'' + (y')^2 = -1$. **Hints:** 110

**9.23** Solve $y'' = y'$ with initial conditions $y(0) = 1$ and $y(1) = 2$.

**9.24** Motion of an object through a fluid can be modeled by $y' = -ky^2$ where $y$ represents velocity and $k$ is a positive constant. Suppose an object starts at time $t = 0$ sec with velocity 10 m/sec and $k = 0.5$. Determine when the object slows to 1 m/sec.

**9.25** We can model the rate that a rumor spreads among a population with the differential equation $\frac{dy}{dt} = ky(1-y)$, where $0 \le y \le 1$ is the fraction of the population that knows the rumor, and $k > 0$ is a constant.

(a) Explain in words why this differential equation is a reasonable model. **Hints:** 4

(b) Solve the equation.

(c) If 10% of the population knows the rumor at noon on Sunday, and 20% of the population knows the rumor at noon on Monday, then approximately when will 90% of the population know the rumor?

**9.26** Solve the differential equation $(\sin x)y' + (\cos x)y = \tan x$. **Hints:** 250

# CHALLENGE PROBLEMS

**9.27** A not uncommon calculus mistake is to believe that the product rule for derivatives says that $(fg)' = f'g'$. If $f(x) = e^{x^2}$, determine, with proof, whether there exists an open interval $(a, b)$ and a nonzero continuous function $g$ defined on $(a, b)$ such that this wrong product rule is true for $x$ in $(a, b)$. *(Source: Putnam)*

**9.28**

(a) Explain how the equation $y' = ay^2 - by$, where $a$ and $b$ are positive real numbers, models a population with a birth rate represented by $a$ and a death rate represented by $b$.

(b) Solve the equation $y' = ay^2 - by$, where $a$ and $b$ are positive real numbers.

(c) Further suppose that $y(0) = m$. How does the behavior of the solutions depend on whether $m > b/a$, $m < b/a$, or $m = b/a$? Does this equation seem like a good model?

**9.29** A **first-order linear differential equation** is a differential equation of the form

$$y' + p(x)y = q(x),$$

where $p$ and $q$ are functions of $x$.

(a) Solve $y' - 2y = e^{-x}$ by multiplying both sides by $e^{-2x}$ and integrating.

(b) Find a function $h(x)$, in terms of $p(x)$, such that $(yh)' = (y' + py)h$. **Hints:** 211

(c) Multiply $y' + py = q$ on both sides by the function $h$ from part (b), and solve the equation.

Note: the function $h$ is called an **integrating factor** for the linear differential equation.

**9.30** We prove that all solutions of $y'' + y = 0$ are of the form $y = c_1 \sin x + c_2 \cos x$ for some constants $c_1$ and $c_2$, as follows:

(a) Show that if $f$ is a function such that $f''(x) + f(x) = 0$ for all $x$, then the function

$$g(x) = (f(x))^2 + (f'(x))^2$$

is a constant function. **Hints:** 138

(b) Using part (a), show that if $f$ is a function such that $f''(x) + f(x) = 0$, and $f(0) = f'(0) = 0$, then $f$ is the constant function 0.

(c) Prove that if $f$ is a function such that $f''(x) + f(x) = 0$, then

$$f(x) = f'(0) \sin x + f(0) \cos x.$$

**9.31** Let $f : \mathbb{R} \to \mathbb{R}$ be a differentiable function such that $f'(x) = f(1-x)$ for all $x$ and $f(0) = 1$. Find $f(1)$. *(Source: HMMT)* **Hints:** 263

**9.32** (This problem is closely based on a problem from [H-H].)

Juliet is in love with Romeo, but Romeo is more fickle. The more Juliet loves him, the more he hates her, and the more she hates him, the more he loves her. On the other hand, Juliet is more sensible: the more Romeo loves her, the more she loves him, and the more he hates her, the more she hates him.

(a) Explain why a reasonable model for their love for each other is

$$\frac{dj}{dt} = kr, \quad \frac{dr}{dt} = -kj,$$

where $j$ and $r$ denote their love (if positive) or hate (if negative) for each other, and where $k$ is a positive constant.

(b) Solve this system for $r$ and $j$. Your answer will depend on $k$ and two other arbitrary constants.

(c) Suppose at time $t = 0$, Romeo is fully in love with Juliet (so that $r(0) = 1$), but Juliet is indifferent to Romeo (so that $j(0) = 0$). Write equations for the solution in terms of $k$.

(d) Sketch the solution from (c), and explain in words what is going on.

(e)$\star$ (If you want to explore further) How would things change if we had

$$\frac{dj}{dt} = kr, \quad \frac{dr}{dt} = -lj,$$

where $k$ and $l$ are positive constants?

**9.33**$\star$ Find all real-valued continuously differentiable functions $f$ with domain $\mathbb{R}$ such that for all $x \in \mathbb{R}$,

$$(f(x))^2 = 2009 + \int_0^x \left( (f(t))^2 + (f'(t))^2 \right) dt.$$

*(Source: Putnam)* **Hints:** 20, 184

**9.34★** Find all continuous, infinitely differentiable functions $f$ with domain $\mathbb{R}$ such that

$$f(x)f(y) = \int_{x-y}^{x+y} f(t)\,dt$$

for all $x, y \in \mathbb{R}$. (Warning: this is quite hard. First just play with the equation a bit, to see if you can discover any facts about such a function. Then try to find all the solutions where $f$ is a polynomial. Then try to find some non-polynomial solution(s). Then try to prove that you've found them all.) **Hints:** 86, 172, 173, 114, 287, 38

## 9.A  EULER'S METHOD

As mentioned in Section 9.1, **Euler's Method** is a method for approximating solutions to differential equations of the form $y' = f(x, y)$. Euler's Method is basically just repeated tangent line approximation, as we shall see.

Let's go back to our first example from Problem 9.3 of $y' = -\dfrac{x}{y}$ with initial condition $y(0) = 1$. We know the solution to this is the circle $x^2 + y^2 = 1$. When $x = 0.3$, we have $y(0.3) = \sqrt{1 - (0.3)^2} = \sqrt{0.91} \approx 0.954$. Let's now see how we can estimate $y(0.3)$ using only the differential equation $y' = -\frac{x}{y}$.

---

**Problem 9.35:** Suppose a function $y$ satisfies $y' = -\dfrac{x}{y}$ and $y(0) = 1$. We wish to estimate $y(0.3)$.

(a)  Using $y(0) = 1$ and the fact that $y'(0) = -\dfrac{0}{1} = 0$, estimate $y(0.1)$ via a tangent line approximation.

(b)  Using the value of $y(0.1)$ that you found in part (a), compute an estimate for $y'(0.1)$.

(c)  Using the values from parts (a) and (b), estimate $y(0.2)$ via a tangent line approximation.

(d)  Repeat steps (b) and (c) to estimate $y(0.3)$.

---

*Solution for Problem 9.35:* Our method is basically to perform repeated tangent-line approximations. We can decide how accurate to make the approximation by choosing how many "steps" to do. Since we want $y(0.3)$ and we're starting with $y(0)$, we'll try steps of 0.1, so we will end up doing three successive tangent-line approximations: first $y(0.1)$, then $y(0.2)$, and finally $y(0.3)$.

(a)  Our first step is to apply our usual tangent line approximation, starting at the point $(0, 1)$ with slope $y' = -0/1 = 0$. As you recall, the expression for the tangent line approximation at $a$ is

$$y(x) \approx y(a) + y'(a)(x - a).$$

(If you don't "recall" this, please go back to Chapter 4 and review it.) Since $y'(0) = 0$, our tangent line is just the horizontal line $y = 1$, and thus our first approximation is $y(0.1) = 1$. If we insist on applying the formula, we get

$$y(0.1) \approx y(0) + y'(0)(0.1) = 1 + 0(0.1) = 1.$$

(b)  Now we're at the point $(0.1, 1)$. We use the differential equation to get the slope for our next tangent line approximation, by substituting $x = 0.1$ and $y = 1$ to get $y'(0.1) = -x/y = -0.1/1 = -0.1$.

(c)  Now we have $y(0.1)$ and $y'(0.1)$, so we can use these to perform a tangent line approximation of $y(0.2)$:

$$y(0.2) \approx y(0.1) + y'(0.1)(0.1) \approx 1 + (-0.1)(0.1) = 0.99.$$

(d)  Now we're at the point $(0.2, 0.99)$, so we substitute $x = 0.2$ and $y = 0.99$ into the differential equation to get $y'(0.2) = -x/y \approx -0.2/0.99 \approx -0.202$. Thus, our final tangent line approximation is

$$y(0.3) \approx y(0.2) + y'(0.2)(0.1) \approx 0.99 + (-0.202)(0.1) \approx 0.970.$$

So our final answer is $y(0.3) \approx 0.970$.

□

We recall the exact answer was approximately 0.954, so our estimate is not that great, but it is considerably better than a 1-step tangent line approximation starting at $(1, 0)$ would give us—that would give us $y(0.3) \approx 1$, since $y'(0) = 0$ would be the slope of our tangent line at $y = 0$. Not surprisingly, performing more steps (for example, increasing $x$ by 0.05 between estimates instead of 0.1) would give a better approximation.

> **Concept:** Euler's Method is just repeated application of tangent line approximation.

Let's see a slightly different example, where we don't even have a differential equation to start with.

**Problem 9.36:** Estimate $e^{0.3}$ using a 3-step Euler's Method approximation starting from $e^0 = 1$.

*Solution for Problem 9.36:* To put this more in the context of Problem 9.35, we use the fact that $y = e^x$ is a solution to the differential equation $y' = y$.

We start at the point $(0, 1)$. The first tangent line approximation uses $y'(0) = 1$. So we have

$$y(0.1) \approx 1 + 1(0.1) = 1.1.$$

Now we're at the point $(0.1, 1.1)$. We have $y'(0.1) = y \approx 1.1$, so we have

$$y(0.2) \approx y(0.1) + (0.1)y'(0.1) \approx 1.1 + (0.1)(1.1) = 1.21.$$

Now we're at the point $(0.2, 1.21)$. We have $y'(0.2) = y \approx 1.21$. So we have

$$y(0.3) \approx y(0.2) + (0.1)y'(0.2) \approx 1.21 + (0.1)(1.21) = 1.331.$$

Thus, we conclude that $e^{0.3} \approx 1.331$. □

Your calculator will say $e^{0.3} = 1.349859\ldots$, so this is not an especially great approximation. We can make the estimate of $e^{0.3}$ more accurate by doing more steps to get from 0 to 0.3. Here's the calculation for 10 steps: in each step, $x$ increases by 0.03:

| $x$ | $y$ | $y'$ | new $y$ |
|----------|----------|----------|----------|
| 0.000000 | 1.000000 | 1.000000 | 1.030000 |
| 0.030000 | 1.030000 | 1.030000 | 1.060900 |
| 0.060000 | 1.060900 | 1.060900 | 1.092727 |
| 0.090000 | 1.092727 | 1.092727 | 1.125509 |
| 0.120000 | 1.125509 | 1.125509 | 1.159274 |
| 0.150000 | 1.159274 | 1.159274 | 1.194052 |
| 0.180000 | 1.194052 | 1.194052 | 1.229874 |
| 0.210000 | 1.229874 | 1.229874 | 1.266770 |
| 0.240000 | 1.266770 | 1.266770 | 1.304773 |
| 0.270000 | 1.304773 | 1.304773 | 1.343916 |

This gives $e^{0.3} \approx 1.3439\ldots$, which is better but still not too good. If we did 100 steps (which I won't torture you by showing, but is a nice computer programming exercise if you are so inclined), we get $e^{0.3} \approx 1.3493\ldots$ which is within 0.0005 of the true value.

**Sidenote:**  Finding numerical solutions to differential equations is a vast area of mathematics, because differential equations appear very frequently in science and engineering applications, but are often quite difficult to solve explicitly. There are many more sophisticated methods for getting numerical solutions to differential equations, some of which you may learn when you take a differential equations or numerical methods course.

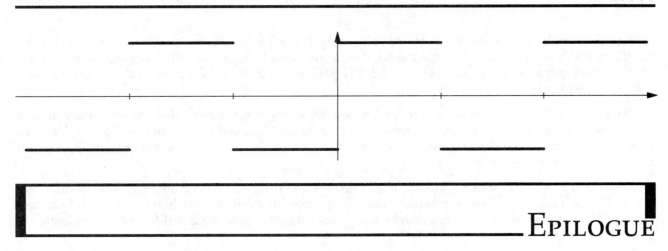

# EPILOGUE

## NOW WHAT?

Congratulations on completing the book! You should now have a good understanding of the fundamentals of single-variable calculus. What do you do now?

Most likely, you are now at the stage of your career where the mathematics that you "have to" study is dictated by what subject you are going to pursue. For many paths of study, you may not "need" any more mathematics! But assuming that most readers of this book will be pursuing careers in mathematics, science, engineering, or some other technically-demanding field, there is probably more mathematics in your future.

One very good option is to study **physics**. You may have already seen some physics, but physics without calculus is like language without verbs: it's hard to do much physics without some basic calculus. For example, one of the most fundamental equations in physics is $F = ma$, but since $a$ (acceleration) is the second derivative of position, what is $F = ma$ if not a differential equation? Virtually all major concepts in physics hinge on calculus—in fact, it's largely why much of calculus was invented!

Another option is to study **statistics**. You've likely already seen some discrete statistics or probability, where you were analyzing finite sets of data or situations with finitely many discrete outcomes. Now that you know calculus, you can explore the much wider arena of probability and statistics of events with continuous outcomes. For example, many events can be modeled by a **normal distribution**, where an event with mean $\mu$ and variance $\sigma^2$ is modeled with the **probability density function**

$$f(x) = \frac{1}{\sigma\sqrt{2\pi}}e^{-\frac{(x-\mu)^2}{2\sigma^2}}.$$

Using this function, the probability that $a \leq x \leq b$ is $\int_a^b f(x)\,dx$. (Note that $\int_{-\infty}^{\infty} f(x)\,dx = 1$ by Problem 6.32, reflecting the fact that the probability of *any* outcome should be 1.)

Within pure mathematics, there are a number of possibilities for the next course after single-variable calculus. The most obvious choice is to continue with **multivariable calculus** or **vector calculus** (these two are essentially the same material with slightly different nuances). This subject extends the tools of calculus that we developed in this book to functions of two or more variables. It also generalizes many of the techniques from Chapter 8 to work with curves and surfaces in 3-dimensional space.

You could also embark on a course of study of **differential equations**. Our work in Chapter 9 barely scratched the surface of this very deep subject.

A third direction is to study **linear algebra**. Linear algebra, at its core, is the study of vectors and matrices, but it is much more than that. Also, many argue that having some background with linear algebra is preferred before beginning multivariable calculus or differential equations, because the tools of linear algebra are necessary in both of these subjects.

Finally, we will repeat what we said in the Preface: we strongly recommend that students study **discrete mathematics**, which broadly includes combinatorics, probability, logic, and number theory. These subjects are often overlooked—especially in high-school curricula—but are vitally important and are broadly applicable to many "real world" problems.

The overall point is that once you've completed a first course in calculus, mathematics is no longer "do A, then B, then C" like it might have been throughout high school. There are many different branches of math to explore, most of them interrelated. Don't be in a rush to pigeonhole yourself—explore lots of different areas of math, and most importantly, have fun!

## EXPLANATION OF TOP-OF-CHAPTER DIAGRAMS

The diagrams at the top of each chapter are graphs of **Fourier series approximations**. Specifically, the picture at the top of Chapter $n$ (where $1 \leq n \leq 9$) is the graph of

$$y = \frac{2}{\pi} \sum_{k=1}^{n} \frac{\sin((2k-1)\pi x)}{2k-1}.$$

As $n \to \infty$, this function approaches the **square wave** function:

$$f(x) = \begin{cases} \frac{1}{2} & \text{if } \lfloor x \rfloor \text{ is even,} \\ -\frac{1}{2} & \text{if } \lfloor x \rfloor \text{ is odd.} \end{cases}$$

The graph of this function is shown at the top of the previous page.

The $n^{\text{th}}$ Fourier series approximation of a function $f(x)$ with period $2L$ is

$$F_n(x) = \frac{a_0}{2} + \sum_{k=1}^{n} \left( a_k \cos \frac{k\pi x}{L} + b_k \sin \frac{k\pi x}{L} \right),$$

where the coefficients are given by:

$$a_0 = \frac{1}{L} \int_{-L}^{L} f(x)\, dx, \quad a_k = \frac{1}{L} \int_{-L}^{L} f(x) \cos \frac{k\pi x}{L}\, dx, \quad b_k = \frac{1}{L} \int_{-L}^{L} f(x) \sin \frac{k\pi x}{L}\, dx.$$

If we extend this to an infinite series, we get the Fourier series for $f(x)$. Part of the reason that the series converges is that the integrals above approach 0 as $k \to \infty$, due to the result from Problem 6.29.

Just as Taylor polynomials compute the best polynomial approximations of a function at a point, Fourier series compute the best approximations of a function as a sum of sine and cosine functions. But whereas Taylor series give an approximation of a function at a single point, Fourier series are instead global in nature, considering the entire function at once, and thus are used to study the global properties of the function.

Fourier series are useful for studying functions which are periodic in nature. Such functions arise in acoustics, cryptography, and signal processing. Fourier series are also essential for studying quantum mechanics and differential equations, and Fourier analysis even makes multiplication of large numbers easier.

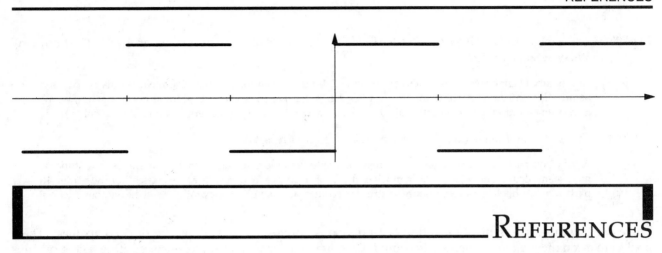

Before studying calculus, you should be ready. If you need to brush up on your precalculus topics, a good source is:

**[Ru]** R. Rusczyk, *Precalculus*, AoPS Incorporated, 2009.

> Covers trigonometry, complex numbers, and an introduction to vectors and matrices. Lots of hard problems, including many problems from advanced US high-school math contests such as the AIME and USAMO.

Next are a couple of "mainstream" calculus textbooks. Most widely-used college calculus textbooks, including the two listed below, come in many varieties: single-variable (like this book) vs. multi-variable (typically the next calculus course after this book) vs. both, and "early transcendentals" (where exp and log are introduced early, as in this book) vs. "late transcendentals" (where exp and log are not introduced until after differentiation and integration are defined).

**[H-H]** D. Hughes-Hallett et al., *Calculus* (6th Edition), John Wiley & Sons, 2012.

> An above-average "mainstream" calculus textbook. The "Single Variable" edition is the version most closely aligned with this textbook. Light on rigor in spots, but a stronger emphasis than most books on using calculus to model "real-world" problems.

**[St]** J. Stewart, *Calculus* (7th edition), Brooks Cole, 2011.

> By far the most widely-used college calculus textbook—reportedly sells more than all other calculus textbooks combined. A competent book designed for typical first-year college calculus courses, with the usual advantages (lots of routine exercises and word problems) and drawbacks (not much rigor in places and not a lot of very challenging problems). The main version (which is now in its 8th edition, combining single-variable and multivariable calculus, with late transcendentals) is 1368 pages long, and at press time retails for $299.95.

Some more advanced calculus texts:

**[Sp]** M. Spivak, *Calculus* (Third Edition), Publish or Perish, Inc., 1994.

> A very thorough, very rigorous treatment of calculus. Spivak covers many topics much more thoroughly than we do, and proves *everything*. If you want to read something more rigorous than this book, that really covers all the nuts-and-bolts of calculus, then you want to read Spivak's book. His detailed construction of the real numbers is particularly illuminating. A new 4th edition was published in 2008.

**[Ap]** T. M. Apostol, *Calculus, Volume 1: One-Variable Calculus with an Introduction to Linear Algebra* (2nd Edition), John Wiley & Sons, 1967.

> Another excellent rigorous treatment of calculus. A bit unconventional in that definite integrals are covered before differentiation. Also, as the title implies, has extensive coverage of beginning linear algebra, which leads into an introduction of vector calculus. (Volume 2 of this textbook covers multivariable calculus.)

**[MacC]** C. R. MacCluer, *Honors Calculus*, Princeton University Press, 2006.

> A very compact (only 168 pages!) treatment of single-variable calculus. Generally assumes that students have seen calculus before, and fills in much of the rigor. Leaves a lot of results as "exercises" for the reader. In particular, the book has a very mature treatment of continuity, using topology rather than the $\delta$-$\epsilon$ construction.

There are a number of essentially identical test-prep books published by various test-prep companies. These books are recommended for students who would like more practice with routine exercises before taking calculus placement tests for the purpose of potential college credit. These books may also contain test-taking tips. While such books are largely interchangeable, one of the more popular choices is:

**[Bar]** S. O. Hockett and D. Bock, *Barron's AP Calculus*, Barron's Educational Services, Inc., 2008.

> Includes four full-length practice exams, a brief review of the topics on the exam, and test-taking tips (including tips on calculator usage).

A definitive source for recent Putnam Competition problems is:

**[KPV]** K. S. Kedlaya, B. Poonen, and R. Vakil, *The William Lowell Putnam Competition Problems & Solutions: 1985–2000*, Mathematical Association of America, 2002.

> All the problems from the Putnam during the period 1985–2000. Contains hints and very detailed solutions, including areas for further study. Warning: the majority of the problems on the Putnam involve branches of mathematics beyond calculus, and Putnam problems as a whole are *very* difficult.

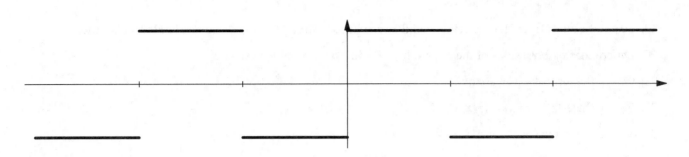

# HINTS TO SELECTED PROBLEMS

1. Letting $u = x^5 + 3x^2 + x$, what happens if we add and subtract $du$ to the numerator?

2. Compare the sum of the first $n$ terms to $\displaystyle\int_1^{n+1} \frac{1}{x}\, dx$.

3. Draw a picture first.

4. The rumor spreads when someone who knows the rumor tells it to someone who doesn't already know it.

5. Try converting to rectangular coordinates.

6. There's no "right answer." Just try to explain what's going on as best as you can. Then read the explanation in the Solutions Manual.

7. Write $\frac{2}{x^4}$ as $2x^{-4}$.

8. If $f$ is even, what is the relationship between $\displaystyle\int_a^b f$ and $\displaystyle\int_{-b}^{-a} f$?

9. Try substituting $u = \sqrt{x}$.

10. Draw a picture first.

11. Let 4-dimensional space be represented by 4-tuples $(x, y, z, w)$. The 4-dimensional sphere is the graph of $x^2 + y^2 + z^2 + w^2 = 1$.

12. The velocity that the snowplow travels is inversely proportional to the amount of time since it started snowing.

13. Use integration by parts twice.

14. First prove it in the case where $f(x) \geq 0$ for all $x \in [a, b]$.

15. Factor out $\frac{1}{n}$. Now what does the sum look like?

16. An ellipse is just a "stretched" circle.

17. Try it first for $n = 2$ to get a better idea of what's happening.

18. Try taking the log of the sequence.

19. To get the slope of the tangent line, you'll have to take a limit. You may also need l'Hôptial's Rule.

20. Differentiating both sides of the equation seems like a reasonable first step.

21. Group the terms by powers of 2.

22. Notice that $f(x) - f(4x) = (f(x) - f(2x)) + (f(2x) - f(4x))$.

23. The statement is false.

24. Don't compute derivatives—start with the Taylor series for $\sin x$.

25. Substitute $u = \sqrt[3]{x}$.

26. Use $\cos^2 x = 1 - \sin^2 x$.

27. Try to make the sum look like a Riemann sum.

28. Draw some points for easy values of $\theta$ and connect the dots.

29. What substitution makes the fractional exponents go away?

30. Note it's about $x = 2$.

31. Slice the surface area into cylindrical strips.

32. There's no need to use l'Hôpital's Rule for the quotient of tangents.

33. Prove by induction, using the fact that $(fg)^{(n+1)} = ((fg)^{(n)})'$.

34. Use $u = \log x$ and $dv = x\,dx$.

35. Use the facts that if $r$ is a double-root, then $a = -2r$ and $b = r^2$.

36. One piece should be $\displaystyle\int \frac{2}{(x^2 + 1)^2}\,dx$. Evaluate this by the trig substitution $x = \tan\theta$.

37. If $\displaystyle\lim_{n\to\infty} \frac{a_n}{b_n} = c \neq 0$, then show that $a_n < 2cb_n$ for sufficiently large $n$.

38. Some functions that work are $0$, $2x$, $\frac{2}{c}\sin cx$ where $c$ is any nonzero constant. There is one other family of functions that works too.

39. There are two basic ways to do this problem, and they might lead you to two very different-looking answers. Check that those two answers are the same.

40. How can we easily extend the proof to arbitrary $f$? Just translate $f$ up until its range on $[a, b]$ is positive.

41. The series looks pretty close to the harmonic series.

42. You don't necessarily need to solve for $a$ and $b$. You just need to find $f(1)$.

43. Try to construct an example where $\displaystyle\lim_{x\to\infty} f'(x)$ does not exist. Trig functions are usually the best examples of functions that don't have nice asymptotic behavior as $x \to \infty$.

44. After simplification, the integral should no longer be improper.

45. Try to find a useful linear combination of the given integrals.

46. Try integration by parts with $u = (1 - x)^7$ and $dv = x^{200}\,dx$. What do you get?

47. It may be easier to work in terms of coordinates rather than angles.

48. Compare the series with an appropriate geometric series.

49. Divide through by the $x$ first.

50. Bring the exponent out to the front of the logarithm, and then you should have something to which you can apply l'Hôpital's Rule.

51. Find $\delta$ so that each of $|f(x)g(x) - f(x)G|$ and $|f(x)G - FG|$ are bounded by $\frac{\varepsilon}{2}$.

52. Note that you're trying to maximize $y = r\sin\theta$ for $\theta \in \left[0, \frac{\pi}{4}\right]$.

53. Show that each set is a subset of the other.

54. Drawing a picture will help a lot.

55. You'll have to use some sort of Squeeze Theorem argument.

56. For $x \neq 0$, you will be able to compute the derivative just using the Product Formula. But at $x = 0$, you'll have to use the limit definition of derivative.

57. Start with a partial fraction decomposition.

58. Try to group the terms of the series is a useful way.

59. It's not as hard as it looks. Just logically work through it step-by-step.

60. Since we're starting with $\sin 2x$, the double-angle formula may help.

61. It's not as hard as it looks. Start with the usual idea of writing it as $\exp\left(\lim_{x \to 1} \log\left(x^{\frac{x}{\sin(1-x)}}\right)\right)$.

62. Use $|g(x) - L| \leq \max\{|f(x) - L|, |h(x) - L|\}$.

63. Note that the odd-power terms of $f$ should cancel out.

64. The relevant equation is $PV = k$, where $k$ is some constant.

65. Show that an odd-degree polynomial gets arbitrarily large as $x$ gets large, and gets arbitrarily small as $x$ gets small, or vice versa.

66. Prove it by induction.

67. Use the Law of Cosines to determine the distance between the tips of the hands in terms of the angle between the hands.

68. First, show that the new parameterization gives the same curve (as a set) as the original parameterization.

69. Look for a function whose derivative is a degree 4 polynomial that is a multiple of $x^2$ (so that it has a double root at $x = 0$).

70. The three different behaviors are $\frac{r}{R} < \frac{1}{4}$, $\frac{r}{R} = \frac{1}{4}$, and $\frac{r}{R} > \frac{1}{4}$.

71. You can assume that Sam first rows in a straight line and then walks the rest of the way. (Why is this OK to do?)

72. Complete the square in the denominator.

73. In $(x, y, z)$-space, let one cylinder be given by $y^2 + z^2 = 1$, and let the other cylinder be given by $x^2 + z^2 = 1$.

74. The best you can do for most $n$ is to get an equation relating $\cos(n - 1)\theta$ and $\cos(n + 1)\theta$. This equation can be solved for $n = 3$, but I wouldn't try it without using a calculator or computer.

75. How many times will this curve touch the lines $x = \pm 1$ and $y = \pm 1$ before returning back to its starting point?

76. As in part (a), you can assume that Sam first rows in a straight line and then walks the rest of the way. (Why is this OK to do?)

77. Use integration by parts.

78. Bound $\int_a^b f(x)g(x)\,dx$ above and below by appropriate multiples of $\int_a^b g(x)\,dx$.

79. Use integration by parts.

80. We know the Taylor series for $e^x$; how is the Taylor series for $e^{-x}$ related?

81. Use a trig substitution.

82. It seems convenient to look for a function such that $\int_{-a}^a f(x)\,dx = 0$ for all $a \in \mathbb{R}$.

83. Look at a partition in which each interval is the same size.

84. Break into a sum of two series that you know how to deal with.

85. First, solve $y'' + 2y' + 2y = 0$.

86. First, try all the things in the remarks accompanying the problem.

87. Use $\sin x = \cos\left(\frac{\pi}{2} - x\right)$.

88. You could try to sketch an example first.

89. Be careful about the range of $\sin^{-1}$.

90. We know that $\lim\limits_{x \to 0} \dfrac{\sin x}{x} = 1$. How does this help?

91. Try letting $b_n = \log_2 a_n$.

92. Do $a = 0$ and/or $b = 0$ as separate cases.

93. Drawing a picture might help to see what's going on.

94. Try the substitution $x = u^6$.

95. You can actually do both parts at once.

96. This is just an (admittedly complicated) application of the Chain Rule.

97. If $a < c < d < b$, show that $\int_a^d f = \int_a^c f + \int_c^d f$.

98. Write the limit as a fraction with the integral in the numerator and $\frac{1}{x}$ in the denominator, and use l'Hôpital's Rule.

99. Let $g(x) = \dfrac{b - x}{b - a} f(a) + \dfrac{x - a}{b - a} f(b)$. Compute $g(c) - f(c)$ for any $c \in (a, b)$.

100. Use integration by parts twice.

101. To integrate $\csc x$, look for trig expressions that have $\csc x$ in their derivatives.

102. Try a "rearranged" version of integration by parts.

103. Note that $f^{-1}(y)$ is a number but $f^{-1}(\{y\})$ is a set.

104. Use integration by parts.

105. Can the integral of a positive function ever be 0?

106. Look for a parameterization similar to part (a), but where the speed is appropriate.

107. Is something in this integral the derivative of something else in the integral?

108. Use the symmetry of the sine and cosine functions.

109. Perform long division first.

110. Substitute $v = y'$, solve for $v$, then integrate.

111. First solve $y' = y$, then worry about the "extra" $x$ term.

112. This is pretty hard to solve. You can try the substitution $y = vx$.

113. Start by showing $\sup(A \cap B) \leq \min\{\sup A, \sup B\}$.

114. At some point you'll want to differentiate both sides. Differentiating multiple times might help too.

115. Write the direction of the string as a function of $t$.

116. You might have to make an educated guess, and then check that your guess works.

117. Use the Mean Value Theorem.

118. Computing the tangent of what you want might be easier.

119. Drawing a picture will help a lot.

120. Try the Limit Comparison Test. What's a good series to compare to?

121. There are two possibilities.

122. Note $f(0) = f(1) = 0$ and $f(x) > 0$ for all $x \in (0, 1)$. Try to find the maximum on $[0, 1]$.

123. Try to create a "hole" in your union.

124. Write the power series for $\sin x^2$, then integrate term-by-term. Be a little careful about the resulting constant of integration.

125. This looks a lot like the previous problem, so the same technique should work.

126. The denominator factors, so use partial fractions.

127. You may find Pascal's Identity useful: $\binom{n}{k-1} + \binom{n}{k} = \binom{n+1}{k}$.

128. It may be easiest to first convert to rectangular coordinates.

129. Try to get powers of 2 in the numerator.

130. What is $\displaystyle\int_0^1 f(x)(\alpha - x)^2 \, dx$?

131. How far around the big circle will the small circle be when the dot first retouches the big circle?

132. An example might help.

133. The substitution $u = x - 1$ will make the integral look more symmetric.

134. Use integration by parts (twice) to find an equation relating $\int \sin^n x \, dx$ and $\int \sin^{n-2} x \, dx$.

135. Multiply and divide by the conjugate: $\sqrt{x^2 + x} + x$.

136. Use integration by parts.

137. Use the function $y = \sqrt{b^2 - (x - a)^2}$ for the cross-section of the upper half of the torus.

138. The easiest way to show that $g$ is constant is to show that $g' = 0$.

139. Just compute it.

140. Prove by induction.

141. Write a function for the total travel time, then minimize it.

142. This is essentially the same argument as Problem 6.4 with some inequalities reversed.

143. Look for a function whose derivative has two roots plus a double root.

144. We compute 4-dimensional volume by integrating over 3-dimensional cross-sectional volumes (just as we compute 3-dimensional volume by integrating over 2-dimensional cross-section areas).

145. After completing the square, use a trig substitution.

146. What is the logical choice for the common ratio of the geometric series?

147. Let $g(x)$ be the function whose graph is the line from $(a, f(a))$ to $(b, f(b))$. Your goal is to show that $g(c) > f(c)$ for all $c \in (a, b)$.

148. It may be helpful to measure angles clockwise starting at the 12:00 position.

149. Try to compute it recursively.

150. Again, try to use partial fractions.

151. Write $\tan x$ as $\dfrac{\sin x}{\cos x}$.

152. Look for $g$ whose range contains both positive and negative values.

153. Write $\dfrac{\sin ax}{\sin bx} = \dfrac{\sin ax}{x} \cdot \dfrac{x}{\sin bx}$.

154. If either $m$ or $n$ is odd, use $\sin^2 x + \cos^2 x = 1$ repeatedly so that we can eventually substitute $u = \sin x$ or $u = \cos x$.

155. This looks a lot like the Intermediate Value Theorem.

156. Convert $f - g$ to a quotient of fractions involving $f$ and/or $g$.

157. Integration by parts seems like a reasonable thing to try.

158. You'll need to use the Triangle Inequality.

159. For the other inequality, show that $\log(n + 1) - \log(n) > \dfrac{1}{n + 1}$.

160. Use partial fractions.

161. Try to turn $f - g$ into a $\frac{0}{0}$ indeterminate form.

162. Start with $\frac{f-g}{1}$ and divide numerator and denominator by $fg$.

163. Show that $\lim\limits_{x \to a} f(x) = 0$ for all $a \in \mathbb{R}$.

164. It doesn't really matter that $r$ is a root.

165. This is just a matter of chasing the definitions.

166. "The tangent lines ... are parallel" means that $f'(a) = f'(b)$.

167. Take a definite integral of areas of appropriate cross-sections.

168. If $x$ is the distance and $\theta$ is the angle, show that $\theta = \tan^{-1}\dfrac{55}{x} - \tan^{-1}\dfrac{45}{x}$.

169. Factor out what you can, then multiply and divide to get rid of terms with negative exponents.

170. It can be false if $g$ is not continuous.

171. All of these parts are actually the same—why?

172. Plugging in nice values for $x$ and/or $y$ is a good strategy.

173. Try substituting $y = 0$.

174. We'd be much happier working with $\sin^2 \theta$ and $\cos^2 \theta$. What's a relationship between $\sin^5 \theta$ and $\sin^2 \theta$?

175. Divide the numerator and denominator by $x^2$.

176. Use the Squeeze Theorem.

177. You'll probably need to use integration by parts 7 times.

178. The integral that you get will likely require a trig substitution to evaluate.

179. Substitute $u = \cos \theta$.

180. Substitute in the more complicated term.

181. Substitute $u = -2x$.

182. Use integration by parts twice.

183. Pick a few points and try to connect the dots.

184. Can you factor the equation that results after differentiation?

185. For a given $\epsilon$, choose a positive integer $n$ such that $\epsilon > \frac{1}{n}$. Then describe how to choose $\delta$ so that $|f(x)| < \frac{1}{n}$ for all $0 < |x - a| < \delta$.

186. Write $g(x)$ as a linear function in terms of $f(a)$ and $f(b)$.

187. Note that $f$ is bounded on a closed interval, so bound $f$ between its minimum and maximum, and use part (a).

188. Use the Series Comparison Test.

189. Note that $\dfrac{ds}{dt} = \dfrac{k}{t}$ for some constant $k$ (where $s$ is the distance traveled by the plow).

190. Integrate the cross-sectional areas as a function of $z$.

191. Start by computing $((fg)h)'$ using the Product Rule.

192. If both $m$ and $n$ are even, try the half-angle formulas.

193. Experiment with some simple functions, and take a guess at the answer. This should help suggest a strategy.

194. Start with the equation of a circle of radius $b$ centered at $(a, 0)$, and rotate it about the $y$-axis using the cylindrical shell method.

195. Use integration by parts with $u = x^z$.

196. $\sqrt{x} = x^{\frac{1}{2}}$.

197. Try the substitution $u = \sqrt[3]{x}$.

198. What substitution would get rid of all the fractional exponents?

199. Multiplying by $r$ may make it easier to convert to rectangular coordinates.

200. Then, find a function of the form $y = se^{-3x}$ that is a solution to the equation, for some constant $s$.

201. Try the Ratio Test.

202. Try the substitution $u = \sin^{-1} x$.

203. What's the relationship between $\lim\limits_{n \to \infty} \dfrac{a_n}{b_n}$ and $\lim\limits_{n \to \infty} \dfrac{b_n}{a_n}$?

204. Factor the denominator first.

205. Use partial fractions to write the sum as a telescoping sum.

206. Note the limaçon passes through the origin when $\sin \theta = -\frac{1}{2}$, and forms the boundary of the inner white region when $\sin \theta < -\frac{1}{2}$.

207. Use the Mean Value Theorem.

208. You shouldn't need to write out $f'(x)$ in order to compute $f'(1)$.

209. The pictures from part (b) should give you a good idea of where the full stops might occur.

210. You should get the sequence $1, -2, 4, -8, 16, \dots$.

211. Show that $h$ should satisfy $h'(x) = h(x)p(x)$.

212. Compute $\Gamma(2)$, $\Gamma(3)$, $\Gamma(4)$ using your formula from part (b). Do you see the pattern?

213. Let $g(x) = f(x) - f(2x)$ and $h(x) = f(x) - f(4x)$. Write an equation relating $h'(x)$, $g'(x)$, and $g'(2x)$.

214. Complete the square in the denominator.

215. Show that if $f$ is odd, then an antiderivative of $f$ is even.

216. What's the equation for a hyperbola?

217. Before computing derivatives, do you recognize this expression as the sum of a series that you know?

218. Try computing in terms of the angle at which Sam chooses to start rowing (relative to the diameter of the lake).

219. The key fact is that $100 \log 2$ is reasonably close to 72.

220. Show that if $\sup(A \cap B) < \min\{\sup A, \sup B\}$, then there is a contradiction, by finding an element of $A \cap B$ strictly larger than $\sup(A \cap B)$.

221. Another method is to differentiate the original series.

222. Use the Ratio Test.

223. Substitute $u = x^2$.

224. Try computing in terms of the angle at which Sam chooses to start rowing (relative to the shore of the river).

225. Let $f$ be an odd function.

226. Use induction.

227. Does $\mathbb{Q}$ contain any intervals of $\mathbb{R}$ as subsets?

228. Compute $\lim\limits_{x \to 0^+} x \int_x^1 \frac{1}{t}\, dt$.

229. There is only one function with range $\emptyset$—what is it?

230. You need to show that for any $c, d \in (a, b)$, that

$$\int_a^c f + \int_c^b f = \int_a^d f + \int_d^b f.$$

231. Write $\frac{1}{1+e^x} = 1 - \frac{e^x}{1+e^x}$.

232. Try drawing a right triangle.

233. Try substituting $u = \sqrt{e^x + 1}$.

234. Use a bounding argument.

235. How is our sum related to $\int_0^1 \frac{1}{\sqrt{1 - x^2}}\, dx$?

236. Use the identity $1 + \sinh^2 x = \cosh^2 x$.

237. Use the tangent double-angle formula to compute $\tan\left(\tan^{-1}\frac{1}{2} + \tan^{-1}\frac{1}{3}\right)$.

238. Use the substitution $u = \frac{\pi}{2} - x$. How does what you end up with relate to the original integral?

239. Break up the series into a sum of two geometric series.

240. What function does this look like the Taylor series of?

241. If $\mathcal{P}_n$ is the partition of $[a, b]$ into $n$ equal-sized pieces, what is $u(f, \mathcal{P}_n) - l(f, \mathcal{P}_n)$?

242. It should be straightforward to show that $a_n < b_n$ for sufficiently large $n$.

243. Given $c, d$ in the interval, you must show that any $x$ with $c \le x \le d$ is also in the interval.

244. $f$ is continuous on $[0, 1]$, so $|f(x)|$ has an upper bound on $[0, 1]$.

245. We can multiply Taylor series.

246. Applying the sine angle-subtraction formula at some stage may make your answer look much nicer.

247. Since the function is differentiable, we must have $f'(a) = 0$.

248. To show this curve is the same as the astroid, you'll need the trig triple-angle formulas.

249. Since we know that the Mean Value Theorem holds for differentiable functions, you should be looking for a function that is not differentiable.

250. Does the left side of the equation look like the derivative of a product?

251. If $\lim\limits_{x \to \infty} f'(x)$ does exist, what must it be?

252. Think about it a bit first before diving into computations. What do you expect the answer to be?

253. Use the fact that the picture is symmetric across the line $y = x$.

254. Use what you know about the ranges of $\sin^{-1}$ and $\cos^{-1}$.

255. Start by drawing a picture.

256. Expand the numerator and then do long division.

257. For the $n = 1$ case, $p$-series are your best examples.

258. Start with $\sin^2 \theta + \cos^2 \theta = 1$ and differentiate.

259. Substitute $u = x^3 + 1$.

260. Find a bound, in terms of $f'$, for $\dfrac{|E(z)|}{(z-a)^2}$, and then use the Mean Value Theorem to write the bound solely in terms of $f''$.

261. Suppose the leading term of $f(x)$ is $cx^n$ for some constant $c$ and some positive integer $n$. What are the leading terms of $f'(x)$ and $f''(x)$?

262. Use Rolle's Theorem.

263. Differentiate the given equation. How are $f$ and $f''$ related?

264. Write out a few terms of $(1 - x - x^2)f(x)$ to see what's going on.

265. Substitute $x = u^6$.

266. Manipulate using differences of squares.

267. Recall $\sin^2 x + \cos^2 x = 1$.

268. When does $P$ first again touch $C$?

269. If we take the area inside the entire limaçon for $\theta \in [0, 2\pi]$, how many times is the small white inner loop region counted?

270. Write the sum as the derivative of some function.

271. How can we introduce some symmetry into the integral?

272. You'll need to express this area as a difference of two integrals.

273. The cross-sections are squares!

274. Recall that $a^x = e^{x \log a}$.

275. Write $\tan\theta = \dfrac{\sin\theta}{\cos\theta}$.

276. Use part (a) with the Product Rule to compute $\left(f\cdot\frac{1}{g}\right)'$.

277. If $f \le g \le h$ and the limit of $f$ and $h$ is $L$, consider the inequality $f(x) - L \le g(x) - L \le h(x) - L$.

278. Consider the function $g(x) = f(x) - x$.

279. Write an expression for $\dfrac{|E(z)|}{z - a}$, then use the Mean Value Theorem to write your expression solely in terms of $f'$.

280. Look first for the "obvious" solutions.

281. Let $G(x) = \displaystyle\int_0^x g(t)\,dt$, and compute $\dfrac{d}{dx}G(f(x))$ using the Chain Rule.

282. Note that $\lim\limits_{x\to 0} g(x) = \lim\limits_{x\to 0} g(-x)$ for any function $g$ (provided either limit is defined).

283. At some point, the substitution $v = e^u$ will probably help.

284. One method is to use partial fractions to split each term into two fractions, then write the original series as a sum of two series.

285. The nature of the graph will depend on the sign of $a - b$.

286. Does the integrand look like the derivative of a product?

287. The next hint will tell you most of the possible functions. If you're stuck, you might be able to reverse-engineer the solution once you know the answer.

288. Does the value of $\epsilon$ matter?

289. Use the Limit Comparison Test with $\sum \frac{1}{n}$. You may need to use l'Hôpital's Rule to evaluate the resulting limit.

290. Factor the denominator, but not all the way.

291. Write $f(x) = px^3 + qx^2 + rx + s$ for some unknown coefficients $p, q, r, s$.

292. Note that $f'(x) = \cot x$, so $\sqrt{1 + (f'(x))^2} = \sqrt{1 + \cot^2 x}$. What trig identity can we now use?

293. Look at trig functions.

294. Substitute $x = 2\tan\theta$. ●

295. Note $\cos^2 x \le \cos x \le 1$ for all $x$. This suggests the Squeeze Theorem.

296. Go for broke—substitute $u = \sqrt{2 + \sqrt{x}}$ and see what happens. The integrand should become a polynomial in $u$.

297. The factor in the denominator is also a factor of part of the numerator.

298. Let $\lim\limits_{x\to a} f(x) = F$ and $\lim\limits_{x\to a} g(x) = G$. Write $f(x)g(x) - FG$ as $(f(x)g(x) - f(x)G) + (f(x)G - FG)$ and use the Triangle Inequality.

299. Compute the Taylor series of $(1 + x)^p$.

300. We'd like to make the substitution $u = x^5 + 3x^2 + x$, but where are we going to find $du$?

301. Suppose the right intersection point of the two curves is at $x = b$. What do you know about $\displaystyle\int_0^b (2x - 3x^3 - c)\,dx$?

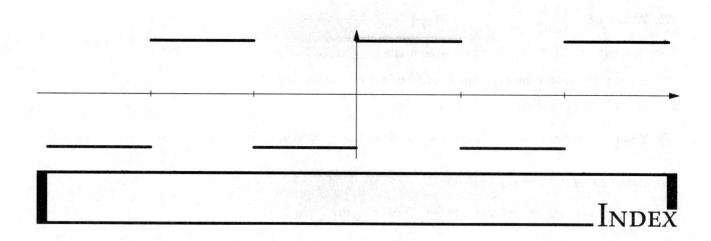

# www.artofproblemsolving.com

The Art of Problem Solving (AoPS) is:

- ## Books

  For over 28 years, the classic *Art of Problem Solving* books have been used by students as a resource for the American Mathematics Competitions and other national and local math events.

  > *Every school should have this in their math library.*
  > – Paul Zeitz, past coach of the U.S. International Mathematical Olympiad team

  The Art of Problem Solving Introduction and Intermediate texts, together with our *Prealgebra*, *Precalculus*, and *Calculus* texts, form a complete curriculum for outstanding math students in grades 6-12.

  > *The new book [Introduction to Counting & Probability] is great. I have started to use it in my classes on a regular basis. I can see the improvement in my kids over just a short period.*
  > – Jeff Boyd, 4-time MATHCOUNTS National Competition winning coach

- ## Classes

  The Art of Problem Solving offers online classes on topics such as number theory, counting, geometry, algebra, and more at beginning, intermediate, and Olympiad levels.

  > *All the children were very engaged. It's the best use of technology I have ever seen.*
  > – Mary Fay-Zenk, coach of National Champion California MATHCOUNTS teams

- ## Forum

  As of December 2022, the Art of Problem Solving Forum has over 930,000 members who have posted over 18,600,000 messages on our discussion board. Members can also participate in any of our free "Math Jams."

  > *I'd just like to thank the coordinators of this site for taking the time to set it up... I think this is a great site, and I bet just about anyone else here would say the same...*
  > – AoPS Community Member

- ## Resources

  We have links to summer programs, book resources, problem sources, national and local competitions, scholarship listings, a math wiki, and a LaTeX tutorial.

  > *I'd like to commend you on your wonderful site. It's informative, welcoming, and supportive of the math community. I wish it had been around when I was growing up.*
  > – AoPS Community Member

- ## ... and more!

Membership is **FREE**! Come join the Art of Problem Solving community today!